Introduction to Probability and Statistics

Introduction to

Probability and Statistics

B. W. LINDGREN and G. W. McELRATH

Department of
Mathematics

Department of
Mechanical Engineering

INSTITUTE OF TECHNOLOGY • UNIVERSITY OF MINNESOTA

The Macmillan Company—New York

First Printing

Library of congress catalog card number: 59-5633

The Macmillan Company, New York
Brett-Macmillan Ltd., Galt, Ontario

Printed in the United States of America

Preliminary edition copyright 1957 by B.W.
Lindgren & G.W. McElrath under title *Brief
Course in Statistical Theory*.

Preface

It is intended that this book serve as a text in a one-quarter or a one-semester course in statistics for undergraduate students who have had mathematics through integral calculus. It is an extensive revision of a mimeographed work published under the title *Brief Course in Statistical Theory*.

The book is neither ultratheoretical nor completely down-to-earth, which reflects our feeling that theory is practical and that practice too far removed from theory is easily led astray. Our plan has been to lay a relatively careful foundation in probability models and on this to build some of the simpler structure of estimation and testing of hypotheses.

In such a brief text, we have had to compromise with completeness and to leave untouched certain areas that could not have been neglected in a more encyclopedic presentation. There are limits to the amount of statistics that the average student can digest in a single semester; thus, we have omitted such theoretical topics as maximum likelihood, likelihood ratio tests, sufficiency, multivariate distributions, and such areas of application as multivariate regression and correlation, time series, and sample surveys. It is our purpose that the book introduce a way of thinking, rather than rush breathlessly over the full field of statistics.

With "malice aforethought" we have presented probability models before discussing the collection and analysis of data. From the points of view of both teachability and development, we find this arrangement virtuous. After the five rather loaded chapters on probability distributions, the simple computations of Chapter 7 will seem to the student like a breath of fresh air. Yet, if he desires, the instructor can conveniently take up Chapter 7 before Chapter 1, ignoring the occasional reference to earlier chapters.

Statistical inference has been treated from the point of view of the Neyman and Pearson theory of testing hypotheses, and the important concept of power function (or its complement, the operating characteristic function) plays a prominent part in the development. Some of the statistical tests called "nonparametric" or "distribution-free" are included along with the more classical tests.

The treatment of the Poisson distribution, although not original (it is adapted from that of T.C. Fry and others), is not yet common in statistics books. It permits the Poisson distribution to be treated as a useful model in its own right, rather than as a mere approximation tool in certain binomial problems. Employing λt as the parameter of the Poisson distribution not only gives the appropriate setting for many direct applications of the distribution but also seems to reduce students' difficulties with it to the vanishing point.

To give the student a hint of some of the directions in which statistics can go, we have included in the last chapter introductions to sequential analysis, analysis of variance, regression, and decision theory. These discussions admittedly open the door but a crack in each case—but perhaps enough to whet the curiosity.

Throughout the book many examples are worked out in preparing the student to attack the problems at the end of each topic. Review problems are provided for each of the earlier chapters, in which the pile-up of ideas warrants such a review. The reader will perhaps observe that many of the problems reflect the fact that the authors teach and consult in an engineering atmosphere, but we hasten to point out that in no case is a background of engineering necessary to comprehend the situation.

We are grateful to those who have seen and criticized the manuscript in its various stages—especially to Professors Charles Hicks and Paul Randolph of Purdue University, and to Professor I.R. Savage of the University of Minnesota. Their comments have been most helpful to us, and we appreciate their encouragement. We are indebted to the editors of *Biometrika*, *The Annals of Mathematical Statistics*, and the *Journal of the American Statistical Association* for permission to adapt material taken from these journals for use in our tables, and to the American Society for Testing Materials for permission to adopt material from the *ASTM Manual on Quality Control Materials*. We are indebted also to Professor Sir Ronald A. Fisher, Cambridge, to Dr. Frank Yates, Rothamsted, and to Messrs. Oliver and Boyd, Ltd., Edinburgh, for permission to reprint a portion of Table II from their book *Statistical Tables for Biological, Agricultural, and Medical Research*. Finally, we extend our thanks to Miss Shirley Hilsen for her excellent work in typing the manuscript.

B. W. Lindgren
G. W. McElrath

Foreword to the Student

Statistics, in its many ramifications, is an exceedingly complex subject, much too involved to be absorbed in a single semester. The material in this book, therefore, is but an introduction to some of the fundamental ideas of statistical estimation and testing. Even so, it can serve some important purposes. It can show that, contrary to the common saying, you *cannot* prove anything with statistics. It can give enough of an introduction to enable you to read scientific literature that uses statistical ideas. And it can provide a good foundation in the notion of a probability distribution. You should not expect to be expert statisticians for having had a course from this book. Yet, what you do learn can be quite useful.

As in a mathematics course, you must be willing to work out problem after problem, regularly, in order to acquire any useful "feeling" for the subject—no matter how clearly the material be presented in the text or in lectures.

Those students expecting to plunge directly into "statistics" are asked to be patient through five chapters of probability theory, with the reward of a better comprehension of the statistics in the following chapters.

Contents

ix

Introduction to Probability and Statistics

1/Simple Probability Models

1.0 Introduction

It is a common experience in drawing samples from a lot or "population" of objects to find that characteristics of the sample vary from sample to sample in a manner which cannot be predicted infallibly. The results are commonly thought of as being "random," or subject to "chance." Nevertheless, it has been found that the notion of "probability" of a chance happening affords a type of prediction which is especially useful over several trials of an experiment with a chance outcome. Probability theory is the mathematical structure which has evolved for the purpose of providing a model for chance happenings.

The gathering of data and computation of statistics are usually prompted by a desire either to learn something about a probability model or to test the correctness of an assumed model. Thus, our study begins with probability models.

1.1 Mathematical Models

An essential part of applying mathematics to a so-called real situation is the construction of a "mathematical model" for the situation. Consider a familiar example. Newton's second law of motion states that an object subject to a force moves with an acceleration proportional to the force: $F = ma$. The *model* consists of the numbers representing the magnitudes of force, mass, and acceleration, together with the equation relating them. The *law* says that this mathematical model can be used for describing and predicting physical phenomena. Proof of the law in a mathematical sense is impossible; it can only be tested by experiment.

For example, working mathematically with the equation $F = ma$, one can derive a formula giving the distance a dropped object will fall in a given time. Agreement between the motion predicted by this formula and the actual motion of a dropped object is then taken as evidence of the usefulness or "correctness" of the model.

1

Similarly, in geometry one sets up mathematical points, lines, circles, etc. These, together with certain axioms, constitute a model. Theorems of geometry are really theorems about this model, *not* theorems about *physical* points, lines, or circles. Of course, the model is found to be useful, and so people study geometry. For that matter, people even study apparently useless models, hoping that someone will later find—as often happens—applications for them.

Now, there are many phenomena in which the cause mechanisms are so complex that it is futile to attempt to set up a deterministic model based on something like Newton's laws. Yet some kind of model is desirable.

Let us consider first what is perhaps the simplest example of an "experiment of chance," the toss of a coin. Surely no one could determine analytically (from the initial position and velocity, from the forces acting during its flight, and from the laws of motion) whether a coin will land "heads" or "tails." However, it is clear that there are just these two possible results if we exclude the rather unstable "on-end" position as impossible. If we examine the coin before the toss, see that it has a heads side and a tails side, and observe the geometrical symmetry, we should undoubtedly decide that we cannot predict the outcome. However, if forced to bet on the outcome, who would not give "even odds"? There is no reason to expect heads any more than tails, and in some sense there should be just as many sets of influencing factors which produce heads as those which produce tails. Furthermore, the feeling is rather universal as to the equal expectancy of heads and tails. We say, in such a case, that the outcomes of the experiment are *equally likely*.

A mathematical model is constructed to depict equal likelihood by assigning equal *numbers* to the equally likely outcomes. If this is done in such a way that the total of the assigned numbers is 1, the number assigned an outcome is called the *probability* of the outcome. Thus, for the coin, we assign the number 1/2 to heads and the equal number 1/2 to tails. We may think of the probability 1/2 for heads as the ratio of the number of equally likely outcomes which are heads to the total number of equally likely outcomes.

The numbers assigned to heads and tails constitute a mathematical model or symbolism for the agreement of equal likelihood. We observe that this model is based on *a priori* considerations, since no experimentation is involved. The probabilities assigned to heads and tails refer to a "mathematical coin"—the coin of the model. Whether the probabilities are meaningful for actual coins is a matter for experience to determine.

There are, of course, situations in which *a priori* considerations do not lead to a complete definition of a probability model. The probability that a machine will produce a defective article, for example, would be impossible to specify with no observation of the machine's performance. Even here, however, there is nothing to prevent us from postulating the *existence* of such a probability. (This postulation is discussed further in Chapter 2.) We still set up the model in such a case but do not assign specific numbers as probabilities, since we do not know what numbers to assign. Experimentation can furnish a crude guide, but it must be realized that in any chance experiment, two series of trials will usually give different results. For instance, in tossing a coin 100 times, the proportion of heads can be .48 one time and .59 another time. The difficulty of idealizing from such *a posteriori* considerations is clear; when intuition fails, we can never know precisely the probabilities involved.

In this chapter we shall learn how to define probabilities—set up models —in simple cases in which the number of outcomes is finite and in which the situation may be reduced to fundamental cases wherein equal likelihood obtains by mutual agreement. We shall not *prove* that the probability of an event is, say, 1/2. Rather, we decree it. And we decree such things only in those cases in which intuition, common sense, symmetry, etc., lead to common consent that certain outcomes are equally likely. We often do this even though we may have no personal experience in conducting the actual experiment—tossing the die, or what have you. However, experiment would be the final test of the worth of the model we decree.

1.2 A Fundamental Principle

As suggested above, we shall calculate the probability of an event E as the ratio of the number of those outcomes of an experiment which result in E to the total number of outcomes of the experiment. This requires some practice in counting such numbers of outcomes or numbers of ways of doing things. Toward this end, we state a principle, which often reduces what would be a tremendous task of enumeration to a simple one of multiplication.

Principle A: If an experiment $\mathcal{E}_1$ can have exactly n_1 distinct outcomes, and if for each of these a second experiment $\mathcal{E}_2$ can have exactly n_2 distinct outcomes, the combined experiment, $\mathcal{E}_1$ and $\mathcal{E}_2$, can have exactly $n_1 n_2$ distinct outcomes.

This principle is so evident as to make a proof seem forced. Consider an example.

Example 1–a

Let us count the number of ways that a coin and die can fall if tossed together. The coin can fall in two ways, and for each of these, the die can fall in six ways; when tossed together they can fall in $2 \cdot 6 = 12$ ways. The following enumeration shows why multiplication yields the correct number:

$$H - 1, H - 2, H - 3, H - 4, H - 5, H - 6$$
$$T - 1, T - 2, T - 3, T - 4, T - 5, T - 6.$$

It is essential to keep track of which experiment is $\mathcal{E}_1$ and which is $\mathcal{E}_2$ in tabulating the different ways counted in the product $n_1 n_2$. To see this, consider the combined experiment of tossing two coins. One might think of counting the number of possible results of this experiment according to several schemes. He might reason that the outcomes are: two heads, two tails, and one of each—a total of *three* outcomes. Or he might consider just *two* outcomes: the coins match, or they don't match. And Principle A tells us to consider the outcomes to be *four* in number: HH, HT, TH, TT. In this last approach, the two coins are considered to be distinguishable—say, one is a nickel and the other a penny. Heads on one with tails on the other is treated as an outcome different from tails on the one with heads on the other.

Which is the *correct* "number of outcomes"? Let us remember that we are learning to count ways for the purpose of specifying probabilities in cases in which we require equally likely outcomes. Experience shows that HH, HT, TH, TT should be considered equally likely and that the three outcomes "both heads," "both tails," and "one of each" should not. However, that the coins match and that they don't match are *also* equally likely results!

Surely a *single* coin falls in one of two ways. Let us speak of these as *elementary outcomes* of the coin toss.

Next let us consider an experiment which is the joint performance of two simpler experiments $\mathcal{E}_1$ and $\mathcal{E}_2$. We define the elementary outcomes of this compound experiment as the results of associating each elementary outcome of $\mathcal{E}_1$ with each elementary outcome of $\mathcal{E}_2$. Then, if there are n_1 elementary outcomes of $\mathcal{E}_1$ and n_2 elementary outcomes of $\mathcal{E}_2$, there are $n_1 n_2$ elementary outcomes of the combined experiment $\mathcal{E}_1$ and $\mathcal{E}_2$, by Principle A. We now state another principle.

Principle B: If the n_1 elementary outcomes of an experiment $\mathcal{E}_1$ are equally likely, and the n_2 elementary outcomes of a subsequent experiment $\mathcal{E}_2$ are equally likely, the $n_1 n_2$ elementary outcomes of the compound experiment $\mathcal{E}_1$ and $\mathcal{E}_2$ are equally likely.

Whether this is an axiom or a theorem depends upon the logical system employed. At this point in the development, we take the principle as simply a tested guide to successful model building. It is consistent with subsequent definitions and rules concerning "conditional probabilities."

Example 1–b

Two coins are tossed. The $2 \times 2 = 4$ *elementary* outcomes are HH, HT, TH, TT. If H and T are equally likely in the case of each coin, these four elementary outcomes are equally likely by Principle B.

Notice that in this example of tossing two coins, we can think of the event "the coins match" as the *pair* of elementary outcomes HH and TT, and the event "the coins don't match" as the pair of outcomes HT and TH. Similarly any "way" in which the experiment may be said to result can be thought of as a set of so many of the elementary outcomes.

Let us next use Principle A to count the number of ways n distinct objects can be arranged in a row. We count by breaking the task of arrangement into subtasks: We have n positions in the row to fill, and the first can be filled with any of the n objects—n ways for this subtask. Next we fill the second position, which can be done in $n - 1$ ways for *each* of the n ways of doing the first subtask. And so on. We find, by Principle A, that the number of ways in which n things can be arranged in a row is

$$n \cdot (n - 1) \cdot (n - 2) \cdots 3 \cdot 2 \cdot 1 = n!$$

Furthermore, if in each choice of an object to fill a position, all candidate objects are equally likely, it follows from Principle B that the $n!$ arrangements are equally likely.

Example 1–c

The four letters A, B, C, D can be arranged in 4! or 24 distinct sequences. These may be enumerated as follows, showing why the product $4 \cdot 3 \cdot 2 \cdot 1$ gives the correct number of arrangements:

ABCD	BACD	CABD	DABC
ABDC	BADC	CADB	DACB
ACBD	BCAD	CBAD	DBAC
ACDB	BCDA	CBDA	DBCA
ADBC	BDAC	CDAB	DCAB
ADCB	BDCA	CDBA	DCBA

A modification of this arrangement problem is the following: In how many *distinct* ways can n things, k of which are alike, be arranged in a row? Let the answer be P, and compute P as follows. Take n distinct objects. These could be arranged in $n!$ ways. Now eliminate the identifying features from k of them, thus making k of them alike, and arrange the n modified objects (k alike). This can be done in P distinct ways. For *each* of these P arrangements, if we restore the identification of the k objects, we may count $k!$ distinct arrangements and in this way attain all of the $n!$ arrangements of n distinct objects. But then we must have, by Principle A, $P \cdot k! = n!$, so that $P = n!/k!$

Using the same type of reasoning it may be seen that if, of n objects, k_1 are alike, k_2 are alike but different from the k_1, etc., the number of distinct arrangements is

$$\frac{n!}{k_1!k_2! \cdots}.$$

Example 1-d

How many different orderings are there of seven names on a ballot, if the names of the three incumbents are listed first?

Here each arrangement is achieved when we order the three incumbents' names in the first three positions—in one of $3!$ ways—and then order the remaining names in the remaining four positions—in one of $4!$ ways. By Principle A, the desired number is $3! \, 4! = 144$.

Example 1-e

Six blocks, of which three are red, two are yellow, and one is blue, can be arranged in a row in $6!/3!2! = 60$ distinct ways. These one can enumerate with patience but without much difficulty.

Problems

1-1. How many equally likely elementary outcomes are there when three coins are tossed?

1-2. How many equally likely elementary outcomes are there when n coins are tossed?

1-3. In how many distinct ways can five distinct objects be distributed among three distinct containers?

1-4. In how many distinct ways can k distinct objects be distributed among m distinct containers?

1-5. How many three-digit numbers are there whose digits are either 4, 5, 6, or 7? (Repeated digits are allowed.)

1-6. How many numbers with three *distinct* digits are there whose digits are either 4, 5, 6, or 7?

1-7. How many equally likely elementary outcomes are there when n dice are tossed?

1-8. How many distinct signals can be made using four flags of different colors in a row?

1-9. How many distinct signals can be made using four flags in a row, if there are available just three red, one white, and two black flags?

1-10. In a certain experiment it is determined whether observations fall above or below (denoted by A and B, respectively) a certain level. In a series of n observations, how many different sequences of A's and B's could result?

1-11. Referring to Problem 1-10, suppose that twenty observations are made and that there are as many A's as there are B's. In how many ways can this come about? (That is, how many distinct arrangements are there of ten A's and ten B's?)

1-12. Of the arrangements counted in Problem 1-11, how many have a string of at least nine A's together? (Such a string is often called a "run." Runs will be discussed in more detail in Chapter 8.)

1.3 Combinations

A handy tool for later use in computing probabilities (but also useful in its own right for simply counting elementary outcomes) is the notion of a *combination*. The basic problem is this: In how many distinct ways can one select k objects from a collection of n objects, *without regard to order* of selection or to arrangement after selection? One bunch, or combination, of k objects selected will be considered the same as another bunch of k if and only if they contain *exactly the same k objects*.

1.3.1 The Combination Symbol

We use the symbol $\binom{n}{k}$ to denote the answer to the problem stated above, namely, the *number* of combinations of k things taken from n. Other symbols for the same quantity are: $_nC_k$, C_k^n, $C_{n,k}$. It remains to compute $\binom{n}{k}$.

This we do as follows. Consider k A's and $n - k$ B's; these n letters are to be arranged in a sequence. The arrangement is accomplished as soon as we *select* k out of the n sequence positions to put the A's in, the B's being consigned to the remaining positions. Thus, there are precisely as many ways of arranging the A's and B's as there are ways of selecting k out of n things. But we have already seen how to count the arrangements, and following this scheme (page 6), we have

$$\binom{n}{k} = \frac{n!}{k!(n-k!)}.$$

Cancelling the $(n - k)!$ in the denominator with corresponding factors in the numerator, we have the following form more suited to computation:

$$\binom{n}{k} = \frac{n(n - 1)(n - 2) \cdots (n - k + 1)}{k(k - 1)(k - 2) \cdots 3 \cdot 2 \cdot 1}.$$

The first formula, in terms of factorials, shows that there is a type of symmetry, namely,

$$\binom{n}{n - k} = \frac{n!}{(n - k)!k!} = \binom{n}{k}.$$

This should be evident in the statement of the problem: If we select a group of k from n objects, we automatically select a group of $n - k$, simply by leaving them behind. The symmetry is well exploited in calculating such an expression as

$$\binom{100}{98} = \binom{100}{2} = \frac{100 \cdot 99}{2 \cdot 1} = 4950.$$

To make the symmetry formula true when $k = n$, we define $\binom{n}{0}$ to be 1, equivalent to defining (as is customary) 0! to be 1.

We have not indicated above the precise manner in which the objects are to be selected. Actually, we may select them simultaneously, in one fistfull, or we may select them one at a time if we don't put any back. The two methods yield the same end results.

It is often useful to know that the $\binom{n}{k}$ selections of k from n objects are equally likely. One may postulate this equal likelihood as a *definition* of selecting the k objects "at random." It is for experience to decide whether a given method of selection and mixing conforms to this definition of "at random."

Another approach is in considering a selection as being accomplished by drawing the objects one at a time. If at each drawing all remaining objects are equally likely to be drawn, we may infer equal likelihood of the selections by using Principle B. Consider, for instance, the drawing of three objects from five. If we were forming *arrangements* of the three objects by selecting one at a time at random, we should have $5 \cdot 4 \cdot 3 = 60$ equally likely arrangements, by Principles A and B. Now, the same group of three letters, say, A, C, and D, would be used in six of these arrangements:

$$ACD, \; ADC, \; CDA, \; DAC, \; CAD, \; DCA.$$

Similarly, each combination of three letters would correspond to six arrangements, a completely different six for each combination. Since the arrangements are equally likely, and since the same number of arrangements is involved in each combination, the ten combinations are equally likely.

Example 1–f

A group of three men may be selected from five available men in ten ways:

$$\binom{5}{3} = \binom{5}{2} = \frac{5 \cdot 4}{2 \cdot 1} = 10.$$

These are easily enumerated. Call the five men A, B, C, D, E. The ten groups of three are as follows:

$$ABC, \ ABD, \ ABE, \ ACD, \ ACE, \ ADE, \ BCD, \ BCE, \ BDE, \ CDE.$$

Observe that (although we have written the names in order) we do not call ACB a selection different from ABC, since the same three men are used. Observe also that corresponding to each selection of three men there is a selection of two men not used:

$$DE, \ CE, \ CD, \ BE, \ BD, \ BC, \ AE, \ AD, \ AC, \ AB.$$

If at any stage of the selection process the remaining men are equally likely to be chosen, the ten combinations enumerated above are equally likely.

Example 1–g

A bowl contains five identical beads. How many selections of three beads can be made?

If the beads were of different colors, the problem would clearly be equivalent to that of the preceding examples. When the beads are identical, say, all white, one might wish to think of just one possible selection, namely, three white beads. Actually, of course, there would still be ten outcomes, in the following sense. The three beads in one of the $\binom{5}{3}$ combinations would be a different set of three beads from those in another combination—*whether or not* we can distinguish the difference!

Example 1–h

Consider a bowl with three white and two black beads. In how many ways can we select a bead?

In one sense, just two ways—a white bead or a black bead. For our purposes of probability computation, however, we shall need to consider that the white beads are actually not the *same* bead, but are three distinct beads. Thus, from this point of view there are still five beads in the bowl, and there are $\binom{5}{1} = 5$ ways of picking one bead, $\binom{5}{3} = 10$ ways of picking three beads, etc. Again, if each bead is equally likely to be picked at any stage of the selection, the $\binom{5}{1}$ combinations, etc., are equally likely. This is why we prefer five (over two) as the number of outcomes when we select one bead; the beads, *not* the colors, are then equally likely.

Example 1–i

Suppose we again have a bowl with three white and two black beads. We select three beads. How many combinations of three beads are there of which one is black and two are white?

Such combinations may be thought of as being formed by selecting first one black bead from the two available black beads, and then two white beads from the three available white beads. These selections can be made in $\binom{2}{1}$ and $\binom{3}{2}$ ways, respectively. Hence, the desired number (by Principle A) is $\binom{2}{1} \cdot \binom{3}{2} = 6$. Observe that the same answer would result had we chosen the white beads first.

1.3.2 Binomial Coefficients

Perhaps it will be recalled from algebra that the value of $\binom{n}{k}$ as given above is precisely the coefficient of a term of a binomial expansion. To see why this is so, consider $(x + y)^n$. This nth power is the product of the n factors:

$$(x + y)(x + y)(x + y) \cdots (x + y).$$

In this product, one obtains 2^n terms by selecting either the x or the y from each factor. (There are two choices at each of the n selections. Hence, by Principle A, there are 2^n terms.) Each term is made up of n factors, some of them x's and the rest y's—say, k x's and $n - k$ y's:

$$\underbrace{x \cdot x \cdots x}_{k \ x\text{'s}} \cdot \underbrace{y \cdot y \cdots y}_{n - k \ y\text{'s.}}$$

Of these terms, there will be certain ones alike, which may be grouped. Namely, there will be as many terms with k x's (and hence $n - k$ y's) as there are ways of selecting k out of the n factors $(x + y)$ from which to use the x. But this number is just $\binom{n}{k}$, and so the coefficient of the term $x^k y^{n-k}$ is $\binom{n}{k}$. Thus,

$$(x + y)^n = \sum_{k=0}^{n} \binom{n}{k} x^k y^{n-k}.$$

For this reason the number $\binom{n}{k}$ is often referred to as a *binomial coefficient*.

Example 1-j

Using $n = 5$, we have

$$(q + p)^5 = \sum_0^5 \binom{n}{k} q^k p^{n-k}$$

$$= \binom{5}{0} q^5 + \binom{5}{1} q^4 p + \binom{5}{2} q^3 p^2 + \binom{5}{3} q^2 p^3 + \binom{5}{4} q p^4 + \binom{5}{5} p^5$$

$$= q^5 + 5 q^4 p + 10 q^3 p^2 + 10 q^2 p^3 + 5 q p^4 + p^5.$$

Problems

1-13. Compute: $\binom{15}{15}, \binom{15}{13}, \binom{15}{0}, \binom{15}{1}, \binom{46}{44}, \binom{52}{5}.$

1-14. How many connecting cables are needed in order that any two of nine offices in a building be able to communicate directly?

1-15. In how many different ways could one pick a committee of four from a group consisting of ten labor and five management representatives?

1-16. Of the committees possible in Problem 1-15, how many
   (a) would have two labor and two management representatives?
   (b) would have at least one representative from each group?
   (c) would have on them the chairman of the labor delegation and the chairman of the management delegation?

1-17. A lot contains fifty articles, six of them defective.
   (a) How many selections of five articles can be made from the lot?
   (b) How many selections of two defective and four good articles can be made from the lot?

1-18. Show that $k \binom{n}{k} = n \binom{n-1}{k-1}.$ Interpret this equality by considering each side as the number of ways of performing a certain task of selection.

1-19. (a) Write the term involving p^8 in the expansion of $(p + q)^{12}$.
   (b) Write the term involving x^{20} in the expansion of $(x + 2y)^{35}$.

1.4 Calculation of Probability

By a *trial* or *experiment of chance* we shall mean a collection of elementary outcomes together with some agreement as to the relative likelihoods of the outcomes. An *event* shall mean any *set* or *collection* of possible outcomes, described either by listing them or by giving some property which they share. We say that an event E has occurred if, when the experiment is performed, the result is one of the outcomes which make up E. That is, E has occurred if the actual outcome has the property which defines E.

When the elementary outcomes of an experiment are finite in number and are agreed to be *equally likely*, we assign a number called "probability" to each event E, as follows:

$$P(E) \equiv \frac{\text{Number of elementary outcomes in } E.}{\text{Number of elementary outcomes in the experiment}}.$$

The symbol $P(E)$ is read "probability of E," or "probability that E occurs."

Example 1–k

The numbers of dots showing (1, 2, 3, 4, 5, or 6) in a throw of a die are the possible outcomes in this experiment. We agree that these are equally likely. Suppose the event E is that the number of dots be even. The event E consists of the outcomes 2, 4, and 6, and then

$$P(E) = \frac{3}{6}.$$

It is sometimes convenient to have the following picture in mind: Let the six outcomes in the experiment of this last example, for instance, make up a "sample space" and be represented by six points. The event E is then just a set of three of these six points, as shown in Figure 1–1. The

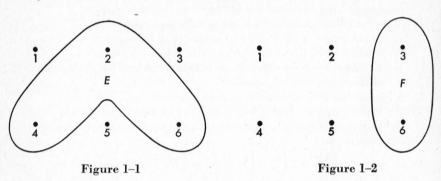

Figure 1–1   Figure 1–2

probability of E is just the ratio of the number of points in E to the total number of points making up the experiment.

Example 1–l

Again consider the toss of a die. Let F be the event: "the number of points is divisible by 3." Then F consists of the two outcomes 3, 6, and clearly has probability 2/6. The set F may be represented as in Figure 1–2.

It is clear, too, that if the event E in these examples is taken to be just the outcome 6, the probability of E is 1/6—as it is also for each of the outcomes 1, 2, 3, 4, and 5. The probabilities of the events consisting of the individual elementary outcomes, assumed to be equally likely, have turned out to be equal. This is no accident. Probability, as we have defined it, is a quantity designed to give numerical expression to the concept of "equally likely," in such a way as to be interpreted as the *fraction* of the time one would expect the event in question to occur. Such a quantity cannot be proved mathematically to be correct; its usefulness depends upon its success in predicting actual experience.

Example 1–m

Suppose that five bad electron tubes get mixed up with eight good tubes. What is the probability that if one is selected at random, it is good?

The phrase "at random" is naturally intended to suggest that all thirteen tubes are equally likely to be drawn—implying an effective mixing or shuffling (which, it is true, may simply be the result of ignorance as to which tube is which). Since the ratio of the number of good tubes to the total number of tubes is eight to thirteen, and since all are equally likely, the desired probability is 8/13.

Example 1–n

If two tubes are drawn from the thirteen tubes of the preceding example, what is the probability
(a) that both are good?
(b) that one is good and one is bad?

For both questions, the denominator is the same: the number of ways one can select two out of thirteen objects, $\binom{13}{2}$; and these are equally likely. Now of these combinations, some satisfy the description "both are good"; there are as many of these as there are ways of selecting two out of eight objects, and hence:

$$P(2 \text{ good tubes are drawn}) = \frac{\binom{8}{2}}{\binom{13}{2}}.$$

Of the $\binom{13}{2}$ combinations, some satisfy the description "one is good and one is bad." We may select one bad tube from five in $\binom{5}{1}$ ways, and one good from the eight good tubes present in $\binom{8}{1}$ ways. Applying the fundamental principle,

$$P(1 \text{ bad and 1 good are drawn}) = \frac{\binom{8}{1}\binom{5}{1}}{\binom{13}{2}} = \frac{20}{39}.$$

Example 1–o

Five cards are drawn at random from a standard deck (four suits, each having 2, 3, . . . , 10, jack, queen, king, ace). What is the probability of drawing two pairs? (An example of such a hand would be a pair of 10's, a pair of aces, and a 4. That is, the pairs are not of the same denomination, and the odd card is of still a different denomination.)

Since five cards are drawn from fifty-two available cards, the denominator of the fraction defining probability is $\binom{52}{5}$, the total number of ways in which such selections are possible. These are equally likely.

In counting the number of ways of selecting the two pairs, we consider the task in several parts. First, we select two of the thirteen denominations from which to draw the pairs and then a denomination from which to draw the odd card. Having decided on the denominations, we then proceed with the selections, one pair from the four of one denomination, another pair from the four of the second denomination, and finally the odd card from the third denomination. The numbers of ways for these subtasks are then multiplied:

$$\binom{13}{2} \binom{11}{1} \binom{4}{2} \binom{4}{2} \binom{4}{1} = 123{,}552.$$

The desired probability is the ratio of this number to $\binom{52}{5}$, or 198/4165.

We note certain facts concerning the number we have termed probability. First, if the event E includes all possible outcomes of the experiment, $P(E) = 1$. The event E is "certain." And if the event E includes none of the possible outcomes, $P(E) = 0$; E is doomed to failure. For instance, in the example just considered, Example 1–n, suppose that eight tubes are selected at random. Then

$$P(6 \text{ out of 8 tubes drawn are bad}) = 0.$$

For, none of the $\binom{13}{8}$ ways in which eight tubes can be selected from thirteen can include six bad tubes, since there are only five bad tubes present.

The probability of every event lies between (or at) these extremes of 0 and 1. And since the event E and the event "not E" (consisting of all outcomes not in E) *exhaust* the set of possible outcomes,

$$P(E) + P(\text{not } E)$$
$$= \frac{(\text{Number of outcomes in } E) + (\text{Number of outcomes not in } E)}{\text{Number of possible outcomes}} = 1.$$

This formula makes clear the fact that a knowledge of $P(\text{not } E)$ is equivalent to a knowledge of $P(E)$:

$$P(E) = 1 - P(\text{not } E).$$

This is an important observation, since in many instances one of these probabilities is considerably easier to compute (directly) than the other.

Example 1–p

If two tubes are drawn from a container with five bad and eight good tubes, what is the probability that at least one is good?

The event "at least one is good" is the opposite of the event "none is good." Hence,

$$P(\text{at least one is good}) = 1 - P(\text{none is good})$$

$$= 1 - \frac{\binom{5}{2}}{\binom{13}{2}} = \frac{34}{39}.$$

Problems

1–20. Four objects are distributed at random among six containers. What is the probability that
   (a) all objects are in the same container?
   (b) no two objects are in the same container?

1–21. A lot consists of ten good articles, four articles with only minor defects, and two with major defects. One is drawn at random. Find the probability that
   (a) it has no defects.
   (b) it has no major defects.
   (c) it is either good or has major defects.

1–22. If, from the lot of articles of Problem 1–21, two articles are selected at random, determine the probability that
   (a) both are good.
   (b) both have major defects.
   (c) at least one is good.
   (d) at most one is good.
   (e) exactly one is good.
   (f) neither has major defects.
   (g) neither is good.

1–23. Suppose a lot of sixteen articles is to be accepted if three articles selected at random have no major defect. What is the probability that the lot in Problem 1–21 is (a) accepted, (b) rejected?

1–24. In a bolt factory machines A, B, C manufacture 25, 35, and 40 per cent of the total. Of their outputs 5, 4, and 2 per cent, respectively, are defective bolts. A bolt is drawn at random and is found to be defective. What are the probabilities that it was manufactured by machines A, B, or C respectively?

1–25. Five cards are drawn from a standard deck (see Example 1–o). What is the probability of "three of a kind"? (This description normally excludes the possibility that the two odd cards themselves form a pair.)

1.5 Combining Probabilities

In this section it is shown how calculations may sometimes be simplified by taking advantage of certain rules of combination of probabilities. These rules of combination are logical consequences of our definition for probability, when that definition applies—namely, in those cases in which we may think of a finite number of equally likely outcomes as making up the experiment. (In other cases, these rules of combination will be taken as axioms!)

1.5.1 The Addition Law

Events E and F are called *mutually exclusive* if the set of outcomes in E does not overlap the set which defines F.

Example 1-q

Consider again the toss of a die. Define the events E and F as follows:

E: The number of points is divisible by 3,
F: The number of points is 4 or 5.

These events are mutually exclusive. This fact is graphically illustrated in the type of diagram we used earlier:

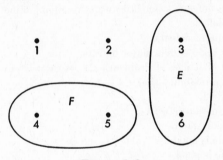

Figure 1-3

The sets of points labeled E and F do not overlap.

For any of two events E and F, mutually exclusive or *not*, the combined event "E or F" is defined as that event consisting of those outcomes which are either in E or in F. Note that if an outcome happens to lie *both* in E and in F, we still say it lies in "E or F."

Clearly, if E and F *are* mutually exclusive, the number of outcomes in the event "E or F" is the sum of the number of outcomes in E and the number in F. Hence, it follows that *when E and F are mutually exclusive*,

$$P(E \text{ or } F) = P(E) + P(F).$$

On the other hand, if E and F are *not* mutually exclusive, those outcomes which lie *both* in E and in F would be counted *twice* in the sum $P(E) + P(F)$. Hence, to obtain $P(E \text{ or } F)$ the number of such twice-counted outcomes must be subtracted once, and we have:

$$P(E \text{ or } F) = P(E) + P(F) - P(E \text{ and } F).$$

The event "E and F," of course, is that event consisting of all outcomes which lie both in E and in F.

Example 1–r

If a die is thrown, what is the probability that the number of points is even or divisible by three? The events "even" and "divisible by three" are not mutually exclusive. Using the formula above,

P(even or divisible by 3)
$= P$(even) $+ P$(divisible by 3) $- P$(even and divisible by 3)
$= \dfrac{3}{6} + \dfrac{2}{6} - \dfrac{1}{6} = \dfrac{4}{6}.$

Again a schematic diagram helps to understand the calculation:

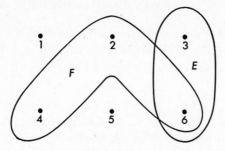

Figure 1–4

Problems

1–26. Two dice are tossed. What is the probability that
   (a) the sum of the points showing is an even number?
   (b) the sum is divisible by three?
   (c) the sum is even or divisible by three?
1–27. A card is drawn from a standard bridge deck (four "suits," each consisting of 2, 3, . . . , 10, jack, queen, king, ace). What is the probability that the card drawn is
   (a) a spade?
   (b) a face card (king, queen, jack)?
   (c) a spade or a face card?

1.5.2 Conditional Probability

Suppose that two men are watching a coin being tossed. Suppose that the coin is tossed, but the result is hidden from one man. These men would have different answers to the question: "What is the probability that the coin landed heads?" One of them would say 1/2—or, at any rate, would still bet at even odds. The other would say 0 or 1, having seen the coin land, depending on whether it fell tails or heads. They have different amounts of information, reflected in their different answers—or what's more to the point, reflected in the different actions they would take.

Next, suppose a die is tossed, and we are told that the number of points is even, but not whether it is 2, 4, or 6. What is the probability that a 6 has turned up? We wish to define a probability which would accord with how one would bet in such situations as these we have described.

Recall that an event E is a set of outcomes of an experiment, often defined by describing a property of the outcomes. The event "E and F" is the event consisting of those outcomes which satisfy both description E and description F. We make the following definition:

$$P(E|F) = \frac{\text{Number of outcomes in the event ``} E \text{ and } F\text{''}}{\text{Number of outcomes in the event } F}.$$

This is called a *conditional probability*, and the symbol $P(E|F)$ is read "the probability of E, given F." Notice that in both numerator and denominator *only those outcomes are considered which satisfy the description F.*

Example 1–s

Consider the toss of a die. Let us compute the probability that the number of points is divisible by three, given that this number is even:

$$P(\text{divisible by 3}|\text{even})$$
$$= \frac{\text{Number of outcomes divisible by 3 and even}}{\text{Number of outcomes even}}.$$

Referring to Figure 1–5, it is readily seen that the numerator is 1 and that the denominator is 3, giving 1/3 as the desired probability.

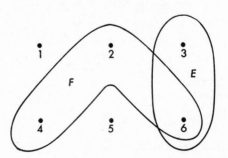

Figure 1–5

If we divide the numerator and denominator of the ratio defining conditional probability by the total number of outcomes possible, we obtain

$$P(E|F) = \frac{P(E \text{ and } F)}{P(F)}.$$

Multiplying this expression through by $P(F)$, we obtain the following *multiplication law:*

$$P(E \text{ and } F) = P(E|F)P(F).$$

This law is often useful in a case in which it is obvious what $P(E|F)$ should be, but it is desired to obtain $P(E \text{ and } F)$.

Example 1–t

A bowl contains two black beads and three white beads. A bead is drawn at random, and then a second bead is drawn at random from these left. What is the probability that, say, both are white?

By the multiplication rule,

P(first is white and second is white)
   $= P$(first is white) P(second is white, given first is white).

The first factor on the right is certainly 3/5, the ratio of the number of white beads to the total number of beads. In computing the second factor we must assume that the first bead selected *was* white; this means that there are two white and two black beads left in the bowl, so that the chances of getting a white one are two out of four. It is two out of four, observe, only under the *condition* that the first bead actually turned out to be white. By the multiplication rule, then, the desired probability is

$$\frac{3}{5} \cdot \frac{2}{4}.$$

(We comment that under the criterion "both white" there is no need for keeping track of order, and we might as well have drawn the beads together. The probability that if two beads are drawn together, both are white, is

$$\frac{\binom{3}{2}}{\binom{5}{2}} = \frac{\frac{3 \cdot 2}{2 \cdot 1}}{\frac{5 \cdot 4}{2 \cdot 1}} = \frac{3 \cdot 2}{5 \cdot 4},$$

with checks the above answer.)

Example 1–u

A bag contains four white and two black beads, and a second bag contains three of each color. A bag is drawn at random, and a bead is then selected at random from the bag chosen. What is the probability that the bead selected is white?

There are two mutually exclusive ways of selecting a white bead: Either a white bead is drawn from the first bag, or a white bead is drawn from the second bag. We have, in the first case,

$$P(\text{white bead from first bag})$$
$$= P(\text{first bag drawn } and \text{ white bead drawn from it})$$
$$= P(\text{white bead}|\text{first bag drawn})\, P(\text{first bag drawn})$$
$$= \frac{4}{6} \cdot \frac{1}{2}.$$

Similarly,

$$P(\text{white bead from second bag}) = \frac{3}{6} \cdot \frac{1}{2}$$

Adding, we obtain

$$P(\text{white bead}) = \frac{4}{6} \cdot \frac{1}{2} + \frac{3}{6} \cdot \frac{1}{2} = \frac{7}{12}.$$

Problems

1–28. A bag contains three luminous white, five luminous green, four nonluminous white, and six nonluminous green beads. A bead is selected at random. What is the probability
(a) that it is white?
(b) that it is luminous, given that it is green (viewed in daylight)?
(c) that it is green, given that it is nonluminous (viewed at night)?
(d) that it is green or luminous?

1–29. A box contains four bad tubes and six good tubes. Two are drawn together, and one of them is tested and found to be good.
(a) What is the probability that the other is also good?
If the tubes are checked by drawing a tube at random, testing it, and repeating the process (not replacing the tube tested) until all four bad tubes are located, what is the probability that the fourth bad tube will be found
(b) at the fifth test?
(c) at the tenth test?
[*Hint:* The fourth bad tube will be found at the fifth test provided that three are found in the first four tests, and then the remaining one is found in the fifth test.]

1.5.3 Independent Events

Consider the simultaneous toss of a coin and a die. There are twelve outcomes—equally likely!—namely:

H–1	H–2	H–3	H–4	H–5	H–6
T–1	T–2	T–3	T–4	T–5	T–6.

Now let us compute the following conditional probability:

P(coin falls H, given that the die shows a 6).

If we define the events E and F as follows:

E: The coin falls heads,
F: The die falls 6,

the computation reads:

$$P(E|F) = \frac{P(E \text{ and } F)}{P(F)} = \frac{1/12}{1/6} = \frac{1}{2}.$$

This number $1/2$ is also $P(E)$, and hence

$$P(E \text{ and } F) = P(E) \cdot P(F).$$

When this relation holds, we say that E and F are *independent events*.

It is easily checked that P(coin falls H, given that the die satisfies F) is always $1/2$, no matter what F is. This is in fact just the probability of heads, *if we completely ignore the die*. Indeed, if E is any property involving the coin only, and F a property involving the die only,

$$P(E|F) = P(E),$$

and therefore

$$P(E \text{ and } F) = P(E) \cdot P(F).$$

In such a case we say that the result of the coin toss and the result of the die toss are *independent*.

In both the multiplication law for dependent events and the above special case for independent events, the "and" in the event on the left corresponds to a multiplication on the right. The difference lies in the fact that when the events are not independent, one of the probabilities on the right must be a conditional probability.

In practice, it is usually intuitively clear when certain phenomena should be considered independent. Probabilities of independent events are then *defined* by means of the multiplication rule.

Example 1–v

In tossing a coin and a die, a person usually postulates the independence of the outcome of the coin toss and the outcome of the die toss. He does this to build into his model the intuitive notion that the outcome of the die toss should have nothing whatever to do with the outcome of the coin toss. Such probabilities as $P(H \text{ and } 4)$ are then obtained by multiplication:

$$P(H \text{ and } 4) = P(H) \cdot P(4) = \frac{1}{2} \cdot \frac{1}{6} = \frac{1}{12}.$$

Example 1–w

One bag contains four white and two black beads, and another contains three of each color. A bead is drawn from each bag. What is the probability that one is white and one is black?

We note that there are two ways of succeeding—drawing a white bead from the first bag and a black one from the second, or the other way around. These are mutually exclusive, so we add their probabilities. Now,

$$P(\text{white from first, black from second}) = \frac{4}{6} \cdot \frac{3}{6},$$

since the drawings from the two bags must be treated as independent experiments. Similarly,

$$P(\text{black from first, white from second}) = \frac{2}{6} \cdot \frac{3}{6}.$$

Hence,

$$P(\text{black from one and white from the other}) = \frac{4}{6} \cdot \frac{3}{6} + \frac{2}{6} \cdot \frac{3}{6} = \frac{1}{2}.$$

Problems

1–30. Two coins and a die are tossed. What is the probability that both coins fall heads and the die shows a 3 or a 6?

1–31. Two dice are thrown three times in succession.
    (a) What is the probability that an 8, 5, and 7 are thrown, in that order?
    (b) What is the probability that the third throw results in a 7, given that the first two throws were an 8 and a 5, in that order?
    (c) What is the probability of throwing exactly one 7 and exactly one 11 in the three throws?

1–32. What is the probability that at least two people in a room of twenty people will be found to have the same birthday?

1.5.4 The Binomial Formula

By and large, problems in probability do not lend themselves to classification, with a formula for each class. Often one must resort to basic principles in order to solve a problem. Surely the student has found by now that he has had to *think* his way through many problems.

Yet there is one important type of problem—with a formula for solution—which is easily identified. We consider it at this point because it illustrates the multiplication law for independent events. This type of problem has the following characteristics.

(1) An experiment is conducted a given finite number of times.
(2) Outcomes of the trials are independent.

(3) In a given trial, one is interested in whether or not an event E has occurred.

(4) The probability (usually called p) that E occurs in a single trial is defined—and is, of course, the *same for each trial!*

(5) It is desired to know the probability that E occurs in exactly a specified number of the total sequence of trials. It is immaterial as to the location of those successes in the sequence.

We shall show how such problems are solved by working out the answer in a specific example.

Example 1–x

Suppose that eight dice are tossed together. What is the probability that three (no more and no less) 6's turn up?

The event E, here, is getting a 6 in a toss of a single die, and the number of trials is eight. To compute the desired probability, let us first compute the probability that three specified dice among the eight turn up 6 and that the remaining five do not. By the multiplication rule for independent events, this probability is

$$\frac{1}{6} \cdot \frac{1}{6} \cdot \frac{1}{6} \cdot \frac{5}{6} \cdot \frac{5}{6} \cdot \frac{5}{6} \cdot \frac{5}{6} \cdot \frac{5}{6} = \left(\frac{1}{6}\right)^3 \left(\frac{5}{6}\right)^5.$$

This same product would be the probability that any other specified set of three of the eight dice turn up 6 and that the remaining five do not. Since these different sets of three correspond to mutually exclusive events, we add the probabilities:

$$\left(\frac{1}{6}\right)^3 \left(\frac{5}{6}\right)^5 + \left(\frac{1}{6}\right)^3 \left(\frac{5}{6}\right)^5 + \cdots,$$

where there are as many (identical) terms as there are ways of selecting three out of eight objects. Hence,

$$P(3 \text{ 6's among 8 dice}) = \binom{8}{3} \left(\frac{1}{6}\right)^3 \left(\frac{5}{6}\right)^5.$$

We observe that tossing eight dice together is equivalent to tossing one die eight times, as far as the question of the number of 6's is concerned.

In the general case, we have n trials and a constant probability p that E occurs in a given trial. That E does not occur in a given trial then has probability $1 - p$, which we denote by q. Reasoning as in the above example, we have the following *binomial formula:*

$$P(k \text{ successes in } n \text{ trials}) = \binom{n}{k} p^k q^{n-k}.$$

Example 1–y

What is the probability that exactly three heads turn up when a coin is tossed five times?

Here, $n = 5$ and the event E is getting heads in a toss of a coin. The probabilities p and $1 - p$ are assumed to be $1/2$. Then,

$$P(3 \text{ heads in } 5 \text{ tosses}) = \binom{5}{3} \left(\frac{1}{2}\right)^3 \left(\frac{1}{2}\right)^2 = \frac{5}{16}.$$

Problems

1–33. What is the probability that if four coins are tossed
   (a) exactly three heads show?
   (b) at least three heads show?
   (c) at most one head shows?

1–34. A certain population of voters consists of forty-five in favor of and fifty-five opposed to a certain proposal. A sample of twenty is canvassed, but the voters are milling about and unknown to the canvasser, so that in effect the voters are drawn one at a time from a bowl, replaced, and then the bowl is mixed before the next is drawn. ("Sampling *with* replacement"—which implies independence of the observations, giving a repeated-trials situation.) What is the probability that the sample of twenty shows a majority in favor of the proposal? (Do not carry out the computations.)

1–35. What is the probability that if the sample of 20 in Problem 1–34 is taken by name from a list of the 100 voters, the sample shows a majority in favor? ("Sampling *without* replacement"—no longer independent observations, and the binomial formula does not apply.) (Do not carry out the computations.)

1–36. Six dice are tossed. What is the probability that
   (a) at most two 1's show?
   (b) at least five 2's or 3's show?

1.6 Expectation

If a reward, say, M (which may be dollars, cents, or the measure of anything which can be quantified), is associated with an event E whose probability is p, we say that the mathematical expectation, or simply expectation, of the event is the product pM. Or, if several mutually exclusive events, E_1, E_2, . . . , are considered, with associated rewards M_1, M_2, . . . , and probabilities p_1, p_2, . . . , we say that the expectation is

$$p_1 M_1 + p_2 M_2 + \cdots = \sum_i p_i M_i.$$

Example 1–z

A man throws a die and receives a dollar if he throws a 6, but receives nothing for any other point. His expectation is the probability of getting a 6, times one dollar, namely, $1/6$ of a dollar.

The practical significance of the expectation in this example is that if he rolls the die again and again, winning a dollar each time he throws a 6, he would expect to average one dollar in every six throws, distributed evenly over all the throws; it is hopefully an "average" amount won. If he were playing against a gambling house, he should then pay 1/6 of a dollar per throw, in order for the game to be fair—that is, in order for the house to take in enough money in sixths of a dollar to be able to pay out on the average of one dollar once in every six throws.

Problems

1-37. What would be a fair bet against $5.00 that two persons picked at random will not have birthdays in the same month, assuming that all months are equally likely?

1-38. How much should one pay to play a game in which the amount won is a number of dollars equal to the number of dots which show in a toss of a die?

1-39. Four coins are tossed. What is the expectation of the number of heads? (This question could have been asked in terms of money, as follows: How many dollars would you pay to play the game if one dollar is won for each head thrown in the toss of the four coins?)

1-40. How much should you pay to play this game? A standard deck of cards is cut, and a dollar is paid if a face card or an ace is turned up. (There are twelve face cards and four aces in the deck.)

Review Problems—Chapter 1

1-R1. In how many ways can eight objects be drawn from eleven?

1-R2. How many distinct code groups of four symbols in a row can be formed, where each symbol is either a dot or a dash?

1-R3. What is the probability that if four dice are tossed, exactly one is a 6?

1-R4. A tester smokes cigarettes of each of three different brands, A, B, and C. He then assigns the name A to one cigarette, B to another, and C to the remaining one. If he does this purely by chance, what is the probability that he correctly identifies just one brand?

1-R5. Suppose that 10,000 tickets are sold in a lottery, and 5000 in another lottery, each lottery having just one winner. A man has one hundred tickets in each. What is the probability that
(a) he wins exactly one prize?
(b) he wins something?

1-R6. What is the probability that five cards drawn together from a standard deck of fifty-two cards are from the same suit and could form a "run" of five? (For example: 9, king, queen, 10, jack of clubs.) Ace counts only high.

1-R7. A child has five blocks, three with the letter A and two with the letter B. How many distinct arrangements of four of these blocks can he make?

1-R8. It is found that in manufacturing a certain article, defects of one type occur with probability .1, and of another type with probability .05. What is the probability that
(a) an article does not have both kinds of defect?

(b) an article is defective?

(c) an article has only one type of defect, given that it is defective?

1–R9. A coin is tossed ten times. What is the probability that the tenth toss results in heads, given that the first nine tosses are heads?

1–R10. A game consists of tossing a coin, the player winning a dollar if heads turns up, and paying a dollar if tails turns up.

(a) What is the probability that in ten plays of the game a player comes out $4.00 ahead?

(b) What are his expected winnings in ten plays?

(c) Given that the player is $4.00 ahead after the first eight out of ten plays, what are then his expected winnings for the ten plays?

1–R11. Each of eight members of a committee flips a coin to decide whether he should attend a certain meeting of the committee.

(a) What is the probability that a majority will show up?

(b) How many different combinations might show up?

1–R12. A man has $7000 to invest in recovering his vacation expenses of $1000. He does this by playing a gambling game in which he is given even odds, but in which his probability of winning is only .4, at a given play. He bets $1000 on the first play and doubles his bet on successive trials if he loses.

(a) What is the probability that he wins (net) the $1000 before going broke?

(b) What is the probability that he wins before going broke on each of eight out of ten annual trips to the casino?

2/Random Variables and Distribution Functions

2.0 Introduction

In Chapter 1 we considered chance experiments in which the possible outcomes were finite in number and (by mutual agreement) equally likely. Defining the probability $P(E)$ of each event E provided a mathematical model to describe the potential result of the chance experiment each time it is performed.

The applicability of the models of Chapter 1 is rather limited. Many experiments of a chance nature defy breakdown into a finite number of equally likely outcomes—either because the number of outcomes is inherently infinite or because of the lack of such a thing as geometrical symmetry to aid our intuition. Even in such cases, however, we shall assign probabilities to events, but we can never know their precise numerical values.

Example 2-a

If a thumbtack is tossed in the air, it will settle in one of two positions of stable equilibrium—point up or point down. These are the possible outcomes. Because of the complex causes involved, the toss of a tack is best considered as an experiment of chance, and we assign probabilities to the two outcomes.

However, there is no obvious way, given the ratio of the length of the tack to the diameter of the head, of determining the proper assignment of probabilities. We postulate the existence of the probability that the tack lands with point up, and call it, say, p. The probability that it lands with point down is then said to be $1 - p$, so that the total of the assigned probabilities is 1.

Considering the toss of a thumbtack, as in this example, and the toss of a coin, as in Chapter 1, there is just as much reason to assign probabilities for the thumbtack as for the coin. In both cases there is a tendency for the proportion of outcomes of a given type in a large number of tosses to

27

approach a limiting value. In both cases we postulate the existence of probabilities. In the case of the coin, we were able to compute useful values for the probabilities, on the basis of intuition, whereas in the case of the tack, intuition fails to suggest the proper values.

Thus, for *every* experiment of chance, we postulate the existence of probabilities of events—that is, of sets of possible outcomes. These probabilities comprise the mathematical model for the experiment. It has been found that in order to obtain a usable and mathematically consistent model, the probabilities assigned to events should satisfy the following properties:

(1) For any event E, $0 \leq P(E) \leq 1$.

(2) $P(E) = \begin{cases} 1, \text{ if } E \text{ contains all outcomes,} \\ 0, \text{ if } E \text{ contains no outcomes.} \end{cases}$

(3) $P(E \text{ or } F) = P(E) + P(F)$, if E and F are mutually exclusive events.

(3') $P(E_1 \text{ or } E_2 \text{ or } \ldots) = P(E_1) + P(E_2) + \cdots$, if the events E_1, E_2, . . . , are mutually exclusive.

These properties are satisfied in the situations considered in Chapter 1, although we never had occasion there to consider infinitely many events, as in (3'), since the total number of outcomes was finite.

With probabilities defined in accordance with the above axioms, we define conditional probability and independence for the present more general models using the same formulas as in Chapter 1 (page 19). The multiplication rules of Chapter 1 *continue* to hold in the more general models.

Example 2–b

Consider two identical thumbtacks. As in Example 2-a, we assume that for each thumbtack there is a number p which gives the probability that it lands with point up when it is tossed. The tacks being identical, this probability is the same for both. Suppose now that both tacks are tossed (together, or one at a time). We ask: What is the probability that both will land with points up?

Surely there is no causal relationship between the ways in which the two tacks land (if they are not stuck together!) This physical independence of the ways the two tacks fall is then translated into the mathematical model as "stochastic" independence. That is, we define the probability that both points turn up using the multiplication rule for independent events:

$$P \text{ (both points up)} = p \cdot p = p^2.$$

Similarly, the probability that, say exactly six out of ten identical tacks land with points up is defined according to the binomial formula (page 23);

$$P \text{ (6 points up out of 10)} = \binom{10}{6} p^6 (1 - p)^4.$$

One might well wonder about the advantage of setting up a model in which one can never know the exact probabilities. Certainly the desirability of having a model available is clear; the point is that even though unknown, probabilities can be estimated through experimentation. Often, estimates of probabilities obtained through experimentation are used in place of the true probabilities for purposes of further argumentation.

Example 2-c

Suppose that the probability that a night lookout on a blacked-out ship detects a periscope under certain weather conditions is .7. What is the probability that a combination of two such lookouts would make the detection?

Assuming that the two lookouts, A and B, operate independently, we have

$$
\begin{aligned}
P(\text{detection}) &= 1 - P(\text{both } A \text{ and } B \text{ fail to detect}) \\
&= 1 - P(A \text{ fails to detect}) \, P(B \text{ fails to detect}) \\
&= 1 - (.3)(.3) = .91.
\end{aligned}
$$

Thus, whether or not .7 is exactly correct for a single lookout, it is clear that the extra lookout increases the probability of a detection.

Problems

2–1. A fire control system consists of a radar and a computer, so connected that the system fails if either of these components fails. If the probability that the radar operates 100 hours without failure is .9 and that the computer operates 100 hours without failure is .7, what is the probability that the combined system operates 100 hours without failure? (Assume failures of the components to be independent.)

2–2. Three alarm devices are so arranged that any one of them will give alarm when something undesirable occurs. If each device has probability .9 of working properly, what is the probability that an alarm is sounded when warranted?

2–3. The probability that a part produced by a certain machine is defective is .05. What is the probability that out of ten parts made by this machine, exactly one is defective?

2–4. The probability that an interceptor can make a successful attack is .6 if he has been "vectored" into position in a certain region with respect to the target. The probability that he is properly directed into position is .8. What is the probability of a successful interception? Suppose that the figure .6 includes a reliability (probability of successful operation) of .7 of the electronic computation system. What would be the probability of successful interception if the electronic system had a reliability of .95, instead?

2.1 Random Variables

In examples considered so far, outcomes of a chance experiment have been of many types: heads and tails, point up and point down, numbers of dots showing on a die, number of successes in several trials, defective or not defective, etc. Some of these are numbers and others are not. Analysis is easier when the outcomes are *numbers;* so when they are not numbers inherently, it is sometimes convenient to *assign* numerical values to the outcomes. This identification of a number with each outcome is quite similar to the notion of a functional relationship in mathematics. The notion of "independent variable" for an ordinary function corresponds here to the set of possible outcomes. For both an ordinary function and the identification introduced here, the "dependent variable" is the assigned value. Here, this assigned value is called a *random variable.* It *depends* for its specific values on the outcome of a chance experiment. In summary, we make the following definition.

Definition: A random variable is a numerical-valued function on the outcomes of a chance experiment.

A random variable is called "random" because the experiment is an experiment of chance. It is called a "variable" because it is a numerical quantity which varies (from one trial to another of the experiment).

When we say that a physical quantity "is a random variable," we mean first of all that it is a variable—a numerical variable—and second that it can be usefully represented by the mathematical model of numbers attached to the possible outcomes of an experiment of chance, in which probabilities of events have been defined as discussed in the preceding section.

We shall use *capital* letters to denote random variables: X, Y, etc. The name X symbolizes the *entire* picture—an experiment, probabilities of events, and numbers assigned to outcomes of the experiment. We write, for example,

$$P(X = 2 \text{ or } 3).$$

This denotes the probability that the outcome of the experiment is one of those to which have been assigned the number 2 or the number 3.

Example 2–d

A coin is tossed; let the possible outcomes be heads and tails. A frequently useful assignment of numbers to these outcomes is this: Let heads correspond to 1 and tails to 0. We have, then, a random variable; call it X. We can now talk about the event $X = 1$ in place of the *equivalent* event that the coin lands with heads up. And

$$P(X = 1) = P(\text{heads}) = \frac{1}{2}; \qquad P(X = 0) = P(\text{tails}) = \frac{1}{2}.$$

Example 2–e

Let us assign the number 1 to the odd numbers of points on the faces of a die, and the number 0 to the even numbers. We again have a random variable which takes on the values 1 and 0 each with probability 1/2, just as in Example 2-d above.

Examples 2–d and 2–e illustrate the fact that the same pattern of values may be obtained from different random variables. The random variables of these two examples are different because they are based on different experiments of chance. However, in each case the probability 1/2 is assigned to each of the values 0 and 1. It is indeed the case that for practical purposes one is interested only in the *values* 0 and 1 together with their *probabilities*. From this point of view, the random variables of Examples 2–d and 2–e are equivalent.

(It is because of this focus of attention on *values* of a random variable that the notation for a random variable makes no reference to the "independent variable"—the outcomes of the underlying experiment—unless these outcomes are themselves, perchance, the values of the random variable. In our subsequent graphical representations of a random variable, we shall also leave out this experiment and shall put the values of the random variable—the dependent variable—on the horizontal axis.)

Example 2–f

A die is tossed. Let

$$X = \text{The number of dots on the up-turned face.}$$

This is a random variable (which happens to have been built into the die by the manufacturer), having—usually—the values 1, 2, 3, 4, 5, and 6 with equal probabilities.

Example 2–g

Consider tossing four coins. For each coin we assign the value 1 to heads and the value 0 to tails. We have then four random variables: X_1, the number 1 or the number 0 depending on whether the *first* coin falls heads or tails; X_2, the same sort of thing for the *second* coin, etc. The assignments of probabilities to values are identical for these four random variables—they are all identical with that of Example 2–d.

One is often interested in yet another random variable, namely:

$$S = X_1 + X_2 + X_3 + X_4.$$

This sum of 0's and 1's is precisely the *number of heads among the four coins*. Probabilities of events relating to S are determined with the aid of the binomial formula.

For example:

$$P(S \leq 1) = P(S = 0 \text{ or } S = 1)$$
$$= P(0 \text{ or } 1 \text{ heads in } 4 \text{ "trials"})$$
$$= \binom{4}{0} \left(\frac{1}{2}\right)^0 \left(\frac{1}{2}\right)^4 + \binom{4}{1} \left(\frac{1}{2}\right)^1 \left(\frac{1}{2}\right)^3 = \frac{5}{16}.$$

Example 2–h

Consider an experiment in which a pointer is spun in a horizontal plane. A linear scale at the tip is marked continuously around the circle from 0 to 1. The outcome of the experiment is that the pointer stops somewhere; the number at which the pointer stops is a random variable, X. Probability would be specified (it seems clear intuitively) in such a way that, for example, $P(.1 < X < .3) = P(.4 < X < .6)$ —in general, in such a way that equal intervals have equal probability.

Example 2–i

The length of a rod is measured with a certain measuring device. Experience shows that repetitions of the measurement yield varying results—in an unpredictable fashion. Here we have a random variable—the *measured* length. In this example we do not have (as in Example 2–h) an intuitive feeling for how probability should be defined, except that in some sense, numbers in the vicinity of the actual length of the rod (whatever that may mean!) should be "most probable."

2.2 The Distribution Function

Having assigned numbers to the outcomes of a chance experiment, it becomes convenient to describe *events* in terms of those numbers. For example, the inequality $2 < X < 7$ describes a certain event—namely, the event that some outcome has occurred to which has been attached a number between 2 and 7.

Consider a probability model given by an *a priori* assignment of probabilities to outcomes of an experiment. These probabilities are automatically transferred to the numbers or sets of numbers which are the values of a given random variable defined on the experiment. However, in constructing a probability model *without a priori* assistance, it is convenient to assign probabilities *directly* to the values or sets of values of the random quantity of interest. This is usually done by specifying the *distribution function* of the random variable.

In defining the distribution function of a random variable, we assign probabilities to all events of a certain simple type, namely, half-infinite intervals such as the event $X \leq 4$. The amount of probability assigned depends on the interval boundary (this boundary is 4 in the case of the interval $X \leq 4$). It is then a *function* of that boundary. We use the name

$F(\,\cdot\,)$ to denote this function and have then, for instance,

$$F(4) = P(X \leq 4), \qquad F(-1) = P(X \leq -1), \text{ etc.}$$

In general, for an arbitrary interval boundary x, we have

$$F(x) = P(X \leq x).$$

This is the distribution function; it is a function of x. If it is necessary to distinguish the distribution function of one random variable from that of another, we use a subscript. Thus,

$$F_X(x) = P(X \leq x), \qquad F_Y(x) = P(Y \leq x), \text{ etc.}$$

The distribution function is of course immediately defined from probabilities of outcomes, when these are the starting point, as in the *a priori* models of Chapter 1.

Example 2–j

Consider any random variable having the two values 0 and 1 each with probability 1/2. We have seen two such random variables in Examples 2–d and 2–e. The distribution function is

$$F(x) = P(X \leq x) = \begin{cases} 0, \text{ if } x < 0, \\ 1/2, \text{ if } 0 \leq x < 1, \\ 1, \text{ if } x \geq 1. \end{cases}$$

The graph has jumps in the amount 1/2 at each of the values 0 and 1, as shown in Figure 2–1.

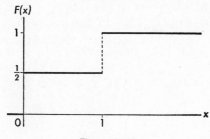

Figure 2–1

Example 2–k

Consider (as in Example 2–b, page 28) two identical thumbtacks tossed on the table. The number, X, of tacks which land with point up is a random variable with values 0, 1, or 2. Corresponding probabilities are $(1 - p)^2$, $2p(1 - p)$, and p^2,

respectively, by the binomial formula.   The distribution function is shown in Figure
2–2.

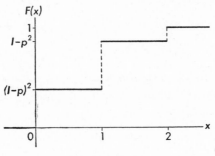

Figure 2–2

If we use the distribution function to set up a probability model, we
must be sure that all types of events which we might have to consider are
assigned probabilities.   For instance, we surely should want to know probabilities of individual values (say, $X = 2$), and probabilities of intervals
(for instance, $2 < X < 7$, or $X > -3$).

A finite interval may be treated as follows.   Since the event $X \leq b$ is
equivalent to the compound event $[X \leq a$ or $a < X \leq b]$, we must have

$$P(X \leq b) = P(X \leq a) + P(a < X \leq b),$$

or, transposing,

$$P(a < X \leq b) = F(b) - F(a).$$

Thus, probabilities of all events of the type $a < X \leq b$ are given by the
"addition rule" (property (3), page 28) as soon as $F(x)$ is specified.

A single value of X may be treated as a limit of intervals containing and
narrowing down to that value.   Thus,

$$P(X = b) = \lim_{a \to b} P(a < X \leq b) = \lim_{a \to b} [F(b) - F(a)]$$
$$= F(b) - \lim_{a \to b} F(a).$$

If $F(x)$ is continuous at $x = b$, this last difference is zero.   Otherwise it
represents the amount of the "jump" in the function $F(x)$ from the limiting
value as x approaches b from the left, up to the value of $F(x)$ at $x = b$.   We
should observe that in the two examples above (Examples 2–j and 2–k) the
distribution functions jumped at certain values of X, indicating non-zero
probabilities of those values.

Although events of considerable complexity may be constructed as combinations of half-infinite intervals and single values, we shall actually need only a few simple kinds, typified in the following examples.

Example 2-l

An interval closed at both ends, such as $2 \leq X \leq 7$, may be constructed from a half-closed interval and a point:

$$P(2 \leq X \leq 7) = P(X = 2) + P(2 < X \leq 7).$$

An interval open at both ends is treated similarly:

$$P(2 < X < 7) = P(2 < X \leq 7) - P(X = 7).$$

Of course, *if individual points carry no probability, it is immaterial whether the inequalities are written < or ≤.*

Example 2-m

The event $|X - 3| < 5$ is just the interval from -2 to 8, since this inequality is simply another way of writing

$$-5 < X - 3 < +5.$$

Adding 3 to each member of this extended inequality yields $-2 < X < 8$. Hence,

$$P(|X - 3| < 5) = P(-2 < X < 8) = F(8) - F(-2) - P(X = 8),$$

where $F(x)$ is the distribution function, $P(X \leq x)$. It is helpful to think of the absolute value of the difference $|X - 3|$ as (what it really is, of course) the *distance* between X and 3. Thus, the inequality $|X - 3| < 5$ is satisfied by any value of X closer than 5 units to the value 3, on either side of 3. Similarly, then, the inequality $|X - 3| > 5$ defines the set of all values of X *farther* than 5 units from 3, and

$$P(|X - 3| > 5) = P(X > 8 \text{ or } X < -2) = P(X > 8) + P(X < -2)$$
$$= 1 - F(8) + F(-2) - P(X = -2).$$

Let us point out that in assigning probabilities to the more complicated events, in several instances above, we have done so in such a way that the rules of combination (1)-(3) on page 28 are satisfied. That is, assigning probabilities by means of the distribution function does not define a new *kind* of probability.

When setting up a probability model by specifying a probability distribution function, it is not always obvious what function to take. Sometimes it is clear from the context what to use, but often one must make an educated guess—and perhaps look for statistical "verification" (such as will be discussed in later chapters). In any event, the function used as $F(x)$ cannot be completely arbitrary; it must satisfy certain conditions as a consequence of being a probability. For example, since probability has been defined as a number between 0 and 1, we must require that

(a) $0 \leq F(x) \leq 1$.

And since we should not want the probability of an interval to be negative, we must have

(b) $F(b) \geq F(a)$, whenever $a < b$.

This means that $F(x)$ must be a nondecreasing function—that is, nondecreasing as we move from left to right. Further, we should have

(c)
$$F(+\infty) = P(X \leq +\infty) = 1,$$
$$F(-\infty) = P(X \leq -\infty) = 0.$$

One would also want, for positive increments h,

(d) $\lim_{h \to 0} P(x < X \leq x + h) = \lim_{h \to 0} [F(x + h) - F(x)] = 0.$

This condition is described by saying that $F(x)$ is continuous from the right.

Summarizing, the properties (a)-(d) above are requirements which must by satisfied by a function before it will serve as a distribution function in a probability model. These properties of a distribution function *are* all satisfied by the function

$$F(x) = P(X \leq x)$$

in those cases in which it is convenient to begin with *probabilities* of events, rather than with the distribution function, in constructing a model.

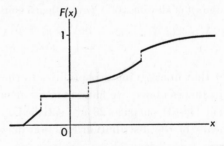

Figure 2–3. A Possible Distribution Function of General Type

A quite *general* distribution function may then look something like that in Figure 2–3. Values of the random variable are plotted horizontally; the vertical axis represents *probability*, and the vertical scale extends from 0 to 1.

The jumps in the above graph correspond to non-zero "lumps" of probability at the x values at which they occur. The probability that X takes on a given x value is the *amount* of the jump in $F(x)$ at that value (which, of course, is zero if there is *no* jump there). Notice that the value of $F(x)$ at a jump point is the higher value. The horizontal sections of the graph correspond to zero probability for those intervals of constancy. And the continuously rising sections correspond to "smears" of probability over intervals, where individual values of x have zero probability, but where a subinterval has non-zero probability given by the amount of the rise in $F(x)$ over it.

In most commonly occurring problems the distribution is either entirely of the "lump" type or of the "smear" type. These are given the names "discrete" and "continuous," respectively, and are both special cases of the general distributions we have been discussing. This classification will be discussed in more detail in Section 2.3 and in later chapters.

A helpful way of thinking of a probability distribution is this: We start at $-\infty$ with a load of probability in the amount 1, and as we proceed along the horizontal axis, we distribute our load—a lump of so much at this point and a smear of so much (in varying thickness) over that interval, etc.,—until we reach $+\infty$ with our load completely distributed. The function $F(x)$ tells us the (accumulated) amount we have distributed by the time we have progressed to the point x.

Example 2–n

Let the distribution function of a random variable X be defined to be

$$F(x) = \begin{cases} 0 \text{ if } x < 0, \\ \dfrac{1 - x^2}{2} + x, \text{ if } 0 \le x \le 1, \\ 1, \text{ if } x > 1. \end{cases}$$

The graph of this function is given in Figure 2–4. We notice that this function satisfies conditions (a)-(d), page 36, and is therefore a legitimate specification of a distribution function.

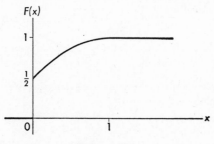

Figure 2–4

From the graph, or from the rule given for computing $F(x)$, it is seen that

$$P(.5 < X < 1) = F(1) - F(.5) = 1 - \frac{7}{8},$$

and

$$P(X > .2) = F(\infty) - F(.2) = 1 - .68 = .32.$$

Also,

$$P(X = 0) = (\text{amount of jump at } 0) = \frac{1}{2},$$

and

$$P(X = 1) = (\text{amount of jump at } 1) = 0.$$

In the chapters to follow, the term *distribution function* will be used to refer exclusively to the *cumulative* quantity:

$$F(x) = P(X \le x).$$

The term *probability distribution*, or simply *distribution*, will be used to refer to a certain assignment of probability to the values of a random quantity—without referring necessarily to a specific manner (such as the distribution function) of describing just how probability is distributed. Thus, the distribution *function* describes a distribution. We shall see subsequently that distributions may also be described by other devices.

Problems

2–5. Let the probability be 1/3 that a certain type of tack lands with point up. Sketch the distribution function of the random quantity which is 1 when the tack lands point up and 0 when it lands with point down.

2–6. A box of articles, four good and one defective, is tested one at a time. Let X denote the number of the test in which the defective article is located. Construct the distribution function of X.

2–7. Consider the function sketched at the right. Check to see that it satisfies the conditions for a distribution function. Express this function algebraically.

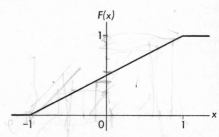

2–8. Let X be a random variable having the distribution function shown in Problem 2–7. Determine from the picture

(a) $P(X < .5)$.

(b) $P(-.2 < X < .8)$.

(c) $P(X > .1)$.

(d) $P(X < 3)$.

(e) $P(X < -2)$.

(f) $P(|X - .4| > .3)$.

2–9. Let $F(x) = 0$ for negative x, and $1 - e^{-x}$ for non-negative x. Check to see that the conditions for a distribution function are satisfied, and determine
(a) $P(X < 1)$.
(b) $P(-1 < X < 1)$.
(c) $P(X > 2)$.
(d) the number m such that $P(X < m) = .5$.

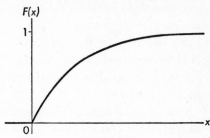

2–10. Let $F(x) = 0$ for negative x, and let it be $1 - 3/4e^x$ for positive x, as shown. Compute
(a) $P(X > 2)$.
(b) $P(X \le 0)$.
(c) $P(X = 0)$.
(d) $P(X = 2)$.
(e) $P(|X - 1| < 2)$.

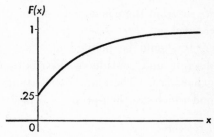

2–11. Table I, page 253, gives the values of a certain distribution function, called there $\Phi(z)$. If Z has this distribution, determine from the table
(a) $P(|Z| > 1)$.
(b) $P(Z < -3.2)$.
(c) $P(|Z| < 2)$.
(d) $P(|Z - .2| > 2)$.

2.3 Classification of Distributions

Because of the different formulas which we shall derive for two commonly occurring types of situations, we shall consider separately,† in the next two chapters, *discrete* probability distributions and *continuous* probability distributions.

A probability distribution is said to be *discrete* if the distribution function $F(x)$, which describes it, is a "step function"—a function which increases only in finite jumps and which is constant between jumps. The distribution of probability is thus made in discrete lumps at the points where the jumps occur, in amounts equal to the sizes of the jumps.

† It is possible to consider both discrete and continuous cases (and more) simultaneously, using a "Stieltjes integral" with respect to the distribution function. This type of integral includes the summations of Chapter 3 and the integrations of Chapter 4 as special cases. The same formulas can be used in both cases, and we should not have needed separate chapters for discrete and continuous variables; but we do not pursue this course.

A random variable is called a discrete random variable if its distribution function is discrete.

A probability distribution is said to be *continuous* if the distribution function $F(x)$ is continuous and if it has a derivative, $F'(x)$, at all but perhaps a finite number of values of x. Since $F(x)$ is continuous, it has no jumps, and there are therefore *no* lumps of probability at any value of x.

A random variable is called a continuous random variable if its distribution is continuous.

A discrete probability distribution is quite analagous to a discrete mass distribution—a collection of "point masses" at certain points along an axis. A continuous probability distribution is analagous to a continuous mass distribution—such as in a long thread of varying thickness—in which case we say that there is no mass *at* any given point, but that there *is* mass in an *interval*.

It should be pointed out that the classification of distributions into discrete and continuous distributions is, although usually adequate, not exhaustive. There are distributions which are a mixture of the two types and which are then properly neither type (cf. Problem 2–10).

Problems

2–12. Determine the nature of the probability distribution (discrete, continuous, or neither) in Examples 2–d through 2–k.

2.4 Functions of Random Variables

Consider the problem of measuring the area of a square with an instrument which measures length. The obvious method is to measure the length of one side (if one is "sure" that it is really a square!) and to square the result. As we have mentioned earlier, the measured length of an object is inevitably a random variable—let us call it X. The computed area is then X^2—a quantity which is a random variable (it varies, and its value depends on a chance experiment), just as much as X is a random variable.

In this simple example, the probability distribution of X^2 is easily obtained from that of X. For, the distribution function of X^2 is just

$$F_{X^2}(x) = P(X^2 \leq x) = P(|X| \leq \sqrt{x}) = \begin{cases} 0 \text{ if } x < 0, \\ F_X(\sqrt{x}) - F_X(-\sqrt{x}), \text{ if } x \geq 0. \end{cases}$$

The first equality is true by definition of the distribution function in terms of probability, or by definition of probability from the distribution function, depending on which has been taken as the fundamental concept. The second equality of probabilities follows from the fact that $(X^2 \leq x)$ and

$(|X| \leq x)$ describe exactly the same event. The third equality follows from the meaning of $|X| \leq \sqrt{x}$, namely, that $-\sqrt{x} < X < \sqrt{x}$.

Actually, such situations are common. One often wishes to perform some functional operation $g(\cdot)$ on the particular observed value of a random variable; as above, such a functional operation yields a new random variable, $Y = g(X)$. As in the case above, the distribution of Y is obtainable from that of X, although care must be exercised if the inverse function is not single valued.

We have even met with a situation in Example 2–g (page 31) in which we had occasion to consider a function of *several* random variables. Such a function is again a random variable.

Problems

2–13. Let X be a random variable with the distribution function of Problem 2–7, namely:

$$F_X(x) = P(X \leq x) = \begin{cases} 0, \text{ if } x < -1, \\ \dfrac{1}{2}(x + 1), \text{ if } -1 \leq x \leq 1, \\ 1, \text{ if } x > 1. \end{cases}$$

Determine the distribution function of the random variable
   (a) $Y = X - 3$.
   (b) $Z = 2X$.
   (c) $U = |X|$.
2–14. Let $X = 0$ if a coin lands tails and $X = 1$ if it lands heads. Sketch the distribution function of the variable $V = X(1 - X)$.
2–15. Two dice are tossed. Let X be the number of points on the first die and Y the number of points on the second die. Discuss the probability distribution of the random variable.
   (a) $T = X + Y$.
   (b) $W = XY$.

2.5 Distribution Percentiles

In tabulating the values of a function $y = f(x)$ it is common practice to give values y (plotted vertically) corresponding to equally spaced values of the independent variable x (plotted horizontally). Indeed, Table I, page 253, gives the value of a certain frequently used probability distribution function according to this scheme.

Another possible scheme, and one which is often convenient, is to give the values of the horizontally plotted variable corresponding to points which are *equally spaced on the vertical axis*. Consider a distribution function, $F(x)$. Its values range from 0 to 1, in increasing fashion. If this range of values is divided into 100 equal parts, the corresponding values of x are called the percentiles. For example, the value of x corresponding to $F(x) = .20$ is called the twentieth percentile of the distribution and is denoted by $x_{.20}$:

$$P(X \leq x_{.20}) = F(x_{.20}) = .20.$$

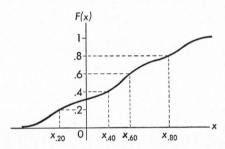

Figure 2-5. Percentiles of a Distribution

Particular percentiles which are assigned special names are the *median:* the fiftieth percentile, and the *quartiles:* the twenty-fifth, fiftieth, and seventy-fifth percentiles.

The above discussion needs a little modification when the distribution is of the discrete type. There may be many values of x such that $P(X \leq x) = .50$, for example. This will occur if the distribution function $F(x)$ happens to be horizontal at the level .50 over an interval, and *any* number in that interval may then be taken as the median. Also, there may be *no* value of x such that $P(X \leq x) = 1/2$. In such a case one takes the median to be a number m, such that

$$P(X \leq m) \geq \frac{1}{2} \quad \text{and} \quad P(X \geq m) \geq \frac{1}{2}.$$

(This definition of median actually applies in *every* case.)

Problems

2–16. Compute the medians of each of the distributions in Problems 2–7, 2–9, and 2–10.

2–17. Discuss $x_{.25}$ (the first quartile) of the distribution of Example 2-k, page 33, in the two cases $p = 1/2$ and $p = 1/3$.

2–18. Determine the fifth and ninety-fifth percentiles of the distribution function tabulated in Table I, page 253.

2–19. Sketch the graph of the "χ^2 distribution with 4 degrees of freedom" as given by the percentiles in Table II, page 256. From the graph, estimate the fortieth percentile of the distribution. Compute also the probability that a random variable with this distribution takes on a value between 4 and 8.

Review Problems—Chapter 2.

2–R1. In a certain series, the probability that A wins the first game is $1/2$; and in any subsequent game, odds are two to one in favor of the previous winner. The first four wins for either player wins the series. What is the probability that A wins in four games? In five games?

2–R2. A random variable X has the distribution function shown. Determine from the graph
  (a) $P(-1/2 < X < 2)$.
  (b) $P(|X - 1| < 1)$.
  (c) $P(X = -1/2)$.
  (d) $P(X > 1)$.

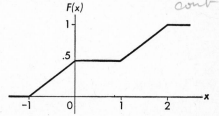

2–R3. A random variable X has the distribution function shown. Determine from the graph
  (a) $P(1/2 < X < 3/2)$.
  (b) $P(X = 1/2)$.
  (c) $P(X = 1)$.
  (d) $P(X \leq 1)$.
  (e) $P(X > 1)$.

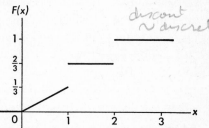

2–R4. For each of the random variables in Problems 2–R2 and 2–R3, determine whether it is discrete, continuous, or not exclusively of either of these two types.

2–R5. A person is to be picked at random from a large group of people and weighed. The weight so obtained is a random variable; discuss the type of probability distribution one might expect.

2–R6. Suppose that both the weight and height of the person picked in Problem 2–R5 are determined. Would these be independent random variables? Is the eye color of the person picked a random variable? Could you *code* eye color so as to construct a random variable?

2–R7. Sketch the graph of the "t distribution with 10 degrees of freedom" as given by the percentiles in Table III, page 257. (Observe the note at the bottom of the page.) From the graph determine approximately the probability that a random variable with this distribution takes on a value exceeding .75 in magnitude—that is, determine $P(|t| > .75)$.

2–R8. A random variable X has the distribution function

$$F(x) = \begin{cases} 0, & x < 0, \\ \dfrac{1 - \cos x}{2}, & 0 \leq x \leq \pi, \\ 1, & x > \pi. \end{cases}$$

  (a) Determine the median of X.
  (b) Compute $P(\pi/4 < X < \pi/3)$.

3/Discrete Distributions

3.0 Introduction

In Chapter 2, a random variable X was said to be discrete if its distribution function is a "step function"—a function which is constant between vertical jumps. In such a case, all of the probability is distributed among the values of X at which the jumps occur. We refer to these numbers as "possible values" of the random variable and denote them by x_1, x_2, ...

In this chapter we shall discuss certain quantities associated with a discrete distribution—quantities which give an idea of the location and extent of the distribution of probability. We shall also discuss a few quite important discrete distributions and their applications.

3.1 The Probability Function

The distribution function of a discrete random variable can be constructed from a knowledge of the list of possible values and the respective probabilities that they occur. It will be convenient to have a symbol for the probability of occurrence of a given value, x_i. We let

$$p(x_i) = P(X = x_i)$$

and call this function of the possible values the *probability function* of the distribution.

The quantity $p(x_i)$, then, is just the amount of the jump in the distribution function $F(x)$ at the point $x = x_i$. Moreover, the function $F(x)$ may be constructed from the probability function as follows:

$$F(x) = P(X \leq x) = \sum_{x_i \leq x} p(x_i).$$

The value of $F(x)$ corresponding to any number x is just the sum of the probabilities of possible values which lie to the left of or at the point x. (Review the discussion on page 37.)

44

Notice that these probabilities $p(x_i)$ must be such that they add up to 1:

$$\sum_{\text{all } x_i} p(x_i) = F(+\infty) = 1.$$

Example 3–a

Consider the toss of a coin, and assign the number 0 to tails and the number 1 to heads. Let X denote the number corresponding to the side which turns up. The possible values of this random variable are just $x_1 = 0$ and $x_2 = 1$, and the probability function is given by $p(0) = p(1) = 1/2$.

Example 3–b

Consider the toss of a die, and let X be the number of dots on the face which turns up. This is a random variable, with possible values 1, 2, 3, 4, 5, and 6. The probability function values are

$$p(1) = p(2) = \cdots = p(6) = \frac{1}{6}.$$

That is, $p(x_i) = 1/6$ for each possible value x_i.

Example 3–c

Consider n identical, independent trials of an experiment, and let p denote the probability that a certain event E occurs at a given trial. Let X denote the number of times E occurs among the n trials. This number X is a random variable, with possible values 0, 1, 2, . . . , n. That is, the possible values (x_i) are integers from 0 to n. The probability function is given by the formula

$$p(k) = P(X = k) = P(k \text{ successes in } n \text{ trials})$$
$$= \binom{n}{k} p^k (1 - p)^{n-k},$$

where k is any one of the possible values.

Example 3–d

A coin is tossed repeatedly; let X be the number of the toss in which heads first appears. Here we have a random variable with an infinite set of possible values: 1, 2, 3, ... Probability function values are as follows:

$$p(1) = P(\text{heads in first toss}) = \frac{1}{2}$$
$$p(2) = P(\text{tails in first toss, heads in second}) = \left(\frac{1}{2}\right) \cdot \left(\frac{1}{2}\right)$$

$$\vdots \qquad\qquad \vdots \qquad\qquad \vdots$$

$$p(k) = P(\text{tails in first } k - 1 \text{ tosses, heads in } k\text{th}) = \left(\frac{1}{2}\right)^k,$$

and so on. Note that $\Sigma p(k)$ is a geometric series and converges to 1.

$$\Sigma \, p(k) \,\dot{=}\, \Sigma \left(\tfrac{1}{2}\right)^k = \Sigma \tfrac{1}{2^k} \quad \text{converges!} \longrightarrow 1$$

Problems

> *Note:* The student should save the work on these problems, since this work will be useful when these same situations are analyzed further in the next two sets of problems.

3–1. Let X be the total number of dots which turn up in a toss of two dice. Construct a table giving the probability function.

3–2. A box of articles, four good and one defective, is tested one at a time. Let X be the number of the test in which the defective article is located. Give the possible values of X and the corresponding probabilities.

3–3. A lot contains ten good and three defective articles. Four articles are selected at random. Construct the probability function for X, the number of defectives in the sample drawn.

3–4. Four articles are taken at random off a production line in which good articles are being produced with probability $1 - p$, defective articles with probability p. Determine the probability function for the number of defectives among the four articles selected.

3–5. A four-sided die is tossed. It is a tetrahedron with one, two, three, and four dots, respectively, on the four sides. Let X be a random variable which assumes the value 1 if an *odd* number of points show and 0 if an *even* number show. Determine the probability function, and compare with that of Example 2–d, page 30.

3–6. Two dice are cast over and over. Let X be the number of the cast in which a 7 is first thrown. List the possible values of X and determine the probability function.

3.2 Expected Value

Let X be a discrete random variable, with possible values $x_1, x_2, \ldots$, which may be a finite or an infinite sequence of numbers. Let the probability function be $p(x_i) = P(X = x_i)$. We define the quantity $E(X)$ to be the weighted sum of the possible values, where the weights are the corresponding probabilities:

$$E(X) = \sum_i x_i p(x_i)$$
$$= x_1 p(x_1) + x_2 p(x_2) + \cdots .$$

This sum is referred to by any one of these names: *expected value, mean, expectation,* or *average* of the random variable X. The notation μ or μ_X is also commonly used for this average.

If the list of possible values of X is finite: $x_1, \ldots, x_n$, and if these are all equally likely (that is, $p(x_i) = 1/n$, for all x_i), the mean value of X reduces to the ordinary average of the possible values: $\Sigma x_i(1/n)$. In cases in which the possible values are *not* equally likely, the various terms in the average become *weighted*—according to their relative likelihoods of occurrence as given by $p(x_i)$.

The above notion of expected value is identical with the notion of expectation defined at the end of Chapter 1. Indeed, the "reward" associated with the outcome of a chance experiment is a common and natural instance of a random variable. The "expected reward" is precisely the expected value defined above, and we have thus extended the definition of expectation to include cases in which the probabilities are not necessarily determined in *a priori* fashion.

Example 3–e

A man wins a dollar for heads and loses a dollar for tails when a coin is tossed. Suppose that he tosses once and quits if he wins, but tries once more if he loses on the first toss. What are his expected winnings?

He can win one dollar, by getting heads on the first toss; he can lose two dollars, by getting tails both times; or he can come out even, by getting tails the first time and heads the second. The number of dollars he wins is a random variable with possible values 1, −2, and 0. These have probabilities 1/2, 1/4, and 1/4, respectively. The expected number of dollars won is then

$$1 \cdot \frac{1}{2} + (-2) \cdot \frac{1}{4} + 0 \cdot \frac{1}{4} = 0.$$

Example 3–f

A die is cast; let X be the number of points thrown. The possible values of X are 1, 2, 3, 4, 5, and 6. Each of these has probability 1/6, and hence the expected number of points thrown is

$$\mu = E(X) = \frac{1}{6} (1 + 2 + 3 + 4 + 5 + 6) = \frac{7}{2}.$$

It is often convenient to arrange this computation in tabular form.

x_i	$p(x_i)$	$x_i p(x_i)$
1	1/6	1/6
2	1/6	2/6
3	1/6	3/6
4	1/6	4/6
5	1/6	5/6
6	1/6	6/6
	$\Sigma p(x_i) = 1$	$\Sigma x_i p(x_i) = 21/6 = 7/2.$

Observe that in this instance the average or expected number of points would never actually be thrown in a single trial—it is *not* one of the possible values.

Example 3–g

As in Example 3–d, page 45, let X be the number of tosses of a coin it takes to get the first heads. The possible values are the integers, 1, 2, . . . , and the probability function is $p(k) = (1/2)^k$. The expected number of tosses required is then

$$E(X) = 1 \left(\frac{1}{2}\right) + 2 \left(\frac{1}{2}\right)^2 + 3 \left(\frac{1}{2}\right)^3 + \cdots = 2.$$

(This sum was computed by the trick of differentiating each of the terms in the identity

$$1 + a + a^2 + \cdots = \frac{1}{1 - a}$$

with respect to a, substituting $a = 1/2$ in the results, and multiplying by $1/2$. The reader was not expected to be familiar with this device.)

In Section 2.4 (page 40) we discussed formation of new random variables by performing operations on the given ones—that is, constructing a random variable $Y = g(X)$ by performing the operations defining $g(\cdot)$ on each of the possible values of X. We saw there how probabilities are transferred from the values of X to the values of $g(X)$ in a natural way: The probability of a given value of $g(X)$ is taken to be the *sum* of the probabilities of all values of X leading to that value of $g(X)$. If we let the values of $Y = g(X)$ be denoted by $y_1, y_2, \ldots$, the expectation of Y is computed in this way:

$$E(Y) = E[g(X)] = \sum_j y_j P[Y = y_j]$$

$$= \sum_j y_j P[\text{a value } x \text{ is obtained for which } g(x) = y_j]$$

$$= \sum_i g(x_i) P[X = x_i] = \sum_i g(x_i) p(x_i).$$

The expectation of $g(X)$ may then be computed either by computing the probabilities for the new variable Y and then computing $E(Y)$ according to definition of $E(\ \ )$ or by the formula

$$E[g(X)] = \sum_i g(x_i) p(x_i).$$

Example 3–h

Again let X be the number of points thrown on a die. Suppose that for some reason we are interested in the random variable

$$Y = (X - 3)^2.$$

In the tables below are carried out the computations of the expectation of $(X - 3)^2$ according to the two methods described above.

x_i	$p(x_i)$	$(x_i - 3)^2$	$(x_i - 3)^2 p(x_i)$
1	1/6	4	4/6
2	1/6	1	1/6
3	1/6	0	0
4	1/6	1	1/6
5	1/6	4	4/6
6	1/6	9	9/6
	1		19/6

y_i	$P(Y = y_i)$	$y_i P(Y = y_i)$
0	1/6	0
1	2/6	2/6
4	2/6	8/6
9	1/6	9/6
	1	19/6

We observe that the results of the two computations are the same:

$$E[(X - 3)^2] = \frac{19}{6}.$$

An examination of these tables shows how the probabilities of the y_i are obtained, and why the two methods are equivalent. For instance, the 1/3 for $P(Y = 1)$ is the sum of the 1/6 for $P(X = 2)$ and the 1/6 for $P(X = 4)$.

Next suppose that we consider two functions of X, $g(X)$ and $h(X)$. The sum of these two is again a random variable. And the mean value of this sum is computed as follows:

$$E[g(X) + h(X)] = \Sigma[g(x_i) + h(x_i)]p(x_i)$$
$$= \Sigma g(x_i)p(x_i) + \Sigma h(x_i)p(x_i) = E[g(X)] + E[h(X)].$$

This additive property of the expection operator $E[\ \ ]$ is actually quite general. We state without proof the following fact: If X and Y are any two random variables,

$$E(X + Y) = E(X) + E(Y).$$

This will be discussed further in Chapter 5.

Two further properties of the expectation operator $E(\ \ )$ should be discussed. Consider that function $g(x)$ which assigns the same value to each x—that is, $g(x) = k$, where k is a given constant. Now consider a random variable X; we may construct the new variable $g(X) = k$. This $g(X)$ is really not random in the usual sense of unpredictability, since no matter how the experiment turns out, the value of $g(X)$ is k. However, we take this to be a very special case of a random variable and compute its average as follows:

$$E(k) = \Sigma k p(x_i) = k \Sigma p(x_i) = k.$$

That is, the expected value of a "variable" which is really constant is that constant value.

Next consider the particular function $g(x) = kx$, where again k is a given constant. For the random variable kX, we have

$$E(kX) = \Sigma kx_i p(x_i) = k\Sigma x_i p(x_i) = kE(X).$$

Example 3–i

If X is the number of points thrown with a die, and one has occasion to consider the random variable $3X + 7$, he may compute the average as follows:

$$E(3X + 7) = 3E(X) + E(7) = 3 \cdot \frac{7}{2} + 7 = \frac{35}{2}.$$

Example 3–j

Let X be any random variable, and let μ be its expected value. Then

$$E(X - \mu) = E(X) - \mu = 0.$$

The calculation of this last example shows that for any discrete variable the "deviation of X from its mean," as the quantity $X - \mu$ is called, has expectation zero. This is the basis for thinking of the expected value of a random variable as measuring the location of the "center" of its probability distribution. Let us explain this using the mass analogy, mentioned in Chapter 2, page 40.

Suppose that we place a point mass of $m(x_1)$ units at x_1, $m(x_2)$ units at x_2, etc. According to the principles of physics, to locate the center of gravity, x_{cg}, of this system of point masses, we compute the "first moment" of the masses about the origin and divide this by the total amount of mass. The formula is this:

$$x_{cg} = \frac{\Sigma x_i m(x_i)}{\Sigma m(x_i)}.$$

But if the masses, $m(x_i)$, are already *relative* masses—expressed as fractions of the whole—the denominator is one unit. The formula is now exactly the same as the formula for the expected value of a random variable with possible values x_1, x_2, . . . and corresponding probabilities $m(x_1)$, $m(x_2)$, ... It is then convenient and correct to think of the expected value of a random variable as a "center of gravity" of the distribution. The property derived in Example 3–j above, that the average deviation about the mean of a random variable is zero, corresponds precisely to a property of a system of masses: The total first moment about the center of gravity is zero.

Problems

3–7—3–12. Determine the expected values of the random variables introduced in Problems 3–1—3–6, page 46.

3–13. Let X be the random variable of Problem 3–5, and determine $E[g(X)]$, where $g(x)$ is the function e^{tx}.

3–14. Compute $E(X^2 - X)$ where X is the variable of Problem 3–1.

3–15. Consider the tossing of two dice. Let X be the number of points on one and Y the number on the other. Compute $E(X)$ and $E(Y)$. Then notice that $X + Y$ is the random variable whose expected value was computed in Problem 3–7 and thus verify that in this case $E(X + Y) = E(X) + E(Y)$.

3.3 Moments

When comparing the distribution of probability with a distribution of mass, we used the term "first moment" to describe the sum

$$E(X) = \sum_i x_i p(x_i).$$

This mean or expected value gives certain information about the distribution—in particular, information about the center of the distribution. Further information about a distribution is provided by moments of higher order; the kth moment is defined to be

$$E(X^k) = \sum_i x_i^k p(x_i),$$

the expected value of the kth power of the variable X. (The number k is any integer: $k = 0, 1, 2, \ldots$.) It is often true that not only can all of these moments be determined from the distribution of probability, but also the distribution of probability is defined by the moments.

The above moments are referred to, more specifically, as moments "about the origin," to distinguish them from moments about other points. For example, the kth moment about the point $x = a$ would be the expected value of the kth power of $(X - a)$:

$$E[(X - a)^k] = \sum_i (x_i - a)^k p(x_i).$$

Moments about the *mean* are important. In particular, the second moment about the mean has a special name; it is called the *variance* of the probability distribution or of the random variable having this distribution. It is denoted by σ^2, by σ_X^2, or by var X:

$$\sigma_X^2 = E[(X - \mu)^2] = \sum_i (x_i - \mu)^2 p(x_i).$$

The positive square root of the variance is called the *standard deviation:*

$$\sigma_X = \sqrt{\sigma_X{}^2} = \sqrt{\Sigma(x_i - \mu)^2 p(x_i)}.$$

This has the same dimension as the variable X itself.

The standard deviation actually measures (and so also then does the variance) the possible variability in an observation on the random variable with the given distribution. It can be shown, for instance, that no more than 1/9 of the probability is distributed outside the interval from $\mu - 3\sigma$ to $\mu + 3\sigma$. That is, the probability is never more than 1/9 that a value outside that range occurs. (In general, according to the "Tchebychev inequality," the probability is never more than $1/k^2$ that a value falls outside the range from $\mu - k\sigma$ to $\mu + k\sigma$.) In specific cases, the situation can be more pronounced. It will be seen from Table I, page 253, that for the continuous probability distribution given there, the probability of getting a value outside $\mu - 3\sigma$ to $\mu + 3\sigma$ is only about .26 per cent (that is, .0026).

Although the first moment about the origin and the second moment about the mean (the mean and variance, respectively) usually do not describe a probability distribution completely, they are adequate for many purposes, as we shall see later. The third and fourth moments about the mean have been used somewhat, but their use has diminished considerably. Even in the case of a mass distribution, it happens that the first two moments are the important ones. Perhaps it will be recognized that the standard deviation, defined above, corresponds to the radius of gyration of a mass distribution about its center of gravity.

The variance has certain properties which are useful. If we expand the squared deviation, we have

$$\sigma^2 = E(X^2 - 2\mu X + \mu^2) = E(X^2) - 2\mu E(X) + \mu^2 = E(X^2) - \mu^2.$$

(We have made use of the additive and homogeneous nature of the expectation operator $E(\;\;)$, discussed on page 49). This is a special case of what is referred to as the "parallel axis theorem" in mechanics. Example 3–k below, shows how it can be used.

Next let a linear change be made on a variable X, yielding a new random variable $Y = aX + b$. Then

$$\sigma_Y{}^2 = E[(aX + b) - (a\mu_X + b)]^2 = a^2\sigma_X{}^2,$$

and taking the positive square root, we have

$$\sigma_Y = a\sigma_X.$$

Notice in particular that the variance is unchanged under a *shift* of the origin, so long as the entire scale is also shifted, with no distortion.

Example 3–k

Let X be the number of heads in a toss of three coins. Here $x_i = 0, 1, 2, 3$, and the probability function is given in the following table, along with certain calculations for μ and σ^2.

x_i	$f(x_i)$	$x_i f(x_i)$	$x_i^2 f(x_i)$
0	1/8	0	0
1	3/8	3/8	3/8
2	3/8	6/8	12/8
3	1/8	3/8	9/8
Sums:	1	12/8	24/8

Thus,

$$\mu = E(X) = \sum x_i \, f(x_i) = \frac{12}{8} = \frac{3}{2},$$

and

$$\sigma^2 = E(X^2) - \mu^2 = \sum x_i^2 f(x_i) - \mu^2 = \frac{24}{8} - \frac{9}{4} = \frac{3}{4}.$$

Example 3–l

If $Y = 4X + 7$, where X is the random variable of Example 3–k, then the expected value and variance of Y are computed from those of X as follows:

$$\mu_Y = 4\mu_X + 7 = 13,$$

and

$$\sigma_Y^2 = 4^2 \sigma_X^2 = 12.$$

Problems

3–16—3–21. Determine the variances of the random variables of Problems 3–1—3–6 and Example 3–b.

3–22. Compute $E(X^k)$ where X is the random variable of Problem 3–5.

3–23. Let X be a random variable with expected value μ and variance σ^2. Determine the variance of $Y = (X - \mu)/\sigma$.

3–24. Calculate the center of gravity of these five point masses: 2 grams at $x = 0$, 3 grams at $x = 1$, 1 gram at $x = 4$, 2 grams at $x = 6$, and 2 grams at $x = 7$.

3–25. Determine the total moment of inertia (total second moment) of the mass points in Problem 3–24 about $x = 2$.

3–26. Determine the radius of gyration about the center of gravity of the mass points of Problem 3–24.

3.4 Some Important Discrete Distributions

Conceivably, any set of values x_1, x_2, . . . , and corresponding probabilities $p(x_1)$, $p(x_2)$, . . . , where $\Sigma p(x_i) = 1$, could serve as the probability model for some situation. However, there are a few particular models which are important because of the large number of instances in which they are useful.

3.4.1 The Poisson Distribution

We consider here a model which is useful in certain situations in which some kind of "event" occurs repeatedly, but haphazardly, such as is indicated in Figure 3–1 (each x represents an occurrence of the event):

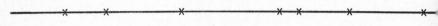

Figure 3–1

The event may be the arrival of a telephone call in an exchange, the breakdown of a piece of equipment, the emission of a radioactive particle, the completion of a repair job by a steadily working repairman, a defect along a long tape or wire or chain, and so on.

These events are quite varied in nature, and it is desirable to have a term which may include them all. Since the word "event" has been used in a technical sense in probability models, we adopt in its place the word "change." In many applications the thing that happens may be considered as a "change of state," which we shorten to *change*.

These changes may occur at random points in time, or at points along a wire, or at points in a plane region, etc. The most common case is that of *time*, so we adopt the letter t as the name of the variable along whose axis the changes occur.

One is interested in particular in the *number* of changes in a *given interval*. Since the changes occur at random times, the number of them in an interval of given size is a random variable—with possible values 0, 1, 2, ... To complete the probability model, we need probabilities for these values. These may be defined in many ways, but a particular specification which turns out to include the cases described above is the one we shall discuss; it is called a Poisson distribution of probabilities. The corresponding random variable, the number of changes in an interval of given size, is called a Poisson random variable.

The Poisson distribution arises when it may be considered that the following postulates hold:

Poisson Postulates:

(a) The numbers of changes in nonoverlapping intervals are independent.
(b) The probability that a change occurs in an interval of width h is approximately proportional to h, when h is small.
(c) The probability that more than one change occurs in an interval of width h is negligible, when compared with the probability of a single change, for small h.

The vague terms "approximately proportional" and "negligible" may be avoided if we use the more precise mathematical formulation of Postulates (b) and (c), namely:

(b') P(one change in interval of width h) $= \lambda h + o(h)$
(c') P(two or more changes in interval of width h) $= o(h)$,

where λ is a constant which characterizes (as we shall see) the particular process at hand. The symbol $o(h)$ is read "some function of smaller order than h," and is used to denote an unspecified function $\epsilon(h)$ having the property that

$$\lim_{h \to 0} \frac{\epsilon(h)}{h} = 0.$$

In rough language, $o(h)$ represents any quantity which for small h is negligible compared to h. For example, h^2, e^{-h}, $\sin^2 h$ are all $o(h)$.

In a process of the above type, we are concerned specifically with the random variable

$$X = \text{Number of changes in an interval of width } t.$$

This random variable has possible values $0, 1, 2, \ldots$, and is said to be of the Poisson type, or to have the *Poisson distribution*. Probabilities in this distribution are given by the *Poisson formula*:

$$p(k) = P(X = k) = e^{-\lambda t} \frac{(\lambda t)^k}{k!}$$
$$= P(k \text{ changes in an interval of width } t),$$

as will be shown at the end of this section. (The λ is of course the constant of proportionality in postulate (b').) For the moment, we accept this formula as correct.

In order that the above Poisson formula give a legitimate distribution of probability, the sum of the probabilities of all possible values should be 1.

This sum is an infinite sum, as follows:

$$\sum_0^\infty p(k) = \sum_0^\infty e^{-\lambda t} \frac{(\lambda t)^k}{k!} = e^{-\lambda t} \sum_0^\infty \frac{(\lambda t)^k}{k!} = 1.$$

We have used the fact, here, that for any number x (and surely then for $x = \lambda t$),

$$e^x = \sum_0^\infty \frac{x^k}{k!}.$$

The Poisson distribution function is obtained by adding up the proper number of Poisson probabilities:

$$F(x) = P(X \le x) = \sum_{k \le x} e^{-\lambda t} \frac{(\lambda t)^k}{k!}.$$

Extensive tables of this function and of the individual probabilities are available (for example: *Poisson's Exponential Binomial Limit*, by E.C. Molina, D. Van Nostrand Company.)

To compute the expected value of a Poisson random variable, we compute, according to the definition, the sum of the products of the possible values and their corresponding probabilities:

$$E(X) = \sum_0^\infty kp(k) = e^{-\lambda t} \sum_1^\infty \frac{(\lambda t)^k}{(k-1)!} = \lambda t.$$

(Again we have used the power series expansion for e^x with $x = \lambda t$.) Hence,

λt = Average or expected number of changes in an interval of length t,

and, therefore, setting $t = 1$,

λ = Average number of changes in a *unit* interval.

With this interpretation of λ and λt, we see that specifying the expected number of changes in an interval of any size (which may, of course, be taken as a "unit" on the t axis) completely determines the distribution of probability among the various possible numbers of changes in an interval of any other size. Notice, for example, that doubling the size of the basic interval of interest doubles the expected number of changes.

Example 3-m

When a company tests new tires by driving them over difficult terrain, they find that flat tires externally caused occur on the average of once every 2000 miles. It is found also that the Poisson process yields a useful model. What is the probability that in a given 500-mile test no more than one flat will occur?

Here the variable t is distance, and the random variable of interest is

$$X = \text{Number of flats in 500 miles.}$$

Since $E(X)$ is proportional to the time interval involved in the definition of X, and since the average is given as one flat is 2000 miles, we have

$$\lambda t = E(X) = \frac{1}{4} \text{ flat in 500 miles.}$$

The values assigned to λ and λt depend on the unit of distance adopted. If we take one mile as the unit, then $t = 500$, $\lambda = .0005$, and $\lambda t = 1/4$. If we take 1000 miles as the unit, then $t = 1/2$, $\lambda = 1/2$, and again $\lambda t = 1/4$, and so on. The important thing is that $\lambda t = 1/4$, no matter what unit is chosen.

Using the Poisson formula, we find:

$$
\begin{aligned}
P(\text{no more than one flat in 500 miles}) &= P(X \leq 1) \\
&= p(0) + p(1) \\
&= e^{1/4}\left[\frac{(1/4)^0}{0!} + \frac{(1/4)^1}{1!}\right] \\
&= \frac{5}{4e^{1/4}} \doteq .97.
\end{aligned}
$$

(The dot over the equal sign is used to indicate an approximate equality.)

We can also answer a question such as this: What is the probability of no flats in a trip of 4000 miles? In this situation,

$$\lambda t = 2 \text{ flats per 4000 miles}$$

and X is the number of flats in a 4000-mile trip. And then

$$P(X = 0) = p(0) = e^{-2}\frac{(2)^0}{0!} = \frac{1}{e^2} \doteq .135.$$

We comment that the variable t, although used above to denote a one-dimensional variable (distance), could also be such a thing as an *area*, with appropriate modifications in the above discussion. For example, flaws may occur "at random" in large sheets of some material, and one may be concerned with the number of flaws per sheet, or per area of a certain size. In such a case, λ has the interpretation of the expected number of changes (flaws) per unit area and λt the expected number of changes in an area of size t.

The variance of a Poisson distribution may be calculated as follows. First compute the expectation of $(X^2 - X)$:

$$E(X^2 - X) = \sum_0^\infty (k^2 - k)f(k)$$

$$= e^{-\lambda t}(\lambda t)^2 \sum_2^\infty \frac{(\lambda t)^{k-2}}{(k - 2)!} = (\lambda t)^2.$$

Then the variance is

$$\sigma^2 = E(X^2) - \mu^2 = E(X^2 - X) + E(X) - [E(X)]^2$$
$$= (\lambda t)^2 + \lambda t - (\lambda t)^2 = \lambda t.$$

Thus the variance turns out to be the same as the expected value.

As promised earlier, we give here an account of the method of obtaining the Poisson formula from the Poisson postulates. It is convenient for this purpose to introduce a notation for probabilities which exhibits their dependence on t, namely:

$$P_n(t) = P(n \text{ changes in an interval of width } t).$$

(We have previously called this expression $p(n)$.)

The method is to obtain a differential relation for $P_n(t)$ whose solution then gives the desired formula. To obtain a derivative of $P_n(t)$ we let t take on an increment h and consider the ratio of the corresponding increment in $P_n(t)$ to the increment in t. Thus, we consider an interval of width $t + h$ and think of it in two parts—a piece of width t and a piece of width h.

$$\begin{array}{ccc} & & \\ 0 & t & t+h \end{array}$$

Figure 3–2

We may then write, using the addition law for mutually exclusive events,

$P_n(t + h) = P(n \text{ changes in the interval of width } t + h)$
$= P(n \text{ changes from 0 to } t, \text{ and none from } t \text{ to } t + h)$
$\quad + P(n - 1 \text{ changes from 0 to } t, \text{ and one from } t \text{ to } t + h)$
$\quad + P(n - 2 \text{ changes from 0 to } t, \text{ and two from } t \text{ to } t + h)$
$\quad + \text{etc.}$

We may factor the first term, using the independence of Postulate (a), and obtain

$P(n \text{ changes from 0 to } t \text{ and none from } t \text{ to } t + h) = P_n(t)[1 - \lambda h - o(h)]$

where we have interpreted "none" as the opposite of "more than one," and used (b'). Similarly, we may factor the second term:

$P(n - 1 \text{ changes from } 0 \text{ to } t \text{ and one from } t \text{ to } t + h) = P_{n-1}(t)[\lambda h + o(h)]$.

For the remaining terms,

$P(n - k \text{ changes from } 0 \text{ to } t, k \text{ from } t \text{ to } t + h) = P_{n-k}(t)[o(h)], \quad (k > 1)$.

Combining these, we have

$P_n(t + h) = P_n(t) - \lambda h P_n(t) + \lambda h P_{n-1}(t) + o(h) \text{ [terms not depending on } h].$

Transposing $P_n(t)$, dividing by h, and passing to the limit as h tends to 0, we obtain

$$P_n'(t) = \lim_{h \to 0} \frac{P_n(t + h) - P_n(t)}{h} = -\lambda P_n(t) + \lambda P_{n-1}(t).$$

It should be noticed, however, that if $n = 0$, the last term is not present:

$$P_0'(t) = -\lambda P_0(t).$$

This last equation and the condition $P_0(0) = 1$ immediately imply that $P_0(t) = e^{-\lambda t}$. Using this, one can successively solve the more general equation for $P_1(t)$, $P_2(t)$, etc. Alternatively, the student can easily check that the expression for $P_n(t)$ in the Poisson formula satisfies the above differential equations.

Problems

3–27. Calls come in to a telephone exchange at random but at a rate of 300 per hour (when taken over a long period). Assume that the number of calls coming in during a given period is a random variable with a Poisson distribution and determine the probability that
(a) one call comes in during a given one-minute period.
(b) at least two calls come in during a given one-minute period.
(c) no calls arrive in an interval of length T minutes.
3–28. A random variable X has a Poisson distribution with variance 1. Calculate $P(X = 2)$.
3–29. Splices in a certain manufactured tape occur at random, but on the average of one per 2000 feet. Assuming a Poisson distribution, what is the probability that a 5000-foot roll of tape has
(a) no splices.
(b) at most two splices.
(c) at least two splices.
3–30. Flaws in the plating of large sheets of metal occur at random, on the average of one in each section of area 10 square feet. What is the probability that a sheet 5 by 8 will have no flaws? At most one flaw?

3–31. Failures of electron tubes in airborne applications have been found to follow closely the Poisson postulates. A receiver with sixteen tubes suffers a tube failure on the average of once every 50 hours of operating time.

(a) What is the probability of more than one failure on an 8-hour mission?

(b) What is the expected number of failures in 1000 hours of operating time?

3.4.2 The Bernoulli Distribution

A random variable which can take on only two values is sometimes said to have a *Bernoulli distribution*. Probability is then divided between these two values. Let the two values be 0 and 1, for simplicity, and let the probabilities be q and p, respectively, where $q + p = 1$. We give below the table showing this probability distribution, together with some entries used in computing the mean and variance.

x_i	$p(x_i)$	$x_i p(x_i)$	$x_i^2 p(x_i)$
1	p	p	p
0	q	0	0
Sums: 1		$p = E(X)$	$p = E(X^2)$

Thus the expected value is

$$\mu = E(X) = p,$$

and the variance is

$$\sigma^2 = E(X^2) - \mu^2 = p - p^2 = p(1 - p) = pq.$$

This model is often useful—in such cases as defective or nondefective articles, yes or no votes, success or failure of a mission—indeed, in any case in which one is interested whether an experiment results in an event E or in the opposite event, not E, whatever E may be.

Problems

3–32. A die is tossed. Let a random variable X be defined by

$$X = \begin{cases} 1 \text{ if a 6 turns up,} \\ -1 \text{ if any other side turns up.} \end{cases}$$

Determine the expected value and variance of X.

3–33. Suppose that 55 per cent of the voters in a community favor a proposal. A voter is chosen at random; let $X = 0$ if he is against, and 1 if he is for the proposal. Determine μ and σ^2.

3.4.3 The Binomial Distribution

We have met the binomial distribution before, in Chapter 1. We consider n identical, independent trials of an experiment, with probability p that a given event E occurs at each of the n trials. Let

$X = $ the number of times E occurs in the n independent trials.

This random variable has possible values $0, 1, \ldots , n$, and the probability function was derived in Chapter 1 (without calling it by that name) to be

$$p(k) = P(X = k) = P(k \text{ } E\text{'s in } n \text{ trials})$$
$$= \binom{n}{k} p^k (1 - p)^{n-k}.$$

A random variable with this probability function is said to be a *binomial random variable*, or to be binomially distributed, or to have a binomial distribution.

The two numbers n and p determine the probabilities and might be called parameters of the distribution. However, the number of trials, n, is almost always known, whereas p is almost never known exactly. The interest is then in p, and one often thinks of p as "the parameter" of the distribution.

A binomial random variable is intimately connected with the Bernoulli variable which, at a given trial of the experiment, takes on the values 1 or 0 depending on whether E occurs or not. If we mark down a 1 for each E and a 0 each time E fails to occur, as the experiment proceeds, we obtain a sequence of n 0's and 1's, such as

$$1, 0, 0, 1, 1, 1, 0, 1.$$

Adding these numbers gives the number of 1's in the list—that is, the number of E's in the n trials:

$$1 + 0 + 0 + 1 + 1 + 1 + 0 + 1 = 5,$$

five E's in eight trials in this instance.

Thus, X, the number of E's in n trials, may be thought of as a sum

$$X = X_1 + X_2 + \cdots + X_n,$$

where each of the terms X_i of the sum represents a 1 or a 0, depending on whether E occurred or not at the ith trial. (Cf. Example 2–g, page 31.) Each X_i is clearly a Bernoulli random variable, having the values 0 and 1 with probabilities $1 - p$ and p, respectively, the p being the binomial parameter.

Expressing a binomially distributed variable X as the sum of n Bernoulli variables enables us to compute the expectation of the former from that of the latter (using the additive property of the expectation operation, page 49):

$$\mu = E(X) = E(X_1) + E(X_2) + \cdots + E(X_n) = p + p + \cdots + p$$
$$= np.$$

Hence the expected value of a binomially distributed random variable is the product of the number of trials and the probability of E at a single trial—the two numbers which determine the distribution. This should not be too surprising when we consider that p was intended to be an idealization of the fraction of a large number of trials in which E occurs.

This formula for μ can be derived from the "generating function"

$$\psi(t) = (pt + q)^n = \sum_{0}^{n} \binom{n}{k} p^k q^{n-k} t^k = E(t^X).$$

One can easily show by differentiating these two expressions for $\psi(t)$ that

$$\psi'(1) = np = \mu.$$

The variance can also be obtained from this function by a second differentiation. The result is

$$\psi''(1) = n(n - 1)p^2 = E(X^2 - X),$$

from which it easily follows that $\sigma^2 = npq$.

Example 3-n

Suppose that we draw a card from a deck five times, replacing each card drawn and shuffling the deck before the next drawing, and consider the random variable X which is the number of spades obtained in the five draws. At each drawing the probability of getting a spade is $1/4$. Replacement and shuffling guarantee that conditions are identical each time and that the results of the five draws are "stochastically independent." The pertinent numbers are then

$$n = 5, \; p = \frac{1}{4}, \text{ and } q = \frac{3}{4}.$$

The table of probabilities (multiplied by 4^5 for convenience) is given below, computed from

$$p(k) = \binom{5}{k} \left(\frac{1}{4}\right)^k \left(\frac{3}{4}\right)^{5-k}.$$

k	$4^5 p(k)$	$k 4^5 p(k)$	$k^2 4^5 p(k)$
0	243	0	0
1	405	405	405
2	270	540	1080
3	90	270	810
4	15	60	240
5	1	5	25
Totals:	$1024 = 4^5$	1280	2560

From the computations of the last two columns of this table we can compute μ and σ^2:

$$\mu = E(X) = \sum kp(k) = \frac{1280}{1024} = \frac{5}{4},$$

$$E(X^2) = \sum k^2 p(k) = \frac{2560}{1024} = \frac{40}{16},$$

and

$$\sigma^2 = E(X^2) - \mu^2 = \frac{40}{16} - \frac{25}{16} = \frac{15}{16}.$$

Of course, using the formulas we obtain the same result with less effort:

$$\mu = np = 5 \cdot \frac{1}{4},$$

and

$$\sigma^2 = npq = 5 \cdot \frac{1}{4} \cdot \frac{3}{4}.$$

This avoids the computations in the table, but it is pleasant to see that the formulas work properly, at least in this one example.

Problems

3–34. A machine produces articles in such a way that there is a probability .01 that a given article has a defect.
  (a) What is the probability that out of four articles none has a defect? At most one has a defect?
  (b) What is the average number of defects in lots of fifty of these articles?

3–35. Four hundred nickels are tossed on a table. What are the expected value and standard deviation of the number of coins which fall heads?

3-36. A die is tossed 1620 times. What are the mean and standard deviation of the number of 6's which are thrown?

3-37. The following is the graph of the distribution function of a binomial random variable X.

(a) Determine n, p, μ, and σ^2.

(b) Determine $P(X \geq 1)$.

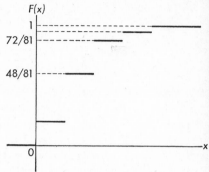

3-38. Verify the formulas for expectation and variance by computing these quantities also from a table of probabilities, as in Example 3-n, in the case of the number of 1's and 2's in four throws of a die.

3.4.4 The Hypergeometric Distribution

Consider a collection of N objects, M having a certain property E, and the remainder, $N - M$, not having this property. We draw n objects from the N objects and are interested in the number of objects with property E that we have drawn in the sample of n. Let this number be X, a random variable. If the objects are drawn one at a time and *replaced* at each drawing, as in Example 3-n, the number in the sample with property E is binomially distributed (cf. that example, page 62), with $p = M/N$. If, on the other hand, the objects are *not replaced* or are drawn simultaneously, the distribution of probability is called *hypergeometric*. We have already seen in Chapter 1 (page 13) how to compute such probabilities:

$$p(k) = P(X = k) = P(k \ E\text{'s in a sample of } n)$$
$$= \frac{\binom{M}{k}\binom{N-M}{n-k}}{\binom{N}{n}}.$$

Example 3-o

Consider a bowl with fifteen beads, ten of them red and five white. Let four beads be drawn together (or one at a time, without replacement), and let

$$X = \text{Number of red beads drawn (out of four).}$$

This has the hypergeometric distribution, with probability function

$$p(k) = P(X = k) = \frac{\binom{10}{k}\binom{5}{4-k}}{\binom{15}{4}}, \ k = 0, 1, 2, 3, 4.$$

The values of this function (multiplied by $\binom{15}{4} = 1365$) are tabulated in the table below, together with some computations for determining μ and σ^2.

k	$1365\ p(k)$	$1365\ kp(k)$	$1365\ k^2p(k)$
0	5	0	0
1	100	100	100
2	450	900	1800
3	600	1800	5400
4	210	840	3360
Totals:	1365	3640	10660

The expectation and variance of X are then computed as follows:

$$\mu = E(X) = \sum kp(k) = \frac{3640}{1365} = \frac{8}{3},$$

$$\sigma^2 = E(X^2) - \mu^2 = \frac{10,660}{1,365} - \left(\frac{8}{3}\right)^2 = \frac{44}{63}.$$

We observe that, at least in this example, the mean value is exactly the same as it would have been in the case in which the objects are replaced each time: $4 \cdot 2/3 = 8/3$. Actually, this will always be the case, since, as with the binomial distribution, we may think of X as the sum $X_1 + \cdots + X_n$, where each X_i (the result of the ith trial) is a 1 if E occurs at that trial and is 0 otherwise. But then, even though $X_1, \ldots, X_n$ are not independent, $E(X) = E(X_1) + \cdots + E(X_n)$, where each $E(X_i)$ is the probability of E at the ith trial—not knowing what has happened at preceding or subsequent trials. Hence,

$$\mu = E(X) = n \cdot \frac{M}{N}.$$

The variance, however, is different in the two cases (replacement and nonreplacement). It can be shown that in the hypergeometric case, the variance is given by the formula

$$\sigma^2 = \frac{N-n}{N-1}\, n\, \frac{M}{N} \frac{N-M}{N}.$$

In Example 3–o above, this formula gives the correct result:

$$\sigma^2 = \frac{11}{14} \cdot \frac{4 \cdot 10 \cdot 5}{15^2} = \frac{44}{63}.$$

(If objects are *replaced* before drawing successive ones, the variance of the number of E's is $npq = n \cdot M/N \cdot (N - M)/N$. *Not* replacing the objects introduces the factor $(N - n)/(N - 1)$.)

Problems

3–39. A lot of ten articles contains two defective articles.
   (a) What is the probability that one drawn at random will be defective?
   (b) What is the probability that in a sample of four articles, k are defective?
   (c) If X is the number of defective articles in a sample of four, determine μ_X and σ_X^2.
3–40. A deck of cards contains thirteen spades, thirteen hearts, thirteen diamonds, and thirteen clubs.
   (a) Determine the probability that a hand of five cards contain three spades and two hearts.
   (b) If X is the number of spades in a hand of thirteen cards dealt at random from the deck, determine μ_X and σ_X^2.
3–41. A deck of cards contains four aces, four kings, four queens, four jacks, and four of each of the denominations, 10, 9, 8, . . . , 2.
   (a) Determine the probability that a hand of five cards has three aces and two kings.
   (b) Determine the probability that a hand of five cards has three of one denomination and two of another.
   (c) If X is the number of aces in a hand of thirteen cards from the deck, determine μ_X and σ_X^2.

3.4.5 Relations Among the Special Cases

The four special discrete probability distributions we have considered here happen to be quite closely related. We have already shown how a binomially distributed variable may be considered as the sum of n identical Bernoulli variables. Let us now show the relation between the *binomial* and *Poisson* distributions by using the binomial formula from the Poisson postulates.

Suppose that the postulates for the Poisson distribution (page 55) hold for changes along a t axis, and consider in particular an interval of size t. Let X be as always the number of changes in an interval of this size, and let λ denote the average number of changes in a unit interval. Now subdivide the interval of width t into n equal parts, each of width t/n. Let us think of each of these subintervals as a "trial" and E as the occurrence of a change in a given trial. Actually, there might be more than one change in a subinterval, but by Postulate (c) this is relatively unlikely if the sub-interval is small.

Thus, in each trial, we have either "E" (a change) or "not E" (no change). The probability of "E" is (by Postulate (b)) approximately $\lambda t/n$, and hence the probability of "not E" is approximately $1 - \lambda t/n$. Using these as the p and q of the binomial formula, we find

$$P(X = k) = P(k\ E\text{'s among the } n \text{ subintervals})$$
$$= P(k \text{ "trials" result in } E) \doteq \binom{n}{k} \left(\frac{\lambda t}{n}\right)^k \left(1 - \frac{\lambda t}{n}\right)^{n-k}$$

We may rewrite this approximation with a slight rearrangement of some of the factors as follows:

$$\frac{n}{n} \frac{n-1}{n} \cdots \frac{n-k+1}{n} \frac{(\lambda t)^k}{k!} \left(1 - \frac{\lambda t}{n}\right)^{-k} \left(1 - \frac{\lambda t}{n}\right)^n.$$

We are interested in what happens to this as $n \to \infty$, because then the sub-interval width approaches zero, and the approximations involved get better and better. But as $n \to \infty$, the first k factors tend to 1, the next factor is fixed, the next tends to 1, and the last factor becomes

$$\lim_{n \to \infty} \left\{ \left[\left(1 - \frac{\lambda t}{n}\right) \right]^{-n/\lambda t} \right\}^{-\lambda t}.$$

Setting $-\lambda t/n = h$, this is

$$[\lim_{h \to 0} (1 + h)^{1/h}]^{-\lambda t} = e^{-\lambda t},$$

since the bracketed quantity is the usual definition of e. Thus the approximation to the probability that $X = k$ approaches the expression claimed earlier, namely:

$$e^{-\lambda t} \frac{(\lambda t)^k}{k!}.$$

Although this limit-type relationship is an interesting application of the binomial probability formula, the practical significance lies in the fact that the approximate equality

$$e^{-\lambda t} \frac{(\lambda t)^k}{k!} \doteq \binom{n}{k} \left(\frac{\lambda t}{n}\right)^k \left(1 - \frac{\lambda t}{n}\right)^{n-k}, \text{ (large } n),$$

may be read the other way around, and the binomial probability may be approximated by the Poisson. If we put $p = \lambda t/n$ in the above expressions, we obtain

$$\binom{n}{k} p^k (1 - p)^{n-k} \doteq e^{-np} \frac{(np)^k}{k!}, \text{ (large } r, \text{ small } p).$$

When using the Poisson distribution as a convenient approximation to the binomial distribution, we should perhaps establish a thumb-rule for "large n" and "small p." It happens that when p is sufficiently small, the Poisson distribution successfully approximates the binomial even for what might be called "small" n. *Let us consider that we can apply the Poisson distribution as an approximation to the binomial distribution when $p < .1$.* Even for n as small as 10, the Poisson approximation is quite good. It depends on how accurate we want to be! Of course, for $p \leq .05$ and $n \geq 20$ the Poisson distribution becomes a *better* approximation to the binomial. In order to get an appreciation for such words as "large," "small," "better," etc., it becomes necessary actually to experience calculating the respective probabilities using both the binomial and Poisson distributions and comparing the answers.

Example 3–p

Let us consider two particular cases to indicate the sort of accuracy one can expect. In the table below are given values of the probability function in two binomial cases, $n = 10$ and $p = .1$, and $n = 20$ and $p = .05$. In each case $np = 1$, and the Poisson approximations using $\lambda t = np = 1$ are also given in the table.

k	Poisson $\lambda t = 1$	Binomial (10, .1)	Binomial (20, .05)
0	.368	.349	.358
1	.368	.387	.377
2	.184	.194	.187
3	.061	.057	.060
4	.015	.011	.013
5	.0031	.0015	.0022

Actually, the entries in this table should continue to $k = 10$ for the binomial case with $n = 10$, to $k = 20$, for the binomial case with $n = 20$, and to $k = \infty$ in the Poisson column.

Example 3–q

Suppose that the probability that a certain type of inoculation has an adverse effect is .005. What is the probability that two out of 1000 people given the inoculation will be adversely affected?

If we let X be the number of people out of 1000 who are so affected, this is binomially distributed, and the probability that $X = 2$ is

$$p(2) = \binom{1000}{2} (.005)^2(.995)^{998}.$$

Rather than compute this, we may compute instead the approximation given by the

Poisson formula, with $\lambda t = 1000 \times (.005) = 5$:

$$p(2) \doteq e^{-5}\frac{5^2}{2!} = \frac{25}{2e^5} \doteq .0842.$$

Similarly, we may compute

$$P(\text{no more than 2 are affected}) = P(X = 0, 1, \text{ or } 2)$$
$$= p(0) + p(1) + p(2)$$
$$\doteq e^{-5}\left[1 + \frac{5^1}{1!} + \frac{5^2}{2!}\right] \doteq .125$$

Next let us consider the relation between the *hypergeometric* and the *binomial* distributions. Each of these gives the distribution of probability among the numbers of occurrences of an event E in n trials. In the binomial case, these trials are independent and identical, as when objects are replaced after each drawing. In the hypergeometric case, n objects are drawn together. The possible values in each case are $0, 1, 2, \ldots, n$, except that when the n objects drawn are *not* replaced, there can be no more objects with property E drawn than are available.

It is certainly intuitively clear that if the size of the collection from which objects are drawn is large, it will not matter too much that objects are not replaced before drawing subsequent ones. That is, one would expect that as the N of the hypergeometric distribution becomes infinite (with the ratio M/N fixed), the probabilities in this distribution would approach the binomial probabilities (with $p = M/N$) which apply when the population *is* infinite. This is the case, and we shall content ourselves with an illustration of the fact. Generally speaking, it is necessary that the population size be "large" with respect to the sample size.

Example 3–r

Consider a bowl with an equal number of black and white beads. Three are selected at random without replacement, and we let

$$X = \text{Number of white beads drawn.}$$

The probability distribution is hypergeometric, and depends on N, the total number of beads. The probabilities are

$$p(0) = p(3) = \frac{\binom{N/2}{0}\binom{N/2}{3}}{\binom{N}{3}},$$

$$p(1) = p(2) = \frac{\binom{N/2}{1}\binom{N/2}{2}}{\binom{N}{3}}.$$

The values of these probabilities are given in the accompanying table for several population sizes, N.

N	$p(0), p(3)$	$p(1), p(2)$
20	.105	.395
50	.117	.383
100	.121	.379
1000	.1246	.3754
∞ (Binomial)	.125	.375

There may well be situations in which a hypergeometric probability can be approximated by a binomial probability and this in turn approximated by a Poisson probability. One such situation is presented as a problem.

Problems

3–42. Let X be the number of defectives in a box of fifty articles taken from the output of a machine which produces articles which are defective with probability .01. *Determine approximately* the probability that $X = 0$, 1, or 2, that is, that the box of fifty contains no more than two defectives.

3–43. An electric light sign is constructed using 10,000 15-watt bulbs. The probability that a new 15-watt bulb will operate for ten hours is given to be .9995. If all the bulbs are new, determine the probability that
(a) the sign will operate the first ten hours without any bulbs burning out.
(b) exactly x bulbs will burn out in the first ten hours.
(c) at least two bulbs will burn out in the first ten hours.

3–44. As an acceptance procedure, a company will buy a shipment of 500 items according to the following plan. The inspector will take a sample of 75 and will pass the shipment if at most two defectives are found in the sample. If a shipment which is 20 per cent defective is submitted by a vendor, what is the probability that the company will accept these items?

3–45. A pole is taken to determine the number of people in a town of population 10,000 who have never left their state. In place of questioning the entire population, a sample of 100 people is selected from the population. Of these, 3 have never left the state. What is the approximate probability of such a result, when in fact 5 per cent of the population have never left the state?

3–46. A sampling plan calls for taking 100 items from a very large lot which is 3 per cent defective. Let X be the number of defectives found in the sample of 100. Construct a table of probabilities,

$$P(X = x) \text{ for } x = 0, 1, 2, 3, 4$$

using first the binomial probability distribution and then the Poisson approximation.

Review Problems—Chapter 3

3–R1. The number X of defects per foot of a long cable is assumed to have a Poisson distribution. If there are, on the average, ten defects per 100 feet of cable, what is the probability that a one-foot length of cable will have at least one defect?

3–R2. If $Y = 2X - 4$, and $\mu_Y = 8$, $\sigma_Y^2 = 4$, what are μ_X and σ_X^2?

3–R3. A lot contains ten articles, and a sample of four is drawn (no replacement) from the lot. Let X be the number of defective articles in the sample of four. Suppose that in a particular case, X turned out to have the value 1. What number of defectives in the *lot* would give the largest probability of getting one defective in the sample of four articles?

3–R4. Given that X is binomially distributed with mean 12 and variance 8, determine n.

3–R5. A discrete random variable has mean 12 and variance 8.
Compute $E(X^2 + 2X)$.

3–R6. Determine approximately the probability of drawing a card at random from a standard deck of cards twenty times (replacing and shuffling between draws) and never getting an ace. (There are four aces in the fifty-two–card deck.)

3–R7. A "signal" consists of a series of pulses of magnitude X, having the values 1, 0, and -1 each with probability 1/3. A "noise" consists of a series of pulses of magnitude Y, having the values 2, 0, and -2 with probabilities 1/6, 2/3, and 1/6, respectively. If noise and signal are mixed, with the pulses synchronized, the sum consists of pulses of magnitude $Z = X + Y$. Construct the probability function for Z, and compute its mean and variance.

3–R8. Referring to the situation described in Problem 1–R4, page 25, let X be the number of cigarettes correctly identified as to brand. Determine the probability function and the mean and variance of X.

3–R9. A box contains four defective and six good articles. Articles are drawn and tested, one at a time. Determine the expected number of tests necessary to locate the defective articles. (Cf. Problem 1–29, page 20.)

4/Continuous Distributions

4.0 Introduction

In Chapter 2, a random variable was said to be continuous if its distribution function is (1) continuous, and (2) differentiable at all but perhaps a finite number of points. Continuous distributions of probability leave no finite lumps at any single point but rather smear it out—smoothly (except perhaps for the finite number of points where $F'(x)$ fails to exist), but not necessarily uniformly—along the axis of possible values.

The probability of occurrence of any single particular value k is zero. For,

$$P(X = k) = \lim_{h \to o} P(k - h < X \le k + h) = \lim_{h \to o} [F(k + h) - F(k - h)].$$

This limit is the amount of the jump in $F(x)$ at $x = k$; and if the distribution function is continuous at $x = k$, there is no jump.

In this chapter we shall derive formulas for the various moments of continuous distributions and discuss some particular continuous distributions. The "probability function" used in the discrete case will be useless here, since individual values have zero probability of occurring. Instead, formulas will be given in terms of a "density function."

4.1 The Density Function

The *derivative* of the distribution function is again a function of x, called the *probability density function*, or the density function, or the distribution density:

$$f(x) = F'(x) = \frac{dF(x)}{dx} = \lim_{h \to 0} \frac{P(x < X < x + h)}{h}.$$

It is assumed to exist except possibly at a finite number of values of x.

Since the density function is a *rate*, we may think of the density function as the rate at which we would accumulate probability if we were to sweep

72

from left to right on the axis of values of the random variable. Over sections of the axis where probability is uniformly spread, for example, this density or rate of accumulation would be constant. In other words, the density function $f(x)$ is a measure of the thickness or concentration of probability at the point x.

Because $F(x)$, the cumulative distribution function, is nondecreasing, it follows that its rate of change or slope is not negative; that is,

$$f(x) \geq 0.$$

And since $F(x)$ becomes horizontal as x becomes infinite, either negatively or positively, its derivative, $f(x)$, tends to zero:

$$\lim_{x \to \pm \infty} f(x) = 0.$$

Since the distribution function $F(x)$ is a function whose derivative is the density function $f(x)$, it follows from the fundamental theorem of integral calculus that

$$\int_a^b f(x)\, dx = F(b) - F(a).$$

We have previously (page 34) interpreted the difference between the value of $F(x)$ at $x = a$ and the value at $x = b$ as the *probability* assigned to the interval from a to b. Hence:

$$\int_a^b f(x)\, dx = P(a < X < b).$$

Notice that we do not have to be careful about whether our inequality signs are $<$ or $\leq$, since the single points which would be left out in any case have zero probability for a continuous distribution.

A definite integral may be interpreted as an area under a curve—as the area under the graph of the integrand function between the ordinates at the endpoints of the interval over which the integral is taken. Thus we have the interpretation that the *area* between two points $x = a$ and $x = b$ represents the probability

$$P(a < X < b) = F(b) - F(a) = \int_a^b f(x)\, dx.$$

This is shown graphically in Figure 4–1. In particular, the total area under the density curve is $F(+\infty) = 1$:

$$P(-\infty < X < +\infty) = F(+\infty) - F(-\infty) = \int_{-\infty}^{+\infty} f(x)\, dx = 1.$$

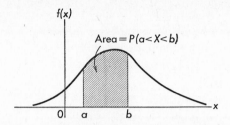

Figure 4–1. Probability Interpreted as Area

As a special case of the above expression of probability in terms of the density function of the distribution we have

$$F(x) = P(X \leq x) = P(-\infty < X \leq x)$$
$$= \int_{-\infty}^{x} f(u)\, du.$$

This relationship is shown graphically in Figure 4–2.

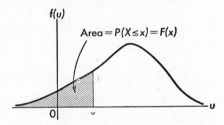

Figure 4–2. The Distribution Function as Area

(When one has the variable x in the limit of an integral it is a good policy to use a name other than x for the variable of integration. This "dummy" variable disappears in the evaluation of a definite integral; the integral depends only on the endpoints of the interval of integration and on the form of the integrand function.)

The probability that X falls in a tiny interval—say, the interval from a point x_o to a nearby point $x_o + dx$, can be approximated without an integration as follows. We first write the *exact* probability:

$$P(x_o < X < x_o + dx) = F(x_o + dx) - F(x_o)$$

and then approximate this increment in the function $F(x)$ by the differential of $F(x)$ to obtain:

$$P(x_o < X < x_o + dx) \doteq dF(x) = f(x_o)\, dx.$$

This approximation amounts to using the area of the rectangle of height $f(x_o)$ and base dx in place of the actual area under the density curve over the base dx. The approximating quantity, $f(x_o)\,dx$, is sometimes called the *probability element*. The approximation is indicated visually in Figure 4–3, somewhat exaggerated, since the approximation would not be very good for the size dx of the interval shown.

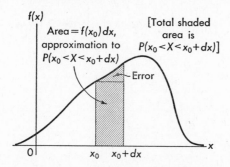

Figure 4-3. The Probability Element

It may be helpful again to consider the analogue discussed in Section 2.3, page 40, in which we thought of probability as mass. Suppose we have mass distributed along the x axis (as in the case of a long wire of variable density). Let

$$M(x) = \text{Amount of mass to the left of (or at) } x.$$

Then $M(-\infty) = 0$, and $M(+\infty) =$ the total amount of mass present (which, if finite, we could make equal to 1 unit of mass). Consider, then, the derivative of $M(x)$. It is defined as the limit of a ratio of increments:

$$m(x) = M'(x) = \lim_{h \to 0} \frac{M(x+h) - M(x)}{h} = \lim_{h \to 0} \frac{\text{Mass between } x \text{ and } x+h}{h}$$

The ratio whose limit is taken is the average mass density over the interval from x to $x + h$, that is, the amount of mass in the interval divided by the width of the interval. The limit is the instantaneous mass density. If one is given this density, he can calculate the mass in an interval from $x = a$ to $x = b$ by integration:

$$\int_a^b m(x)\,dx = M(b) - M(a).$$

Example 4–a

Consider a random variable X with probability distribution defined by the *distribution* function

$$F(x) = \begin{cases} 0, \ x < 0, \\ x^2, \ 0 \le x \le 1, \\ 1, \ x > 1. \end{cases}$$

Observe first that this is indeed a distribution function. It is, further, continuous and has a derivative everywhere except at $x = 1$. This derivative is the *density* function, $f(x)$:

$$f(x) = \begin{cases} 0, \text{ if } x < 0 \text{ or } x > 1, \\ 2x, \text{ if } 0 \leq x \leq 1. \end{cases}$$

Probabilities can be expressed in terms of this density; for example,

$$P(X < .5) = \int_{-\infty}^{.5} f(x) \, dx = \int_0^{.5} 2x \, dx = x^2 \Big|_0^{.5} = .25.$$

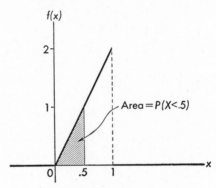

Figure 4–4

Also

$$P(.5 < X < 1.5) = \int_{.5}^1 2x \, dx = .75.$$

Notice that in computing the integrals in this last example we essentially compute $F(x)$ afresh as the integral of the density function. Thus, if $F(x)$ is known, it is foolish to calculate probabilities as integrals. Rather, we should compute, for instance, in the above example,

$$P(.5 < X < 1.5) = F(1.5) - F(.5) = 1 - .25 = .75.$$

Often, however, the distribution is described *initially* by means of the density function. The distribution function is then obtained as an integral:

$$F(x) = \int_{-\infty}^x f(u) \, du.$$

It is often impossible to evaluate this integral, and so express the distribution function, in terms of what are usually called the "elementary functions" (algebraic functions, exponentials, logarithms, trigonometric and inverse trigonometric functions). The integral is nevertheless a bona fide function and can be studied as much as any other function; tables of values can be constructed by numerical integration or other devices.

Example 4–b

Consider the function $1/(1 + x^2)$. This is a non-negative function, and it tends to zero as $x \to \infty$ or as $x \to -\infty$. However, the total area under the graph of this function is π. Dividing the function by π yields a function which can serve as the probability density of a random variable X. The result is this:

$$f(x) = \frac{1}{\pi(1 + x^2)}.$$

Probabilities can be computed by integration; for example,

$$P(X > 1) = \int_1^\infty \frac{dx}{\pi(1 + x^2)} = \frac{1}{4}.$$

The distribution function, which is a probability, can be computed similarly:

$$F(x) = \int_{-\infty}^x \frac{du}{(1 + u^2)} = \frac{1}{\pi} [\text{arc tan } x - \text{arc tan } (-\infty)]$$

$$= \frac{1}{\pi} \left(\text{arc tan } x + \frac{\pi}{2} \right).$$

Example 4–c

Consider the distribution given by the distribution function

$$F(x) = \begin{cases} 0, \text{ for } x < 0, \\ (1 + x)/2, \text{ for } 0 \le x \le 1, \\ 1, \text{ for } x > 1. \end{cases}$$

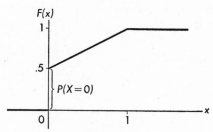

Figure 4–5

This is a proper distribution function and is differentiable except at $x = 0$ and $x = 1$:

$$F'(x) = \begin{cases} 0, \text{ for } x < 0 \text{ or } x > 1, \\ 1/2, \text{ for } 0 < x < 1. \end{cases}$$

But it is *not continuous* (there is a jump in the amount $1/2$ at $x = 0$). It is therefore not a continuous probability distribution according to our definition. There is a lump of $1/2$ at $x = 0$, and the remaining $1/2$ is smeared uniformly over the interval from 0 to 1. The derivative $F'(x)$ is not a true density of the entire distribution, and the area under the graph of $F'(x)$ is $1/2$, not 1. Probabilities can be computed directly from the cumulative distribution function, however, in the usual way (see Chapter 2).

Problems

Note: Save your work for reference in later problems.

4–1. The density function of a random variable X is

$$f(x) = \begin{cases} (\sin x)/2 \text{ for } 0 \leq x \leq \pi, \\ 0 \text{ for } x < 0 \text{ or } x > \pi. \end{cases}$$

(a) Determine the distribution function, and sketch its graph.
(b) Compute $P(X > \pi/3)$.
(c) Determine the point m such that $P(X > m) = P(X < m) = 1/2$.

4–2. The distribution function of a random variable X is

$$F(x) = \begin{cases} kx, \text{ for } 0 \leq x < 1, \\ 0, \text{ for } x \leq 0, \\ 1, \text{ for } x \geq 1. \end{cases}$$

(a) What value of the constant k would make this a *continuous* distribution? Use this value of k in the following.
(b) Determine the density function of X.
(c) Compute $P(X = 1/2)$.
(d) Compute $P(|X| < 1/2)$.

4–3. Determine geometrically the value of k which would make

$$f(x) = \begin{cases} kx, \text{ for } |x - 2| < 1, \\ 0, \text{ for } |x - 2| > 1 \end{cases}$$

a density function.

4–4. Suppose that "changes" occur at random in time according to the Poisson law (Section 3.41). Let X denote the time between successive changes. Show that X is a continuous random variable, and determine its density function. [*Hint:* Write $F(x)$ as $1 - P$ (no changes in interval of length x).]

4–5. In a certain material strength problem, an orientation angle is assumed to have the density $\cos \theta$ on the interval $0 \leq \theta \leq \pi/2$. Determine the distribution function, $F(\theta)$.

4.2 Expected Value; Moments; Median

As a guide in choosing a definition for the expected value of a continuous random variable, let us argue in terms of a discrete approximation and then pass to the limit. It will be convenient to suppose that we have a random variable X whose probability is distributed over a finite interval from $x = a$ to $x = b$.

Let the interval from a to b be subdivided into n equal parts, of width $\Delta x = (b - a)/n$. Let x_i denote the left endpoint of the ith subinterval and round off all values of X in that interval to x_i (for $i = 1, 2, \ldots, n$). The rounded-off values are values of a new random variable X^*, which is discrete, inasmuch as it can take on only the endpoint values $x_1, \ldots, x_n$. The probability that this new variable X^* takes on a particular one of these possible values, say, x_3, is the probability that the original variable X takes on a value which would be rounded off to x_3. This happens if X takes on a value in the third subinterval; thus,

$$P(X^* = x_3) = P(x_3 < X < x_3 + \Delta x).$$

We have seen (page 74) that this may be approximated by the "probability element," as follows:

$$P(X^* = x_3) = P(x_3 < X < x_3 + \Delta x) \doteq f(x_3) \, \Delta x.$$

This approximation becomes more and more exact as the number of sub-intervals is increased.

Now, the expected value of the discrete variable X^* is (as defined in Chapter 3) the sum

$$E(X^*) = \sum_{k=1}^{n} x_k P(X^* = x_k) \doteq \sum_{k=1}^{n} x_k f(x_k) \, \Delta x.$$

As $n \to \infty$ and $\Delta x \to 0$, we expect that the discrete variable X^* should approach the continuous variable X and that the limit of the above expression for $E(X^*)$ should therefore be taken as the expected value of X. But the limit of the last sum above defines a definite integral, namely:

$$\int_a^b xf(x) \, dx,$$

which is of course equal to the integral of the same function, $xf(x)$, over the infinite interval $x = -\infty$ to $x = \infty$.

In general, then, we *define* the *expected value* or *expectation* or *mean valu* *of the continuous random variable* X to be the integral:

$$E(X) = \mu = \int_{-\infty}^{\infty} xf(x) \, dx.$$

This expression depends on the *probability distribution* associated with the random variable X. We speak either of the expected value of X or of the expected value of the distribution of X.

We shall also need a formula, in terms of the density function of X, for the expectation of a random variable which is obtained as a function of X, say, $g(X)$. As in the case of a discrete variable, we use the same type of average for $g(X)$ as for X, but replace the values x by the new values $g(x)$:

$$E[g(X)] = \int_{-\infty}^{\infty} g(x)f(x) \, dx.$$

Again, we have a weighted "sum" of the values of $g(x)$, the weighting being provided by the probability element $f(x)\ dx$. (This definition is consistent with what would be obtained were we to work with the distribution of $Y = g(X)$ directly.)

Taking the particular functions $g(x) = k$, and $g(x) = kx$, we find that the properties obtained for the operator $E(\ )$ in the discrete case hold again with the present definition of expectation, namely:

$$E(k) = k$$

and

$$E(kX) = kE(X).$$

Further, the expectation of the sum of two functions of X is the sum of the expectations; but again we have (without proof) the more general property that for any continuous random variables X and Y which have expectations,

$$E(X + Y) = E(X) + E(Y).$$

The moments of a continuous variable are defined in terms of the expectation operator $E(\ )$ exactly as they were for a discrete variable. The kth moment about the origin is

$$E(X^k) = \int_{-\infty}^{\infty} x^k f(x)\ dx,$$

and the *variance* σ^2 is the second moment about the expected value μ:

$$\text{var } X = \sigma^2 = E(X - \mu)^2 = \int_{-\infty}^{\infty} (x - \mu)^2 f(x)\ dx.$$

The *standard deviation* σ is again the positive square root of the variance.

Thinking of a continuous probability distribution as a continuous mass distribution, as we have done before, we again have the interpretation of expected value and standard deviation as center of gravity and radius of gyration, respectively.

Example 4–d

Let X be a random variable with distribution density as given in Example 4–a, namely,

$$f(x) = \begin{cases} 0, \text{ for } x < 0 \text{ or } x > 1, \\ 2x, \text{ for } 0 < x < 1. \end{cases}$$

Let us compute the expectation and variance of this distribution:

$$\mu = E(X) = \int_{-\infty}^{\infty} xf(x)\ dx = \int_0^1 x(2x\ dx) = 2\frac{x^3}{3}\bigg|_0^1 = \frac{2}{3},$$

and

$$E(X^2) = \int_0^1 x^2(2x\ dx) = \frac{1}{2}, \qquad \sigma^2 = E(X^2) - \mu^2 = \frac{1}{18}.$$

In this example we have used a formula from Chapter 3:

$$\sigma^2 = E(X^2) - \mu^2.$$

It should be observed that we are justified in using this formula for continuous variables also, since it depends on the properties of the operator $E(\ )$ which hold, as we have seen, for both discrete and continuous variables.

Example 4–e

Suppose that a density function $f(x)$ is symmetrical about the value $x = a$. That, is, suppose that

$$f(a - x) = f(a + x).$$

Then, if the mean exists, it is given as follows:

$$\mu = \int_{-\infty}^{\infty} xf(x)\ dx = \int_{-\infty}^{\infty} (x - a + a)f(x)\ dx$$

$$= \int_{-\infty}^{\infty} (x - a)f(x)\ dx + a \int_{-\infty}^{\infty} f(x)\ dx$$

$$= \int_{-\infty}^{\infty} uf(a + u)\ du + a = a.$$

(The last integral vanishes because the integrand is an "odd function"—it is symmetrical about the origin.) Thus, the mean of a *symmetrical* distribution is the point of symmetry. This can often save a tedious integration.

The median and percentiles of a continuous distribution, defined for any distribution in Chapter 2, may be interpreted in terms of the density function. The median m of a continuous distribution is any value such that $F(m) = 1/2$. That is, the probability is $1/2$ that a random variable with this distribution takes on a value less than the median—and the probability is also $1/2$ that it takes on a value greater than the median. This means, then, that a vertical line at the median divides the area under the

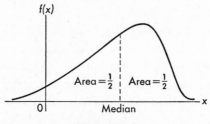

Figure 4–6

graph of the density function into *two equal parts*. In particular, if a density is symmetrical, the center of symmetry is the median.

Similarly, the twentieth percentile, say, is a value of the random variable such that 20 per cent of the total area under the density function lies to the left of that value. And so on.

Example 4–f

Let X again have the distribution defined in Example 4–d above. It is clear geometrically that the median is $m = 1/\sqrt{2}$.
The seventy-fifth percentile could be computed as follows:

$$\int_0^{x_{.75}} 2x \, dx = (x_{.75})^2 = .75,$$

or

$$x_{.75} = \sqrt{.75} \doteq .866.$$

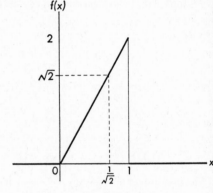

Figure 4–7

Problems

4–6—4–9. Compute the expected value and variance of the random variables described in Problems 4–2—4–5 respectively.

4–10. Referring again to Problem 4–4, a certain strength per unit area is computed as $k \sin \theta$ where k is a constant for the particular material used. This strength is a random variable; determine its expected value.

4.3 Important Special Cases

Any non-negative function $f(x)$ could conceivably serve as the model for some continuous chance quantity, provided that the area under its graph is 1. However, as in the discrete case, there are here certain special density functions which occur so frequently as to warrant special mention. We give some of them, together with their means and variances below. In each case the name given refers to a *type* of distribution. Particular distributions are obtained by specializing the parameters involved to particular values.

The uniform, triangular, and Laplace density functions are sufficiently simple that the student can easily compute the means and variances given. The normal density introduces indefinite integrals which cannot be expressed as "elementary functions"; we shall consider this important distribution in subsequent sections. The chi-square distribution is quite important, but involves such complications as a proper definition of the factorial when ν is an odd number. We shall be using it in a later chapter (by means of a table of values of its distribution function), but the associated mathematical details will not be discussed.

The last density in Table 4.1, the Cauchy density, is perhaps not so important for its practical applications (although they do occasionally arise) as for its use as an example of a density function which has no moments of any integral order, including no expected value. Examples of this kind make it necessary in stating certain theorems to include the qualification "if these moments exist," which may seem to the novice like a waste of ink.

Table 4.1   Some Important Continuous Distributions

Name	Density	Parameters	Mean	Variance
Uniform	$\dfrac{1}{b-a}$ for $a < x < b$	a, b	$\dfrac{a+b}{2}$	$\dfrac{(b-a)^2}{12}$
Triangular	$\dfrac{1}{a}\left(1 - \dfrac{\|x-b\|}{a}\right),$ for $\|x-b\| < a$	a, b	b	$\dfrac{a^2}{6}$
Laplace (or Exponential)	ke^{-kx}, for $x > 0$	k	$\dfrac{1}{k}$	$\dfrac{1}{k^2}$
Normal (or Gaussian)	$\dfrac{1}{\sqrt{2\pi}\,\sigma} e^{-\frac{1}{2}\left(\frac{x-\mu}{\sigma}\right)^2}$	μ, σ^2	μ	σ^2
Chi-Square	$\dfrac{x^{\nu/2-1}e^{-x/2}}{(\nu/2-1)!\,2^{\nu/2}}$	ν	ν	2ν
Cauchy	$\dfrac{1/\pi}{1 + (x-m)^2}$	m	(none)	(none)

4.3.1 The Uniform Distribution

If the density function of a random variable X is constant over some region of values and zero elsewhere, the variable X is said to be uniformly distributed over that region. Thus, a random variable with the density function given first in Table 4.1 is uniformly distributed over the interval from $x = a$ to $x = b$. Such a density is symmetrical about the center of the interval, $(a + b)/2$, and hence this number is both the mean and the median of the distribution.

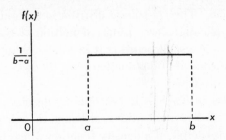

Figure 4–8. Density of a Uniform Distribution

Because of the constant height of $f(x)$, the probability of obtaining a value on some subinterval is proportional to the length of that subinterval.

Example 4–g

Subway trains on a certain line run every 10 minutes between rush hours.   What is the probability that a man entering the station at a random time will have to wait at least 8 minutes?

The random variable

$$T = \text{Time to the next train}$$

is assumed, by definition of "random time" of the man's arrival at the station, to have a *uniform* distribution on $0 \leq T \leq 10$.   The probability that he has to wait at least 8 minutes is then

$$P(T \geq 8) = P(8 \leq T \leq 10) = \frac{2}{10} = \frac{1}{5}.$$

The expected wait is, clearly, 5 minutes.

Example 4–h

An acceleration has a magnitude A and a random direction in the plane described by an angle θ, with respect to a fixed direction, which is uniformly distributed over the range from $-\pi$ to π. What are the mean and variance of the component of acceleration along the fixed direction?

The acceleration component is $A \cos \theta$, and the probability element for the angle θ is

$$f(\theta) \, d\theta = \frac{1}{2\pi} \, d\theta, \qquad \text{for } -\pi < \theta < \pi.$$

Hence,

$$E(A \cos \theta) = AE(\cos \theta) = A \int_{-\pi}^{\pi} (\cos \theta) \frac{1}{2\pi} \, d\theta = 0,$$

and

$$\operatorname{var} (A \cos \theta) = A^2 E(\cos^2 \theta) = A^2 \int_{-\pi}^{\pi} (\cos^2 \theta) \frac{1}{2\pi} \, d\theta = \frac{A^2}{2}.$$

A uniform probability distribution is quite analagous to a uniform distribution of mass along a line—such as in the case of a uniform rod, or a uniform thread. The formula given in mathematical tables for the moment of inertia about the center of gravity of a thin rod of mass m and length l is $ml^2/12$, and this result gives also the variance of a uniform probability distribution. However, in the case of probability, $m = 1$.

Problems

4–11. Let X be uniformly distributed on the interval $-2 \leq X \leq 2$.
    (a) Determine and sketch $f(x)$.
    (b) Compute $P(|X| > 3/2)$.

4–12. What is the probability that, coming at a random time upon a traffic signal which is 20 seconds green and 40 seconds red, one finds the signal red? (What is the uniformly distributed random variable here?)

4–13. Referring to the situation of Example 4–g, suppose that the man lives mid-town, has an office uptown, and has an office downtown. He takes whichever train comes first, the uptown or downtown, but finds himself downtown nine times out of ten. Does this contradict the assumptions that his arrival is "random" or that the trains run on schedule with 10-minute spacings between uptown trains and the same for downtown trains?

4.3.2 The Standard Normal Distribution

If we choose the parameter values $\mu = 0$ and $\sigma = 1$ in the density called "normal" in Table 4.1, we obtain the following function, denoted by $\phi(x)$:

$$\phi(x) = \frac{1}{\sqrt{2\pi}} e^{-x^2/2}.$$

The probability distribution with this density function will be called the *standard normal distribution*.

We should like to know that the area under the graph of $\phi(x)$ is 1 and to be able to compute the moments of the distribution. For these purposes we give (without derivation) an integration formula, as it is usually found in tables of definite integrals:

$$\int_{-\infty}^{\infty} x^{2n} e^{-ax^2} \, dx = \frac{1 \cdot 3 \cdot 5 \cdots (2n-1)}{(2a)^n} \sqrt{\frac{\pi}{a}},$$

where the numerator is understood to have the value 1 when $n = 0$, and a is any positive constant. If we set $a = 1/2$ and $n = 0$ in this integration formula, we find that the constant $1/\sqrt{2\pi}$ has been well chosen. That is,

$$\int_{-\infty}^{\infty} \phi(x) \, dx = 1.$$

All moments of odd order (first, third, etc.) are zero because of the symmetry of the density function about $x = 0$. In particular, the *expected value* of a random variable with this standard normal distribution is *zero*. The variance is then the second moment about $\mu = 0$, obtained from the integration formula by setting $a = 1/2$ and $n = 1$. The result is

$$\text{var } X = \int_{-\infty}^{\infty} x^2 \phi(x) \, dx = 1.$$

The "standard" parameters $\mu = 0$ and $\sigma^2 = 1$ are thus the mean and variance of the distribution, respectively, as the notation would imply:

$$\mu = E(X) = 0, \text{ and } \sigma^2 = \text{var } X = 1.$$

The cumulative distribution function corresponding to the standard density, $\phi(x)$, will be denoted by $\Phi(x)$ and is obtained by integration in the usual fashion.

$$\Phi(x) = \int_{-\infty}^{x} \phi(u) \, du = P(X \leq x).$$

A table of values of this cumulative distribution function is given in Table I, page 253. This table may be used to calculate such probabilities as

$$P(a < X < b) = \Phi(b) - \Phi(a),$$

when X is a standard normal variable.

Graphs of the density and distribution functions of the standard normal distribution are shown in Figures 4–9a and 4–9b.

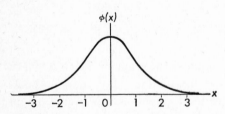
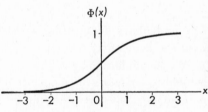

Figure 4–9a. The Standard Normal Density Function

Figure 4–9b. The Standard Normal Distribution Function

Problems

4–14. A random variable X has the standard normal distribution (mean zero and variance 1). Determine, using Table I, page 253,
    (a) $P(X < 0)$.   (d) $P(X = -1)$.
    (b) $P(1 < X < 3)$.   (e) $P(X > 2 \text{ or } X < -2)$.
    (c) $P(|X| < 3)$.

4–15. Show that, when X is a standard normal variable,
  (a) $P(|X| > k) = 2(1 - \Phi(k))$.
  (b) $P(|X| < k) = 2\Phi(k) - 1$.
  (c) $E(X^2) = 1$.

4.3.3 The General Normal Distribution

Let μ and σ be fixed, and consider a random variable X with probability distribution given by the normal density function

$$f(x) = \frac{1}{\sigma\sqrt{2\pi}} e^{-\frac{1}{2}\left(\frac{x-\mu}{\sigma}\right)^2}.$$

Let us introduce the random variable

$$Z = \frac{X - \mu}{\sigma}.$$

This random variable has a distribution function determined as follows:

$$P(Z \leq z) = P\left(\frac{X - \mu}{\sigma} \leq z\right) = P(X \leq \mu + \sigma z)$$

$$= \frac{1}{\sigma\sqrt{2\pi}} \int_{-\infty}^{\mu+\sigma z} e^{-\frac{1}{2}\left(\frac{x-\mu}{\sigma}\right)^2} dx$$

$$= \frac{1}{\sqrt{2\pi}} \int_{-\infty}^{z} e^{-u^2/2} du,$$

where, in order to obtain the last integral, we have made the substitution $x = \mu + \sigma u$ in the preceding integral. This calculation shows that the variable Z has precisely the distribution of what we called the "standard" normal variable in the preceding section, having mean 0 and variance 1. Hence,

$$E(X) = E(\mu + \sigma Z) = \mu,$$

and

$$\text{var } X = \text{var } (\mu + \sigma Z) = \sigma^2 \text{ var } Z = \sigma^2.$$

Thus, the mean and variance of X are the parameters μ and σ^2 used in defining its density function. Anticipation of this fact, of course, is what led us to use those symbols for the parameters.

We shall occasionally speak of this change of a random variable by subtracting its mean and dividing by its standard deviation as "standardizing" the variable. This change always yields a variable with mean zero and variance unity. It amounts to a shift in origin to the center of the distribution and a change of scale so that one standard deviation becomes the new unit of measure on the axis of values of the variable. In the case at hand, where X is *normal*, the standardized variable Z turns out to be normal also.

The various moments about the mean of a general normal random variable can now be easily computed in terms of corresponding moments of the standardized variable Z:

$$E[(X - \mu)^k] = E[(\sigma Z)^k]$$
$$= \sigma^k E(Z^k) = \begin{cases} 0, \text{ if } k \text{ is odd,} \\ 1 \cdot 3 \cdot 5 \cdots (2m - 1)\sigma^{2m} \text{ if } k = 2m. \end{cases}$$

Thus, the kth moment about μ is just σ^k times the kth moment of the standard normal distribution about 0, which kth moment is given in the preceding section. Notice that this means that all odd-order moments about μ are zero and that all even-order moments about μ are expressible in terms of the variance, σ^2.

Finally, it is important to see that the table of values of the distribution function of a *general* normally distributed variable X is contained implicitly in the table of values of the *standard* normal distribution. For, if X is a general normal variable, its distribution function is

$$F_X(x) = P(X \le x) = P(\mu + \sigma Z \le x) = P\left(Z \le \frac{x - \mu}{\sigma}\right) = \Phi\left(\frac{x - \mu}{\sigma}\right).$$

Example 4–i

Suppose that X is normally distributed with mean 16 and variance 7. Compute $P(|X - 16| > 3)$.

We first express the inequality in terms of the distribution function, and then use Table I, page 253:

$$P(|X - 16| > 3) = 1 - P(|X - 16| < 3)$$
$$= 1 - P(-3 < X - 16 < 3)$$
$$= 1 - P(13 < X < 19)$$
$$= 1 - F_X(19) + F_X(13)$$
$$= 1 - \Phi\left(\frac{19 - 16}{\sqrt{7}}\right) + \Phi\left(\frac{13 - 16}{\sqrt{7}}\right)$$
$$= 1 - \Phi(1.17) + \Phi(-1.17)$$
$$= 1 - .8790 + .1210 = .2420.$$

Problems

4–16. A random variable X is normally distributed with mean 50 and variance 25. Determine
  (a) $P(X > 62)$. (c) $P(X = 60)$.
  (b) $P(|X - 50| < 8)$. (d) $P(|X - 40| > 5)$.

4–17. A random variable X is normally distributed. If $E(X^2) = 68$ and $P(X < 10) = .8413$, determine μ and σ^2.

4–18. Suppose that a doorway being constructed is to be used by a class of people whose heights are (approximately) normally distributed with mean 5 feet

10 inches and standard deviation 3 inches. How low may the doorway be without causing more than 2 per cent of the people to bump their heads?

4–19. It is found that following a certain crushing process, rock diameters are approximately normally distributed with mean diameter 1.5 inches and standard deviation .3 inch.

(a) What percentage of the rocks would have diameters exceeding 2 inches?

(b) What characteristic of rock diameters makes the normal distribution necessarily inexact in describing them?

(c) Assuming the weight of a rock to be kd^3, where d is the diameter, what is the expected weight (in terms of k)?

4–20. The acceptability of a capillary tube for a freezer is found by measuring the pressure drop in pounds per square inch between the two ends of the tube. The pressures obtained from a manufacturing process of capillary tubes shows an average of 130 pounds per square inch and a standard deviation of 4 pounds per square inch. Assume that these pressures are random and normally distributed. Determine

(a) what per cent of the pressures are below 121.5 pounds per square inch.

(b) what value is exceeded by 75 per cent of the pressure readings.

(c) what limits include the middle 90 per cent of the pressure readings.

(d) what per cent of the pressure readings lie between 121.5 and 134.5 pounds per square inch.

Review Problems—Chapter 4

4–R1. A random variable X is uniformly distributed on the interval from 0 to 6. Compute $P(|X - 2| < 3)$.

4–R2. The function whose graph is shown at the right is a probability density function. What is the height above the x axis of the highest point?

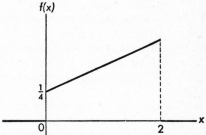

4–R3. The density function of a random variable X is shown at the right. Compute

(a) $P(X > 1/2)$.

(b) $E(X)$.

(c) the number m such that $P(X > m) = 1/2$.

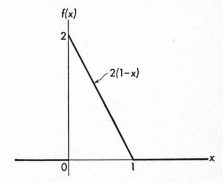

4–R4. A random variable has the density function

$$f(x) = \begin{cases} x/8, \ 0 < x < 4, \\ 0, \ \text{elsewhere.} \end{cases}$$

Compute $E(X)$, $E(X^2)$, var X, $E(2X - 1)$.

4–R5. A random variable X is normally distributed with mean 10 and standard deviation 2. Determine
   (a) $P(8 < X < 11)$.
   (b) $P(X = 12)$.
   (c) $P(|X - 10| < 3)$.

4–R6. Of a large group of men, 4 per cent are under 63.3 inches in height, and 52 per cent are between 63.3 and 69 inches. Assuming an approximately normal distribution of heights, what would be the mean and standard deviation of the distribution?

4–R7. On his way to work, a man passes traffic signals A, B, and C located several miles apart so that traffic variations cause him to arrive at these signals at random and independent times. Suppose each signal is on a 60-second cycle, A showing green for 20 seconds, B for 30 seconds, and C for 45 seconds.
   (a) What is the probability that he makes signal A without stopping? Signal B? Signal C?
   (b) What is the probability that he makes all three?
   (c) What is the probability that he makes the last one, given that he has made the first two?
   (d) What is the probability that he makes the first two, but not the last?
   (e) What is the probability that he makes exactly two of the signals?
   (f) What is the probability that he makes just the *first* two, given that he makes exactly two of the signals?

4–R8. Referring to Problem 4–19, a better approximation to the distribution of particle sizes in a crushing process is obtained by assuming that the variable $X = \log d$ (where d is the particle "diameter") has a normal distribution. These relationships can then be obtained:

$$\sigma_X{}^2 = \log [1 + (\sigma_d/\mu_d)^2], \qquad \mu_X = \log \mu_d - \frac{1}{2}\sigma_X{}^2.$$

With this model, recompute the percentage of rocks having diameters exceeding 2 inches, again taking $E(d) = 1.5$ inches, and $\sigma_d = .3$ inch. (The distribution of e^X, where X is normal, is called the *log-normal* distribution.)

5/Sums of Random Variables

5.0 Introduction

Sums of random variables are of interest for many reasons. Often random quantities under study are inherently sums of other random quantities. For example, we have already discussed in detail how a binomial random variable can be thought of as the sum of Bernoulli random variables. Another instance of a sum of random variables is the accumulated winnings in a game where the winnings at each play are random. A third instance is in the study of errors, where it is common that errors from many sources combine in an additive fasion to produce the over-all system error.

The statistics we shall study in later chapters are often sums of random variables or depend on sums of random variables. For instance, the "sample mean" will be defined to be a constant times the sum of the observations in a sample, and the "sample variance," a constant times the sum of squares of certain random variables.

The *sum* of several random variables *is itself a random variable* and as such has a probability distribution. This distribution of the sum naturally depends on the distributions of the terms in the sum. It is to be expected, then, that one should be able to calculate the distribution of the sum if the distributions of the summands are known. In principle this is so; however, when the summands are not independent, one must have a knowledge of the nature of the dependence. It is common that actual computation of the distribution of a sum is quite complicated.

In this chapter we shall consider the *expected value* of a sum of random variables, the *variance* of a sum of independent random variables, the *distributions* of sums of certain types of variables, and the *asymptotic distribution* of the sum of a large number of identical, independent variables. Derivations of most of the facts to be discussed will be omitted; they are to be found in any text on mathematical statistics.

5.1 Expected Value of a Sum

We have mentioned earlier that the expectation or averaging operation, symbolized $E(\ )$, has an additivity property. Specifically, if X_1, X_2, . . . , X_k are any random variables which have expected values, then,

$$E(X_1 + X_2 + \cdots + X_k) = E(X_1) + E(X_2) + \cdots + E(X_k),$$

or, using "sigma" notation:

$$E(\Sigma X_i) = \Sigma E(X_i).$$

Example 5–a

A bowl contains four chips marked with numbers on each side as follows: $(1, 1)$, $(2, -1)$, $(3, 1)$, $(4, -1)$. A chip is drawn at random. Let the chip drawn be (X, Y). Then, clearly, $E(X) = 2.5$ and $E(Y) = 0$. The sum $X + Y$ can have the values 2, 1, 4, and 3, each with probability $1/4$, and hence $E(X + Y) = 2.5$, which is equal to $E(X) + E(Y)$.

We shall not prove this additivity property in general, but content ourselves with showing it in the discrete case. In establishing the property it is only necessary to do so for the sum of *two* variables, since the principle of induction would extend it to the sum of any finite number of variables. Consider, then, the two discrete random variables X and Y, and let $Z = X + Y$. Let X have possible values x_1, x_2, . . . and Y have possible values y_1, y_2, ... The possible values of Z (z_1, z_2, . . .) are obtained by pairing the possible values of X and Y in all possible ways and forming the sums. The expected sum is computed as follows:

$$E(X + Y) = E(Z) = \sum_k z_k P(Z = z_k)$$

$$= \sum_i \sum_j (x_i + y_j) P(X = x_i \text{ and } Y = y_j)$$

$$= \sum_i x_i \left\{ \sum_j P(X = x_i \text{ and } Y = y_j) \right\}$$

$$+ \sum_j y_j \left\{ \sum_i P(X = x_i \text{ and } Y = y_j) \right\}.$$

Now, since for each i the events

$$(X = x_i \text{ and } Y = y_1), (X = x_i \text{ and } Y = y_2), \ldots$$

are mutually exclusive and make up the event $(X = x_i)$, it follows that

$$\sum_j P(X = x_i \text{ and } Y = y_j) = P(X = x_i).$$

Similarly,

$$\sum_i P(X = x_i \text{ and } Y = y_j) = P(Y = y_j).$$

Using these, we find for the expected sum:

$$E(X + Y) = \sum_i x_i P(X = x_i) + \sum_j y_j P(Y = y_j)$$

$$= \quad E(X) \quad + \quad E(Y).$$

We observe that we did *not* need to assume independence of the variables added in order to show additivity of the expectation.

5.2 Variance of a Sum

The random variables $X_1, \ldots, X_k$ are said to be *independent* if and only if

$$P(X_1 \leq x_1, \ldots, \text{ and } X_k \leq x_k)$$
$$= P(X_1 \leq x_1)P(X_2 \leq x_2) \ldots P(X_k \leq x_k),$$

a definition which is in accord with the discussion in Chapter 1, page 21. In the *discrete* case one obtains an equivalent concept by using the condition

$$P(X_1 = x_1, \ldots, X_k = x_k) = P(X_1 = x_1)P(X_2 = x_2) \cdots P(X_k = x_k).$$

This definition is found to be "correct" in the sense that it puts into our probability models the intuitive notion of independence in a way which experience shows to be satisfactory.

It can be shown that if $X_1, X_2, \ldots, X_k$ are *independent* random variables,

$$\text{var } (X_1 + X_2 + \cdots + X_k) = \text{var } X_1 + \text{var } X_2 + \cdots + \text{var } X_k,$$

or,

$$\text{var } (\Sigma X_i) = \Sigma \text{ var } X_i.$$

Example 5–b

Letting 1 and 0 denote heads and tails in the toss of a coin, we have a Bernoulli variable with variance $\sigma^2 = pq = 1/4$. If we toss ten coins, the total number of heads among the ten is the sum of the 1's and 0's for the ten coins and is binomially distributed. The variance of the sum, or the variance of the number of heads among the ten coins, is $npq = 5/2$ (with $n = 10$, $p = 1/2$), the sum of the ten variances of the results for the individual coins. The additivity property is applicable in this case because of the assumption of independence of the results of the individual coins.

Again we do not prove the additivity property in general, but show why it works in the case of discrete random variables. As in the case of the expectation, it suffices to consider two variables, X and Y. For convenience let us use the notation $U = X - \mu_X$ and $V = Y - \mu_Y$, so that

$$\text{var } X = E(U^2), \text{ and var } Y = E(V^2).$$

Then

$$\begin{aligned} \text{var } (X + Y) = E[(U + V)^2] &= E[U^2 + V^2 + 2UV] \\ &= E(U^2) + E(V^2) + 2E(UV) \\ &= \text{var } X + \text{var } Y + 2 \text{ cov } (X, Y), \end{aligned}$$

where

$$\text{cov } (X, Y) = E[(X - \mu_X)(Y - \mu_Y)],$$

called the *covariance* of X and Y. If this covariance is zero (in which case X and Y are said to be *uncorrelated*), the variance is additive. But this will certainly be the case when X and Y (and hence U and V) are *independent*, for then

$$\begin{aligned} E(UV) &= \sum_i \sum_j u_i v_j P(U = u_i \text{ and } V = v_j) \\ &= \sum_i \sum_j u_i v_j P(U = u_i) P(V = v_j) \\ &= \sum_i u_i P(U = u_i) \sum_j v_j P(V = v_j) = E(U)E(V), \end{aligned}$$

which is zero for the given U and V.

We should observe from this derivation that although, as stated above, independence implies additivity of variances, really all that is required for this additivity is that the terms of the sum be pairwise uncorrelated.

5.3 Distribution of a Sum

In order to be able to compute probabilities of events concerning a sum of random variables, we usually need more than the mean and variance of the sum, namely, the entire probability distribution of the sum.

In simple discrete cases the distribution of the sum can be calculated directly, as was done in Example 5–a. It is not always so easy, however, to obtain the distribution of the sum as in that example; on the other hand, there are certain cases in which we have an additivity property for the distribution *type*, which saves the day. For instance, if one adds together independent, normal variables, the sum is normally distributed; and parallel statements hold for the binomial, Poisson, and chi-square distributions. In each case, of course, the expected sum is the sum of the expectations, and the variance of the sum (of independent summands) is the sum of the variances.

Example 5–c

Let X denote the number of "successes" in ten independent trials of an experiment and Y the number of successes in twenty independent trials. Then $X + Y$ is the number of successes in thirty independent trials. The variable X is binomial $(10, p)$, the variable Y is binomial $(20, p)$, and the sum is binomial $(10 + 20, p)$. Also, $E(X) = 10p$, $E(Y) = 20p$, and $E(X + Y) = 10p + 20p = 30p$. And the variances also add: var $X = 10p(1 - p)$, var $Y = 20p(1 - p)$, and var $(X + Y) = 30p(1 - p)$.

Example 5–d

Suppose that a system consists of two components, one with a Poisson breakdown pattern with $\lambda_1 = 1$ (the average number of breakdowns in a unit time) and the other with a Poisson breakdown pattern with $\lambda_2 = 4$. The number of system breakdowns in a given time interval is then the sum of the number of breakdowns for the one component and the number for the other. This sum has the Poisson distribution, since the Poisson postulates are satisfied. For example:

$P(1 \text{ breakdown in } \Delta t)$
$= P(1 \text{ breakdown in one component and none in the other})$
$\quad + P(1 \text{ breakdown in the other and none in the first})$
$= [\lambda_1 \Delta t + o(\Delta t)][1 - \lambda_2 \Delta t + o(\Delta t)] + [\lambda_2 \Delta t + o(\Delta t)][1 - \lambda_1 \Delta t + o(\Delta t)]$
$= (\lambda_1 + \lambda_2) \Delta t + o(\Delta t) = 5 \Delta t + o(\Delta t).$

The λ for the sum is thus the sum of the λ's for the summands. In the case at hand, the average number of system breakdowns per unit interval is 5, the sum of 1 and 4.

Problems

5–1. What is the average weight of a box of 100 screws, if the weight of an individual screw is a random variable with expected value 1 ounce? What is the standard deviation of the weight of a box of screws, if the standard deviation of the weight of an individual screw is .01 ounce?

5–2. Two dice are thrown. Let X be the number of points on one and Y the number of points on the other. Construct probability tables for X, Y, and $X + Y$ and compute the expected values and variances. Then verify the additivity properties of μ and σ^2.

5–3. Ten four-digit numbers presumed accurate are to be added. If the numbers are rounded off to three digits each and then added, what are the expected value and standard deviation of the error committed in this process? (Treat the error made in rounding off a number as a discrete random variable, assuming that the fourth digit is 0, 1, . . . , 9 with equal probabilities.)

5–4. A missle is fired at a point in a plane, and the amount of the miss is measured by X and Y, the components in two perpendicular directions. If each of these components has expectation zero and standard deviation 1000 feet, what is the expected value of $(X^2 + Y^2)$, the square of the radial miss?

5–5. Given that the sum of squares of ν standard normal variables has the chi-square distribution with ν degrees of freedom, use Table II, page 256, to determine the probability that, referring to Problem 5–4, the radial miss exceeds 1550 feet.

5–6. An electronic device contains sixteen electron tubes each of which has the Poisson failure pattern, with average life 50 hours. Determine the average time between failures of the device (caused by tube failures). [*Hint:* The average time between Poisson "changes" is the reciprocal of the λ, as is seen from the result of Problem 4–4 and the table on page 83. Determine the λ for the individual tubes and from this the λ for the entire unit.]

5.4 Limiting Distributions

A remarkable thing happens when a great many independent random variables are added together. It turns out to be unnecessary to know the precise distribution of the sum, since the distribution is approximately normal—no matter what the distributions of the *terms* in the sum may be, subject to certain mild conditions. This type of result is called a "Central Limit Theorem." One form of this important theorem treats sums of identically distributed variables. This situation is important for us since the sum of the observations in a random sample will be the sum of independent, identically distributed random variables. The theorem, in this form, is given now without proof.

Central Limit Theorem: If X_1, X_2, . . . are identically distributed random variables, each with expectation μ and variance σ^2, and if every finite set of these is independent, then the probability distribution of the sum

$$S_n = X_1 + \cdots + X_n$$

is asymptotically normal, as $n \to \infty$; that is,

$$\lim_{n \to \infty} P \left\{ \frac{S_n - n\mu}{\sigma \sqrt{n}} \leq z \right\} = \frac{1}{\sqrt{2\pi}} \int_{-\infty}^{z} e^{-t^2/2} \, dt.$$

The probability on the left is the distribution function, not of the sum S_n, but of the standardized quantity, as discussed on page 87. This is why we find the *standardized* normal distribution function, $\Phi(z)$, in the conclusion of the theorem. By the definition of a limit, the quantity approaching the limit (as $n \to \infty$) can be made arbitrarily close to the limiting value by taking an n sufficiently large. It follows that we can estimate the probability distribution of a sum of independent, identically distributed, random variables as follows. We note that for large n

$$P \left\{ \frac{S_n - n\mu}{\sigma \sqrt{n}} \leq z \right\} \doteq \int_{-\infty}^{z} \frac{e^{-t^2/2}}{\sqrt{2\pi}} \, dt = \Phi(z),$$

from which we see that we can express the distribution function in terms of the standardized normal distribution function:

$$F_{S_n}(y) = P(X_1 + \cdots + X_n \le y) \doteq \Phi\left(\frac{y - n\mu}{\sigma\sqrt{n}}\right).$$

One would naturally inquire as to how large is "large," so as to know when the asymptotic distribution may be used. This question does not have a simple answer; the rate of approach towards normality depends on the distribution of the population. If the population is normal, any sample sum is already normal. Otherwise the rate of approach depends on how nearly the population distribution resembles the normal distribution (in having a single hump and being rather symmetrical, for example). As a rule of thumb, when nothing is known about the population distribution, a sample size of twenty-five or more is usually adequate in using the asymptotic normal distribution. Whether the approximation is successful depends, of course, on how precise an answer is required.

Example 5-e

Boxes of cereal are filled by machine, the net weight being a random variable with mean 10 ounces and variance .5 ounces². A carton of forty-eight boxes of this cereal would have a combined average weight of 48×10 or 480 ounces, and the variance of the total weight would be $.5 \times 48$ ounces². Further, this total weight would be approximately *normally* distributed with parameters 480 ounces and 24 ounces². With this information we can compute such things as the probability that a carton weighs more than 31 pounds:

$$P(\text{total weight} > 31 \text{ lbs.}) = 1 - P(\text{total weight} < 31 \text{ lbs.})$$
$$\doteq 1 - \Phi\left(\frac{496 - 480}{\sqrt{24}}\right) = .0006.$$

Example 5-f

A die is cast sixty times. At a given throw, the expected number of points is 3.5, with variance 35/12. Hence, the sum of the points thrown in the sixty trials is approximately normally distributed, with mean $60 \times 3.5 = 210$ and variance $60 \times 35/12 = 175$. And, for example,

$$P(\text{total number of points} \le 200) \doteq \Phi\left(\frac{200 - 210}{\sqrt{175}}\right) = .225.$$

Example 5-g

A machine produces parts with a probability p that a part is defective. If the numbers 1 and 0 are assigned to defective and good parts, respectively, the expectation of the assigned number is p and the variance $p(1 - p) = pq$. Among ten parts, the number of defectives would be the *sum* of the 1's and 0's, a random variable with mean $10p$ and variance $10pq$. However, the probability distribution of this number of defectives would not be considered "normal enough" since ten is not very large and since the underlying distribution is usually "skewed" (assuming that p is small). On the other hand, we know that in this case the sum is *binomially* distributed; the asymptotic distribution is therefore not needed. Of course if p is small enough, a Poisson approximation is permitted (see Section 3.45 and Example 5–m).

Example 5–h

A lot contains 100 parts, a fraction p being defective. Again, using 1 and 0 for defective and good, the number assigned to a part drawn at random has the same distribution as in Example 5–g, namely, a Bernoulli distribution with parameter p. However, suppose that ten parts are drawn (*without* replacement) from the lot. The number defective among the ten, which is again the sample sum, is a random variable with expectation $10p$ and variance

$$10pq \frac{100 - 10}{100 - 1} = \frac{100}{11} pq.$$

Again, the Central Limit Theorem in the form given is not of use, for the observations are not independent, and the sample size is small. But we know the exact distribution of the sum—namely, the hypergeometric distribution—and so can determine probabilities associated with the problem.

Problems

5–7. Estimate the probability that a total of 190 or fewer points result from sixty throws of a die. (Cf. Example 5–f, page 97).

5–8. Referring to Example 5–e, page 97, determine an approximation to the probability that a carton of forty-eight boxes weighs in excess of 30.5 pounds.

5–9. Suppose that packages of "100" screws are filled until the weight is at least 10 ounces, when individual screws weight a random amount, with expectation .1 ounce and standard deviation .008 ounce. What is the probability that a box actually containing 98 screws is counted as containing 100?

5.5 Normal Approximation to the Binomial Distribution

We have seen that a random variable which is binomially distributed (n, p) may be considered as the sum of n independent, identically distributed Bernoulli variables with parameter p. These Bernoulli variables are the results of the individual trials in the repeated trials situation in which the number of "successes" is the binomial variable.

Applying the Central Limit Theorem in this instance, we find that a binomial distribution (n, p) becomes asymptotically normal, as $n \to \infty$ with

p fixed. More precisely, if X is the binomially distributed variable,

$$\lim_{n \to \infty} P\left\{\frac{X - np}{\sqrt{npq}} \leq z\right\} = \frac{1}{\sqrt{2\pi}} \int_{-\infty}^{z} e^{-t^2/2} \, dt.$$

whence

$$P(X \leq x) \doteq \Phi\left(\frac{x - np}{\sqrt{npq}}\right) = \Phi(z)$$

where $\Phi(z)$ is again the standardized normal distribution function.

The function on the left of the last approximate equality is a step function—the distribution function of a discrete random variable. The function on the right is a continuous function. Yet the values of the functions for each abscissa are (for large n) approximately equal, the continuous function more or less passing through the middle of the steps of the step function.

Example 5-i

Consider the case $n = 8$ and $p = 1/2$. Here $np = 4$ and $npq = 2$. Hence,

$$P(X \leq x) = \sum_{k \leq x} \binom{8}{k} \left(\frac{1}{2}\right)^{k} \left(\frac{1}{2}\right)^{n-k}.$$

From the above discussion, we can approximate this probability using the normal distribution:

$$P(X \leq x) \doteq \Phi\left(\frac{x - 4}{\sqrt{2}}\right).$$

The graphs of these two functions are shown in Figure 5–1. The approximation is

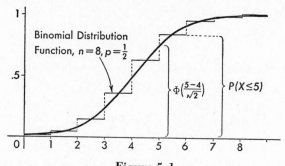

Figure 5–1

good for x about halfway between integers, but it is usually at the integers that we want the value of the distribution function. From the graph it is clear that a much better approximation (but still an approximation) to the value of $P(X \leq k)$ is obtained by taking the ordinate on the continuous curve a half unit to the right of k:

$$P(X \leq k) \doteq \Phi\left(\frac{k + 1/2 - np}{\sqrt{npq}}\right).$$

Using the correction given in this last example, the normal approximation can be quite good even for rather small values of n, as in the following example.

Example 5–j

Consider the normal approximation to the binomial when $n = 4$ and $p = 1/2$. Using the correction of the preceding example, we have

$$P(X \leq k) \doteq \Phi \left(\frac{k + 1/2 - 2}{\sqrt{1}} \right).$$

The results are given in the following table.

k	0	1	2	3	4
$F_X(k)$	.0625	.3125	.6875	.9375	1.0000
Normal Approx.	.0668	.3085	.6915	.9332	.9938

Probabilities of individual values of a binomially distributed variable can of course be estimated, too, since they can be expressed as differences between adjacent values of the distribution function—that is, as the jumps.

Example 5–k

Let X be binomially distributed with $n = 8$ and $p = 3/8$. What is the probability that $X = 5$?
From the binomial formula, we have

$$P(X = 5) = \binom{8}{3} \left(\frac{3}{8} \right)^5 \left(\frac{5}{8} \right)^3 \doteq .1014.$$

Using a normal approximation (with $\mu = np = 3$, and $\sigma^2 = npq = 15/8$), we find

$$\begin{aligned} P(X = 5) &= P(X \leq 5) - P(X \leq 4) \\ &= F_X(5) - F_X(4) \\ &\doteq \Phi \left(\frac{5 + 1/2 - 3}{\sqrt{15/8}} \right) - \Phi \left(\frac{4 + 1/2 - 3}{\sqrt{15/8}} \right) \doteq .1032. \end{aligned}$$

Although for p near $1/2$ we can take n quite small and still get useful accuracy, values of p near 0 or 1 result in a rather skewed distribution, and the accuracy is not so good.

Example 5–l

Consider a binomial variable X with $n = 20$ and $p = .8$. What is the probability that $X \geq 16$?

Using the exact, binomial distribution, we have

$$P(X \geq 16) = P(X = 16,17,18,19, \text{ or } 20)$$

$$= \sum_{16}^{20} \binom{20}{k} (.8)^k (.2)^{20-k} \doteq .6296.$$

The normal approximation ($np = 16$ and $npq = 3.2$) gives

$$P(X \geq 16) = 1 - P(X \leq 15) = 1 - F_X(15)$$

$$\doteq 1 - \Phi\left(\frac{15 + 1/2 - 16}{\sqrt{3.2}}\right) = .6103.$$

(Without the 1/2-correction, we should have obtained .7123.)

For the case of large n and small p (or small q) we have the alternative of using a Poisson approximation, as discussed in Section 3.4.5 (page 66).

Example 5–m

The following table gives a comparison between the normal and Poisson approximations to the binomial distribution function, in the case $n = 8$ and $p = 1/8$. We should perhaps be interested in $k = 5, \ldots, 8$, in addition to the entries $k = 0, \ldots, 4$ shown, but the binomial distribution function has already reached 1 (to four decimal places) at $k = 4$. The Poisson approximation is not quite 1 at $k = 4$, and in fact is still not quite 1 at $k = 8$, since it assigns probability to the values beyond $k = 8$. The same is true of the normal approximation, which also assigns probability to values less than $k = 0$.

Table 5.1   Binomial Distribution Function $P(X \leq k)$
and Approximations

k	Binomial ($n = 8, p = 1/8$)	Normal Approx.	Poisson ($\mu = 1$)
0	.3516	.300	.368
1	.7443	.704	.736
2	.9407	.946	.920
3	.9961	.996	.981
4	1.0000	1.000	.996

These examples would indicate that the success of the normal approximation to the binomial distribution depends on the value of p as well as the value of n. If p is near 0 or 1, a larger value of n is required to have the same success as in cases in which p is near 1/2. A rule of thumb sometimes used is that if $np > 5$ and $nq > 5$, the normal approximation is satisfactory, even though p be, say, lower than .1 or higher than .9. Of course, in these latter instances, the Poisson approximation is usually more successful.

Problems

5–10. Suppose that a process yields 20 per cent defective units. If 100 units are to be taken from the production line for inspection, what is the probability that 15 or less will be defective?

5–11. Determine an approximation to the probability that in 180 throws of a die
(a) more than 40 result in 6's.
(b) the number of 6's is between 25 and 35 (inclusive).
(c) the number of 5's and 6's is less than 50.

5–12. If 55 per cent of the voters of a (large) city are in favor of a given proposal, what is the probability that a random sample of 100 voters would not show a majority in favor?

5–13. Observations are drawn from two identical populations in pairs. We mark down a plus sign ($+$) if the observation from population A exceeds that from B, otherwise a minus sign ($-$). Assuming that the probability is $1/2$ that the A observation exceeds the B at a given drawing, determine the probability that in 144 independent drawings we get 85 or more $+$'s (with the rest $-$'s).

5–14. Two dice are cast seventy-two times. What is the probability of two or less 12's? (Compare the answers obtained using the normal approximation and the Poisson approximation. Which is more accurate?)

5.6 Errors and Tolerances

It is frequently appropriate to consider errors in computation or measurement as random variables. Indeed, it is usually the *random* nature of the quantity which requires treating it as an error, since a predictable miscalculation could be avoided by compensation. One often finds, too, that there are contributions to total error coming from several sources, which combine additively or approximately additively to make up the total error. The total error is then a sum of random variables.

Example 5–n

Consider a measurement A' of the concentration A of a certain chemical solution. The discrepancy may be attributable to random fluctuations in the measuring process and to small variations in concentration from one portion of the solution to another. That is, we may think of A' as

$$A' = A + \epsilon_1 + \epsilon_2.$$

where ϵ_1 and ϵ_2 are independent, random errors. If these errors have zero expectation, $E(A') = A$; or one might define the concentration A of the solution to be $E(A')$. The variance of the total error can be computed from the variances of the components using the additivity property:

$$\text{var } (A' - A) = \text{var } \epsilon_1 + \text{var } \epsilon_2.$$

The standard deviation is then the square root of this sum.

Example 5-o

In analyzing the over-all error in a complex mechanical or electrical computing system caused by errors in various components (such as gyros, accelerometers, multipliers, summers, integrators, etc.), it is often the case that the total error can be expressed (at least to a first-order approximation) as a *linear* combination of component errors:

$$\epsilon = a_1\epsilon_1 + a_2\epsilon_2 + \cdot \cdot \cdot + a_k\epsilon_k.$$

The variance of this over-all error (assuming independence) is

$$\text{var } \epsilon = a_1{}^2 \text{ var } \epsilon_1 + a_2{}^2 \text{ var } \epsilon_2 + \cdot \cdot \cdot + a_k{}^2 \text{ var } \epsilon_k.$$

That standard deviations do not add, to yield the standard deviation of the sum, is an important observation, since the root-sum-square combination which is correct yields in general a *smaller* result than a straight addition. The root-sum-square takes into account the frequent cancellations provided by errors of opposite signs, whereas a straight sum would be overly pessimistic.

It is sometimes more important to consider *maximum* errors than their standard deviations. The relationship between these depends on the distributions of the errors and would usually be different in different situations. However, it has been found practical to assume that the errors are *normally* distributed and then to take $\pm 3\sigma$ as limits beyond which individual observations "never" occur. It can be seen from Table I, page 253, that the probability of occurrence of a value of a normally distributed variable outside those limits is .0026, which is quite small—but not sacred. Thus, it is convenient to take $\pm 3\sigma$ as maximum departures from the mean, although one could (and perhaps in some cases should) take 2σ or 4.3σ or some other multiple of σ in place of 3σ.

The quantities $\mu \pm 3\sigma$ are thought of as "tolerance" limits. We think of them as "natural tolerances" if they describe actual errors. The "tolerance" terminology is especially common in fitting together manufactured parts. Let us introduce the notation $T = 3\sigma$ to signify such a tolerance. We observe that since σ's must be combined in root sum-square fashion, so must tolerances. For example, if

$$\sigma = \sqrt{\sigma_1{}^2 + \sigma_2{}^2},$$

then for the corresponding tolerances:

$$T = \sqrt{T_1{}^2 + T_2{}^2} = \sqrt{9\sigma_1{}^2 + 9\sigma_2{}^2} = 3\sigma.$$

The $T = 3\sigma$ relation is still appropriate for the combination, since if the individual errors are normally distributed, so is a linear combination of them.

Example 5–p

Suppose that bearings are manufactured with inside diameter $.5000 + \epsilon_1$ and that shafts on which the bearings are to fit have outside diameter $.4995 + \epsilon_2$, where ϵ_1 and ϵ_2 are assumed to be independent, normal random variables with tolerances .0006 and .0007, respectively. What percentage of misfits (due to interference) could be expected?

The "clearance" is the difference $.0005 + \epsilon_1 - \epsilon_2$. The combined tolerance is

$$T = \sqrt{(.0006)^2 + (.0007)^2} \doteq .00092,$$

and the corresponding standard deviation is .000307. The proportion of misfits expected is then the probability:

$$P(\text{clearance} < 0) = \Phi\left(\frac{0 - .0005}{.000307}\right) = \Phi(-1.63) = .052,$$

or 5.2 per cent.

Example 5–q

Suppose that two sides of a rectangle are $X = 5 \pm .3$ centimeter and $Y = 2 \pm .3$ centimeter. The area is $A = XY$, and the differential of area provides a first-order approximation to the error in area:

$$dA = d(XY) = X\,dY + Y\,dX.$$

Taking the differentials as random errors, we have then for the corresponding tolerances

$$T_A = \sqrt{X^2 T_Y{}^2 + Y^2 T_X{}^2} = \sqrt{25(.09) + 4(.09)} = 1.62 \text{ cm}^2.$$

The area would then be expressed as 10 ± 1.62 cm². (The expected value of A is of course $E(XY) = E(X)E(Y)$, assuming independence of X and Y, the measured dimensions.) Percentage or relative error computations can be made from the relation

$$\frac{dA}{A} = \frac{dX}{X} + \frac{dY}{Y}.$$

The percentage errors in X and Y are 6 and 15 per cent, respectively. Thus, the percentage error in A is

$$\sqrt{6^2 + 15^2} = 16.2 \text{ per cent.}$$

Problems

5–15. It is desired to make resistors of 200 ohms with a tolerance $\pm 3/4$ per cent. These would cost 25 cents apiece. An employee suggests putting in series two 100-ohm resistors, with tolerances of ± 1 per cent each; these 100-ohm resistors cost 2 cents apiece. Does he rate a bonus?

5–16. Referring to Example 5–p, determine the mean outside diameter of the shafts in order that the percentage of misfits be reduced to 1 per cent.

5–17. Gear A has basic width .500 inch and a tolerance of $\pm .001$ inch. Gear B has basic width .300 inch and a tolerance of $\pm .004$ inch. Gear C has basic width .700 inch and a tolerance of $\pm .002$ inch. These are to be assembled side by side on a single shaft. What is the basic width and tolerance of the assembly?

5–18. The position error (in nautical miles) in a certain guidance system, after a given time of operation is given by

$$\epsilon = 5\delta_a + 20\delta_g,$$

where δ_a is random accelerometer error (in feet per second per second) and δ_g is random gyro error (in degrees per hour). Determine the standard deviation of position error corresponding to standard deviations of .1 ft/sec² and .05 degrees per hour of the accelermoter and gyro errors, respectively.

Review Problems—Chapter 5

5–R1. In a certain system of contract bridge bidding, cards are assigned points as follows: ace, 4 points; king, 3 points; queen, 2 points; jack, 1 point; and 0 points to each of 2, 3, . . . , 10. The number of points assigned to a card chosen at random from the deck is a random variable with possible values 0, 1, 2, 3, and 4.

    (a) Determine the probability distribution of the number of points assigned to a card chosen at random and from it the expected number of points and the variance of the number of points.

    (b) A hand of thirteen cards is dealt (drawn at random). Does the Central Limit Theorem apply in determining the approximate distribution of the *total* number of points in the hand?

    (c) Determine the expected total number of points in a hand of thirteen cards.

    (d) Determine the variance of the total number of points in a hand of thirteen cards, using the factor $(N - n)/(N - 1)$, which enters here, as in Section 3.44, to take into account the finite population size (fifty-two).

5–R2. Each of 400 gear blanks is measured for concentricity. Given that the probability that a single blank is defective, what is the probability that the sample will contain 80 or less defective units?

5–R3. Assume that weights of people in a certain population are normally distributed with mean 162 pounds and standard deviation 20 pounds. Six people are chosen at random to ride in a car; what is their expected total weight? What is the probability that their total weight exceeds 1000 pounds?

5–R4. Measurements of the altitude and radius of a cone are subject to independent random errors having standard deviations of .2 and .1 inch, respectively.

What is the (approximate) standard deviation of the error in computed volume of the cone if the actual dimensions are $r = 5$ inches and $h = 10$ inches?

5–R6. The life L (in hours) of an electron tube in a certain type of application is a random variable with the distribution function $P(L \leq t) = 1 - e^{-.01t}$. What approximately is the probability that a supply of twenty tubes will not last more than 1900 hours, if they are used one at a time successively?

6/Sampling

6.0 Introduction

Despite the unpredictability in individual chance experiments, experimentation often furnishes the only approach to construction of a useful probability model. Even when a model can be constructed from *a priori* considerations, experimentation is necessary to establish in a sense the usefulness of the model. Thus it is that the collecting, analyzing, and describing of data are motivated by a desire to know something about a probability model—about a random variable, together with its probability distribution. The data—that is, the specific values observed in an experiment—comprise what is called a *sample*. The collection of possible values which can result in a given observation is sometimes called a *population*. The process of obtaining a set of specific observations from the population is called *sampling*.

That which one wants to know about a population depends on the problem at hand. It might range anywhere from the value of some simple parameter of the population, such as the expected value, to a complete description of the population as given by the distribution function.

Example 6–a

Consider an object whose length is L. Measurements of length tend to include a random error of measurement. They give, in place of L, the incorrect quantity $X = L + \epsilon$, where ϵ is an unpredictable quantity which is subject to "statistical" fluctuation. Thus, it is expedient to think of ϵ (the error) and hence of X (the *measured* length) as random variables. It is often considered that in such a case the error ϵ has expected value zero—the error is as likely to be negative as positive and, further, has complete symmetry of distribution about L. Assuming a zero average error is equivalent to *defining* the "true" length of the object to be the expected value of the probability distribution of the measured length:

$$E(X) = E(L + \epsilon) = L + E(\epsilon) = L.$$

The reason for taking several measurements, then, is to get information about the probability distribution of the measured length for the purpose of inferring the expected value, or true length. One might also want to know the variance of the

107

measured length, to have some indication of the reliability of future observations of this type as estimates of actual length. Indeed, one could not answer a probability question concerning a measured length without knowing completely the distribution of probability.

The process of guessing (for that is really all one can do) something about a population from a given sample of so many observations is called *statistical inference.* Though it be guessing, of course, it is more properly described as educated guessing, or perhaps as "playing the odds." Chapter 8 will discuss the means whereby in our guessing we may play the odds.

Guessing the value of a population parameter using a set of specific observed values (a sample) as the basis of the guess is called *statistical estimation.* Two questions must be answered when deciding how to use the data to estimate a parameter: First, what quantity can we calculate from the observations in a sample which will be a good estimate of the parameter? Second, what do we mean by a "good" estimate of the parameter? In their full generality these questions and their answers are quite involved, and we shall not discuss them in great detail. In Chapter 9, however, we shall discuss the estimation of the expected value of a random variable, and in Chapter 10 we shall consider the estimation of the variance.

6.1 *Sample Observations As Random Variables*

An individual observation of a value of a random variable is again a random variable. As a random variable, its probability distribution is identical with that of the population of values of the given random variable.

Example 6–b

A bowl contains eight numbered chips, three with the number 1 and five with the number 2. Two chips are drawn, one at a time. The possible samples are as follows:

First Chip	Second chip	Probability
1	1	$\dfrac{3}{8} \cdot \dfrac{2}{7} = \dfrac{6}{56}$
1	2	$\dfrac{3}{8} \cdot \dfrac{5}{7} = \dfrac{15}{56}$
2	1	$\dfrac{5}{8} \cdot \dfrac{3}{7} = \dfrac{15}{56}$
2	2	$\dfrac{5}{8} \cdot \dfrac{4}{7} = \dfrac{20}{56}$

Observing that the number *first* drawn is a random variable, let us call it X_1. This random variable takes the value 1 for the first two samples listed and the value 2 for the last two. The probability that it takes the value 1 is the sum of the probabilities for the first two samples and that it takes the value 2, the sum of the probabilities for the last two. We have this distribution for X_1:

Values	Probabilities
1	$21/56 = 3/8$
2	$35/56 = 5/8$

Similarly, if we denote the *second* number drawn by X_2, we find this distribution for X_2:

Values	Probabilities
1	$3/8$
2	$5/8$

Each of these distributions, for X_1 and for X_2, is *identical with that of the population.*

A single observation is random in the same sense that any quantity may be called random—it has a certain pattern of potential values. After actually obtaining a value, of course, this observed value is not random. Sometimes these observed values are spoken of as *realizations* of the random quantity. We have used capital and lower case letters, respectively, to differentiate between a random variable and particular realizations.

The observed values comprising a sample, then, are random variables when we think *not* of a *specific* sample or set of realizations, but of the possibilities and their probabilities. When thinking of a sample in this sense, we use capital letters to denote the observations: X_1, X_2, etc. Each of these variables has the same pattern of potential values as any other, and this is precisely the pattern of values in the population. When speaking of a *specific* set of numbers which have been obtained by sampling, we denote them by lower case letters: x_1, x_2, ... Thus, we can speak of the probability, say, that $X_1 = 4$, or even (for an arbitrary fixed number x_1) that $X_1 = x_1$. That is, we speak of the probability that the first observation in a sample (not yet drawn) will turn out to have the specific value x_1.

If, now, the observations in a sample are admitted to be random variables, the conclusion follows that any quantity which is computed from these observations is a random variable. Such things are called *statistics*. Various statistics will be introduced in subsequent chapters for the purpose of drawing inferences about probability models from samples. The following examples show how the probability distributions of two simple statistics can be computed from the population distribution.

Example 6–c

Consider the bowl with three chips numbered 1 and five chips numbered 2, as in Example 6–b. The *sum* of the numbers on two chips drawn, $X_1 + X_2$, is a random variable computed from the sample observations—i.e., a statistic.

Referring to the possible samples given in Example 6–b, we see that the possible sums are 2, 3, and 4, with probabilities as follows:

Values of $X_1 + X_2$	Probabilities
2	6/56
3	15/56 + 15/56
4	20/56

Example 6–d

Consider a set of three independent observations of a normally distributed random variable with $\mu = 0$ and $\sigma^2 = 1$. The *largest* of the three observations is a function of those observations—it is a statistic. As a random variable, its probability distribution function is as follows:

$$P(\text{largest observation} \leq x) = P(\text{all observations} \leq x)$$
$$= P(\text{first obs.} \leq x) \, P(\text{second obs.} \leq x) \, P(\text{third obs.} \leq x)$$
$$= \Phi(x)\Phi(x)\Phi(x) = [\Phi(x)]^3.$$

From this we could compute, for instance, the probability that the largest observation exceeds 2:

$$P(\text{largest observation} > 2) = 1 - P(\text{largest observation} \leq 2)$$
$$= 1 - [\Phi(2)]^3 = 1 - (.9772)^3 = .0669.$$

Problems for Class Discussion

A. A sample is taken by using the last name on every tenth page of a telephone directory. Discuss the nature of this sample and the population from which it is taken.

B. The people whose names are selected in Problem A are called (once) on a certain evening. Do those that answer provide a random sample from the same population as that from which the names are drawn?

C. Fishing licenses are numbered from 1 to N, where N is the number of licenses issued. A game warden records the numbers on licenses of twenty licenses he inspects one morning. Is this set of numbers a random sample from the population of license numbers? Would you have to know something about how licenses are issued?

D. An experiment is performed in a chemical research laboratory on a "new" purification process. Ten observations of purity are taken. Discuss the nature of the sample and the population from which it was taken.

E. To determine the acceptability of an hour's production of certain spot welding process, ten strips of metal are spotted together in pairs. The welds are then tested for tensile strength. How should the inspectors be instructed so that the five welds will constitute a random sample? What is the population?

6.2 The Types of Sampling

In some situations there is a collection of objects which may be thought of naturally as a population, from which a sample is taken. For example: the people in a city; a collection of chips in a bowl; a deck of cards; the names in a telephone directory; a box of parts produced by a given manufacturing process. Each of these might be a population, from which we can actually draw one or more objects and observe some numerical characteristics. It is this *numerical characteristic* which becomes the *random variable* of interest, and the term *population* is also used to designate the *collection of possible values of this characteristic.*

Sometimes one may wish to observe more than one numerical characteristic. For example, one might want both the height and weight of a person, or several dimensions of a manufactured part. In such cases, a given population of objects has generated two or more populations of values—that is, two or more random variables.

For the kind of population of objects described above, there are essentially two important methods of obtaining data, or samples. These have already been introduced in Problems 1–34 and 1–35, (page 24). If the objects of a sample are drawn simultaneously, we have what is called "sampling without replacement," since the same end effect may be achieved by drawing the objects one at a time without replacement.

When one object is drawn from a finite population, the characteristics of the population are changed. If the object is not replaced, the population from which the second drawing is made is different, though perhaps only slightly, from the population from which the first object was taken. In this type of sampling it is possible to discover all there is to know about the population by taking all of the objects of the population as the sample.

A second method of sampling is to draw objects one at a time, replacing each one and mixing the population before drawing the next. This is termed "sampling with replacement." The essential feature of this type of sampling is that the outcome of any one drawing or any set of drawings has no effect on any other drawing. Surely these individual observations are then *independent*.

If a population is very large compared with the number of sample objects drawn from it, sampling without replacement resembles sampling with replacement. Going to the extreme, if the population is infinite, removing any finite number of objects will not alter the proportions of values in the population. Hence it does not matter if individual objects are replaced or not. (Indeed, it might be better not to replace the objects to avoid having to mix the population after the replacements.)

There are situations in which it is not so clear what the population is, or even that there is one. For instance, when a coin is tossed, from what population is an object being "drawn"? Actually it is not essential that there be a population, but the language of "drawing from a population" is handy and is commonly used. To use it, we must imagine a population. One way is to think either of the collection of all possible values of the random variable involved, or of the collection of all possible outcomes of the underlying experiment as the population.

Example 6–e

When a coin is tossed, the result is either heads or tails. We can think of these two outcomes as the population, but must imagine that the object drawn is replaced before another drawing in order to represent the fact that when the coin is tossed again, both outcomes are again possible. One could even replace the coin-tossing experiment by drawing a chip from a bowl containing as many chips marked heads as marked tails. The bowl of chips would be the population; and if we imagined infinitely many chips in the bowl, replacement would not be required.

When a physical or chemical measurement is made, there is no obvious population. Here again, however, we can imagine the collection of all possible results of the measurement as the population. If the measured value is a continuous variable, it would be hard to construct a bowl full of chips as an equivalent; but even so we could imagine such a bowl, with numbers marked on the chips in such a way as to produce a weighting to correspond with the probability density.

In both of these instances in which no population is obvious, the conceptual population is either finite, with the requirement of replacement before each successive drawing, or infinite. They are better described, then, not according to the nature of the population, but by stating that the observations are independent and that they have the same pattern of potential values. On the other hand, the type of sampling referred to as sampling without replacement requires the existence of a real, tangible population from which to draw, and this population is finite.

6.3 Random Samples

In (1) sampling with replacement and mixing, (2) sampling without replacement from an infinite population, and (3) sampling in cases in which the population has to be imagined, the observations of the sample are independent, and they share a common pattern of potential values. Furthermore, that pattern of potential values for each observation is exactly that of the underlying random variable of population. We introduce, then, the following terminology:

Definition: A *random sample* is a sample whose n observations may be represented by the mathematical model of n independent random variables, each a replica of the population from which the sample is taken.

We have used the symbols $X_1, X_2, \ldots, X_n$ to denote the observations in a sample. If the sample is a random sample, these n random variables are independent and identically distributed. Perhaps it should be pointed out that even though the observations are identically distributed when thought of as random variables—in terms of what *could* happen when observations are made, it is the usual thing that the actual observations in a *specific* sample which has been obtained, $x_1, \ldots, x_n$, are all different.

Notice that the term *random sample* refers not to a specific set of observations $x_1, \ldots, x_n$ but to the observations considered as random variables. A given set of observations (such as 17.1, 19.3, 24.0, 18.6) cannot be said either to be random or to be nonrandom. The real question is this: Was the sample obtained by a method which ensures independence of the observations? Thus, whether a sample in practice is a random sample or not depends on the means used to obtain it.

We shall consider principally random samples, giving an occasional modification of a formula to cover the case of sampling without replacement from a finite population. We shall not consider the great many facets of the practically important problem of how to obtain a random sample, or any other kind of sample. The various devices used ("stratified random sampling," for instance) are of great interest, especially in survey work. It is also important in industrial production applications to know how to obtain a sample properly. However, in instances in which there is no real population to put one's finger on, as is usually the case in scientific work, obtaining a random sample is rather a matter of maintaining identical conditions for each observation and avoiding, if possible, the bias of a human observer who often sees what he wants to see, or what he has seen previously.

7 / Presentation and Description of Data

7.0 Introduction

Although chance phenomena cannot be logically analyzed without an "ideal" model, such as the probability models discussed in previous chapters, it is quite common that the precise features of the model in question are not known—and, possibly, cannot be known. In order to have a useful model, however, these features must be known at least approximately. For this approximation we exploit an idea which was used in setting up certain probability models on the basis of experience, namely, that the relative frequency of occurrence of an event in a large number of trials should be a good estimate of the probability of the event. Such is actually the case in theory, and this is perhaps the principal reason why probability theory is used as a mathematical basis for statistics.

In cases in which the probability model underlying an experiment is not known, or only partially known, one's only recourse is to gather data and to study it. Even in cases in which theory suggests that a certain probability model is appropriate, the skeptic (and skepticism is sometimes a virtue) would want to test its appropriateness by gathering data and studying it. A model which bears little relation to observed behavior is not very useful.

In this chapter we shall discuss the presentation of data and introduce certain descriptive measures—called "statistics"—which are useful in two respects: (1) They enable one better to digest the information contained in a set of data and to compare one set with another, and (2) they are useful in estimating corresponding quantities associated with the probability model describing the underlying chance variable.

For purposes of description, then, we shall consider the following concepts:

114

(1) Patterns of variation (frequency distributions).

(2) Measures of central value (mean and median).

(3) Measures of variability (variance and range).

7.1 Patterns of Variation

The pattern of variation in a set of data is usually not easy to grasp from unprocessed data, and we are aided by tabulation and graphical representation. Rather than consider generalities, let us work in terms of a specific set of data. Table 7.1 gives 200 observations of the viscosity of a particular solution as determined by an Ostwald Viscosimeter. Looking at the set of 200 observations we obtain but a scant appreciation of the nature of the data. Perhaps the smallest and largest values are noted, together with evidence that the other values seem to scatter themselves somehow between these two extremes. Clearly a more systematic tabulation would be helpful.

7.1.1 The Frequency Distribution: Original Data

Collecting like values, and arranging them numerically, forms a "frequency distribution" of the original data. We say that the measurements of viscosity are then divided into a number of classes or *class intervals*. The *class boundaries* are the limits between which the values that belong to a given class lie. Thus, although the data in Table 7.1 are inherently continuous, they have been measured and recorded to the nearest tenth of a unit, and any viscosity reading which is between the class boundaries of 32.15 and 32.25 is recorded as 32.2. The value 32.2 is called the midpoint or "class mark" of the class—the value halfway between the two boundaries.

A frequency distribution can easily be represented graphically by a *histogram*. This is formed by marking off the class intervals on a horizontal scale and constructing a rectangle, above each class interval, whose height is the total tally for that class interval. Such a construction assumes equal-sized class intervals; if for some reason class intervals of unequal sizes are used, the rectangle heights are again chosen so that frequency is proportional to *area* in the histogram. Figure 7–1 presents a histogram of the data in Table 7.1.

A justification for using a rectangle above the class interval—rather than a "rod" erected at the midpoint—might be this. If the viscosity measurement is a continuous random variable, any value within a class interval is possible and would have contributed to the frequency for that interval; and there is then no reason to favor the midpoint of the interval. On the other hand, if the random variable giving rise to the data is basically

Table 7.1 Characteristic Measured—Viscosity; Method of Measurement— Ostwald Viscosimeter

Individual Measurements in Subgroups of 5

37.0	36.2	34.8	34.5	32.0
31.4	31.0	30.8	30.0	33.9
34.4	33.5	32.9	32.8	31.3
33.3	33.7	34.3	35.9	31.0
34.9	33.4	33.3	32.4	32.0
31.7	32.8	27.6	31.6	35.0
30.0	30.7	32.2	35.3	35.5
34.4	30.2	32.0	31.3	31.6
32.0	33.1	31.2	31.9	31.8
29.8	29.6	31.7	32.0	29.9
31.6	34.4	33.3	35.9	35.4
31.6	32.1	34.2	33.8	33.4
31.3	33.1	32.2	33.3	31.2
34.6	32.7	32.1	32.0	30.5
32.6	31.5	30.8	31.2	31.0
31.5	30.7	32.5	33.0	32.9
34.5	33.7	32.0	31.3	30.9
32.3	32.0	31.9	30.0	33.9
33.8	34.8	34.2	33.8	33.8
31.1	31.8	26.8	32.3	32.8
31.7	33.5	34.5	33.6	32.5
32.5	32.7	32.4	33.6	34.1
31.8	30.5	30.8	30.6	30.7
31.9	31.4	30.9	32.0	30.8
29.9	31.6	29.5	31.7	30.4
30.7	31.3	28.7	28.8	31.0
27.6	31.9	31.3	29.9	32.1
31.2	30.5	30.9	29.8	28.7
30.0	29.1	29.7	31.0	29.0
30.9	28.9	29.5	28.8	29.3
28.4	30.0	29.3	30.2	31.5
31.3	30.3	32.5	31.8	30.8
28.7	30.7	32.3	33.5	32.9
32.1	29.8	29.9	30.8	30.7
31.9	32.0	29.5	30.6	30.1
32.8	31.0	30.0	29.2	32.5
30.2	31.3	29.5	29.0	30.3
30.2	30.7	30.8	31.6	32.7
.32.4	32.8	31.3	31.4	30.7
30.7	30.6	31.3	30.6	31.7

discrete, frequencies might be more appropriately represented as "rods" at the discrete possible values, with heights proportional to frequency.

7.1.2 Regrouping the Data

The original data are often of such a nature that simply grouping the data into a frequency distribution does not clearly delineate the significant features of the data. This is especially true when the refinement of the original measurements is such that the class frequencies are all relatively small. A clearer picture can then be obtained by regrouping the observations into (fewer) new classes, with new class boundaries. Such regrouping

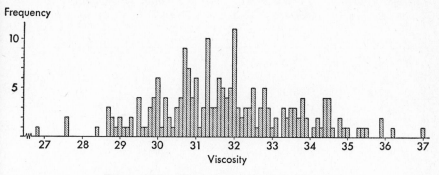

Figure 7-1. Histogram—Original Data

into fewer classes is, of course, equivalent to a coarser rounding off of the original data.

The frequency distribution of the regrouped data is clearly different from that of the original data. The observations in the new classes have lost their original identifications and have taken on the value of the midpoint of the new class. Some justification for considering the new distribution in place of the original one lies in the fact that the features of the original distribution which have been lost in the process are precisely those features which are not repeatable. They are chance variations—variations from sample to sample—which are usually not characteristics of the underlying model.

There is no rigorous set of rules for determining the length of class interval in grouping the data in optimum fashion. The number of intervals chosen is arbitrary. However, there are rules of thumb, one of which suggests that from eight to twenty class intervals is reasonable when there are, say, more than fifty observations. Certainly such factors as the number of observations, the range of values, and for whom and for what purpose the data is to be used, would play a part in deciding the number of class intervals.

Consider again the data in Table 7.1. The range of the viscosity readings is from 26.8 to 37.0, an interval of 10.2. Divide this range, say, into ten intervals with 1.1 as the interval length. The first interval can be defined by the boundaries 26.75 and 27.85 with midpoint 27.3. The second interval is defined by the boundaries 27.85 and 28.95, and so on. With this choice of interval length, the question of an observation's occurring at a

Table 7.2 Frequency Table for Grouping the 200 Viscosity Measurements

(1)	(2)	(3)	(4)	(5)	(6)	(7)
Interval Number i	Interval Boundaries	Interval Midpoint x_i	Frequency f_i	Relative Frequency f_i/n	Cumulative Frequency F_i	Cumulative Relative Frequency F_i/n
1	26.75–27.85	27.3	3	.015		
					3	.015
2	27.85–28.95	28.4	7	.035		
					10	.050
3	28.95–30.05	29.5	25	.125		
					35	.175
4	30.05–31.15	30.6	42	.210		
					77	.385
5	31.15–32.25	31.7	56	.280		
					133	.665
6	32.25–33.35	32.8	30	.150		
					163	.815
7	33.35–34.45	33.9	22	.110		
					185	.925
8	34.45–35.55	35.0	11	.055		
					196	.980
9	35.55–36.65	36.1	3	.015		
					199	.995
10	36.65–37.75	37.2	1	.005		
					200	1.000
		Totals:	$n = 200$	1.000		

boundary value does not arise, and further, the midpoint of the interval is of the same order of refinement as the original readings. In contrast, consider an alternative interval length of 1.0. This choice leads to one of two inconvenient situations. If the class boundaries of the first interval are 25.8 and 26.8, etc., we are faced with a decision as to the proper class interval for a measurement which is at a boundary, such as 26.8. (One could make the decision by flipping a coin.) On the other hand, if we choose 26.75 and 27.75 as the class boundaries, 27.25 is the midpoint of the interval—a number which gives a false sense of refinement when compared with the original data.

Table 7.2 gives the frequency distribution of the data in Table 7.1 which has been regrouped into ten class intervals, as discussed above. The class intervals are *numbered* in column (1), the *interval boundaries* are given in column (2), and the *interval midpoints* are given in column (3). The individual values of the original data are *tallied*, according to the class interval in which they lie. The *frequency* and *relative frequency* are found

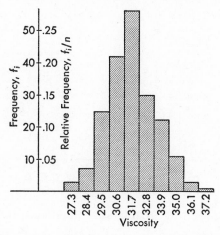

Figure 7–2.   Histogram—Regrouped Data

in columns (4) and (5). The relative frequency is simply the frequency divided by the number of observations, giving the fraction of the data in the corresponding class interval.

Cumulative frequencies and *cumulative relative frequencies* are given in columns (6) and (7). The cumulative frequency associated with a class interval is the sum of the frequencies in that and in all lower numbered class intervals.

As before (cf. Figure 7–1) the frequency tabulation may be represented graphically as a histogram. This is done for the regrouped data in Figure 7–2. In the histogram, area represents frequency of occurrence. The area of each rectangle is proportional to the frequency associated with the class interval which is its base. It is also, then, proportional to relative frequency—the quantity which is an estimate of the *probability* of obtaining a value in the class interval in question.

Hence, the histogram may be thought of as an *estimate* of the probability density function—recalling that area under the graph of the density function between two x values is the probability that the random variable takes on a value in that interval. Of course, if the underlying chance variable is of the *discrete* type, there is no density function, and the histogram is not so appropriate.

The *cumulative frequency* graph is another popular way of representing grouped data graphically. In this, the numbers in columns (6) and/or (7) are plotted vertically versus the class interval upper boundary horizontally. This is done for Table 7.2 in Figure 7–3.

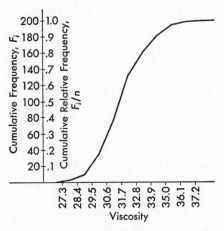

Figure 7–3. Histogram—Regrouped Data

Using the *upper* boundary of the class interval as abscissa in a cumulative graph is simply a convention adopted in this discussion. However, it is a convention with a reason. For, if we think of the horizontal top of a rectangle in a histogram as an estimate of density—constant over each class interval—the cumulative frequency graph would correspond to the cumulative probability distribution function, in that it is essentially the integral of the histogram function. That is, for example, the integral of the simple histogram-type function shown in Figure 7–4 is the broken line function drawn beneath it.

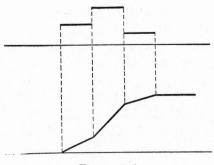

Figure 7–4

Problems

Note: The student should save his work on these problems for use later in this chapter.

7-1. (a) Select a page at random from a phone book, and, from each of the phone numbers in the right-most column, take the last digit. Tabulate these in a frequency table and represent the tabulation graphically. Is the population being sampled discrete or continuous?

    (b) Repeat the process; is this second tabulation identical with the first? Are there any similarities?

    (c) Combine these two sets of data into a single frequency distribution and compare.

7-2. Regroup the data of Table 7.1, using a class interval width of .5. Construct a table similar to Table 7.2, and draw a histogram and a cumulative frequency distribution graph for this modified data.

7-3. Repeat Problem 7-2, but using a class interval width of 2.5.

7-4. Consider the following coating weights as measured by reflectance density.

40	44	37	70	63	45	48	51
53	66	58	62	62	60	47	50
53	67	75	64	48	66	52	55
62	28	51	59	45	67	48	72
50	60	46	60	47	61	28	50
49	42	33	48	51	56	44	45
50	43	41	49	50	28	67	48
34	45	38	37	59	53	70	49
57	63	47	40	74	52	64	55
57	83	48	28	52	45	66	
83	53	48	62	53	61	72	
63	52	46	67	55	66	55	
43	52	59	66	45	56	55	

    (a) Make a histogram of the above original data.

    (b) Regroup the above data using a class interval length of 5 units. Construct a frequency table and draw the histogram.

    (c) Construct the cumulative frequency distribution for this modified data.

7-5. Select a page at random from a (nonmathematical) book, and count the number of words in each line. Make a frequency table and histogram.

7.2 Measures of Centering

In the probability models of previous chapters, the notion of average value of a random variable or "center" of its probability distribution was used extensively. Perhaps with the thought in mind of guessing this average from the data in a sample—or, more simply, just with the desire to describe the data as to general location on the scale of values—it is natural to define some number computed from the data which gives this location, or "center" of the data. At this point, the only guides to defining such a quantity are intuition and a desire for simplicity. Following these, two quantities are suggested, the sample *median*, and the sample *mean*, which we now discuss.

7.2.1 The Sample Median

The median is the *middle value*—if there is one—when the numbers comprising the data or sample are listed in *numerical order*. If there is an odd number of observations in the sample, there is a middle value; if there is an even number of observations, there is no middle value, and the median is usually taken as the ordinary arithmetic average of the *two* numbers which are in the middle. Thus, the median of the set of numbers 23, 26, 30, 31 is the average of 26 and 30, or 28.

There are as many numbers above the median of a sample as there are below, if we interpret "above" to mean "greater than or equal to," and "below," to mean "less than 'or equal to." For, there may be several numbers in the list which are equal to the median. For example, the median of the numbers

$$2, 7, 88, 88, 88, 88, 88, 88, 95$$

is the middle one, 88. This example illustrates a characteristic of the median, namely, that it is not affected by how extreme the extreme values are. The same median, 88, would have been obtained if the last value had been 10,000 rather than 95. This may or may not be a good feature, depending on whether the extreme values are accidents or really indicate something concerning the underlying distribution.

A principal virtue of the median lies in its simplicity of calculation. In the case of grouped data, the median is easily located by referring to the columns in the tabulation which give frequency or relative frequency. It is also obtainable graphically from the cumulative relative frequency graph; starting at the 50 per cent point on the vertical (cumulative relative frequency) scale, one proceeds horizontally over to the graph, and then down, reading the number on the horizontal scale. This estimate of the sample median is not in general exactly equal to one of the numbers in the tabulation, since those numbers have all been rounded off to midpoint values.

7.2.2 The Sample Mean

The *mean* of a set of data, or the *sample mean*, as we shall usually call it (to distinguish it from the expected value of the underlying chance variable which also goes sometimes under the name "mean," or "population mean"), is just the average which one learns in grade school arithmetic—it is the sum of the values divided by the number of values. The mean of the numbers in the preceding section is thus:

$$\frac{2 + 7 + 88 + 88 + 88 + 88 + 88 + 88 + 95}{9} = 70.$$

Note that in spite of the large number of 88's, the extreme values 2 and 7 shift the mean to a point considerably below 88. All of the observations contribute to the mean directly.

To determine properties of the sample mean, let us consider a less specific set of numbers, namely, the n numbers x_1, x_2, . . . , x_n. Their mean is usually denoted by $\bar{x}$, and computed as described above:

$$\bar{x} = \frac{1}{n}(x_1 + x_2 + \cdots + x_n) = \frac{1}{n}\sum_{i=1}^{n} x_i.$$

For simplicity of notation we abbreviate summations by omitting the limits $i = 1$ to n. Thus, $\bar{x} = (1/n)\Sigma x_i$. Observe that the sum of the observed values is n times the mean:

$$\Sigma x_i = n\bar{x}.$$

An interesting property of the mean is that it is the "center of gravity" of the numbers (recall a similar property of the expected value of a random variable!). If we imagined a unit mass placed at each number, this mass system would balance at the mean. Mathematically this is expressed in the fact that the sum of the deviations of the numbers from the mean is zero. The *deviation* of x_i from $\bar{x}$ is the difference $x_i - \bar{x}$, and a simple calculation shows what we have claimed:

$$\Sigma(x_i - \bar{x}) = \Sigma x_i - n\bar{x} = n\bar{x} - n\bar{x} = 0.$$

For computational purposes, it is of interest to see that if we transform the numbers x_i into new numbers y_i by a linear process,

$$y_i = \frac{x_i - b}{a}, \qquad x_i = ay_i + b,$$

the mean values are similarly related:

$$\bar{x} = \frac{1}{n}\Sigma x_i = \frac{1}{n}\Sigma(ay_i + b) = a\bar{y} + b.$$

A slightly different formula for computing the mean, equivalent to the one we have, is used for a set of numbers which have been grouped. It is obtained as follows. Suppose that we have the distinct numbers $x_1, x_2, \ldots$ x_k, with corresponding frequencies (as discussed in Section 7.1.1, page 115) $f_1, f_2, \ldots, f_k$, where the total number of observations is n:

$$f_1 + f_2 + \cdots + f_k = \sum_{i=1}^{k} f_i = n.$$

The mean is then

$$\bar{x} = \frac{1}{n} (x_1 + \cdots + x_1 + x_2 + \cdots + x_2 + \cdots\cdots + x_k + \cdots + x_k)$$

$$= \frac{1}{n} (f_1 x_1 + \cdots + f_k y_k) = \frac{1}{n} \sum_{i=1}^{k} f_i x_i = \sum_{i=1}^{k} x_i \left(\frac{f_i}{n}\right).$$

We have written the last expression to show the analogy between $\bar{x}$ and the expected value of a discrete random variable. In this analogy, the *relative* frequencies play the role of probabilities.

To illustrate calculation using the above formula for grouped data, let us compute the mean value of the data given in Table 7.2, page 118. We repeat part of this table, giving also the additional columns needed for computation of the mean:

x_i	f_i	$y_i = \dfrac{x_i - 31.7}{1.1}$	$f_i y_i$
27.3	3	-4	-12
28.4	7	-3	-21
29.5	25	-2	-50
30.6	42	-1	-42
31.7	56	0	0
32.8	30	1	30
33.9	22	2	44
35.0	11	3	33
36.1	3	4	12
37.2	1	5	5
	200		-1

$$\bar{y} = \frac{1}{200} (-1) = -.005$$

$$\bar{x} = 1.1\bar{y} + 31.7$$

$$= 31.6945 \doteq 31.7$$

The transformation to y's has been made to simplify the arithmetic and is sometimes referred to as a "coding." We have selected a value which looks to be about in the center, called this by the new name 0, and numbered the other values in steps of one on either side of 0. This is a linear transformation if the class intervals are of equal size, and the equation relating x and y is given at the head of the third column of the table. In that equation, the denominator, 1.1, is the class interval width and the 31.7 in the numerator is the new, arbitrarily chosen origin. The equation is solved for x_i to yield $x_i = 1.1y_i + 31.7$. This implies, as we saw earlier, that

$$\bar{x} = 1.1\bar{y} + 31.7.$$

Problems

7-6. Compute the median and the mean of the following set of numbers: 9, 23, 16, 13, 19, 17, 10, 20, 7, 13.

7-7. Estimate the median of the data in Table 7.2 using the cumulative frequency graph, Figure 7-3.

7-8—7-12. Using the frequency tables of Problems 7-1 to 7-5, compute the mean value and estimate the median from the cumulative frequency graph, in each case.

7.3 Measures of Variability

In addition to a measure of location or centering, it is desirable to have an idea as to whether the numbers in a sample are closely bunched about the center or are widely spread. We wish to measure *dispersion*, or *variability*. The commonly used descriptive measures in this connection are the sample *range* and the sample *variance* (or its square root, the *standard deviation*).

7.3.1 The Sample Range

The sample range is defined as the difference between the largest and smallest sample values:

$$R = \text{Largest value} - \text{Smallest value}.$$

This statistic is one of the simplest to compute—and this is one reason for its importance. It is especially valuable, it turns out, in samples which are not large (say, not over 10).

The range of the following observations:

$$2, 7, 88, 88, 88, 88, 88, 88, 95,$$

is $95 - 2 = 93$, a quantity which is determined only by the extreme values and *not* at all by the way in which the other values fall between these extremes. It is certainly a measure of the "width" or dispersion of the data.

7.3.2 The Sample Variance

In attempting to characterize the spread of a set of numbers by an average deviation of some sort, one is quickly led to square the deviations from their mean. Squaring the deviations from the mean prevents cancellation. Other operations, such as taking the absolute value, or raising to the fourth power, also would prevent cancellation, but the result of squaring is more amenable to analysis. The sum of squared deviations about $\bar{x}$,

$$\sum_{1}^{n} (x_i - \bar{x})^2 = (x_1 - \bar{x})^2 + \cdots + (x_n - \bar{x})^2,$$

is a measure of dispersion of the data. It is large if the numbers are spread over a wide range and small if they are clustered about $\bar{x}$. All of the observations contribute to it, but especially those far from $\bar{x}$.

To eliminate the effect of the number of terms in the sum of squared deviations on its size, it is natural to average, by dividing through by n. However, because of the way in which tables to be used subsequently are made up, it is more convenient to divide the sum of squared deviations by $n - 1$. Therefore, we define the *sample variance* as follows:

$$s_x{}^2 = \frac{1}{n-1} \sum_{i=1}^{n} (x_i - \bar{x})^2.$$

The effect of this choice of division constant will be discussed in Chapter 10. For the present we simply observe that whether we use n or $n - 1$, the results are not appreciably different except in the case of small samples.

The sample *standard deviation* is defined as the positive square root of the sample variance—a root-mean-square quantity:

$$s_x = \sqrt{s_x{}^2} = \sqrt{\frac{1}{n-1} \sum_{1}^{n} (x_i - \bar{x})^2}.$$

Certain properties of the sample variance are useful. One is the parallel axis theorem:

$$(n-1)s_x{}^2 = \Sigma(x_i - a)^2 - n(\bar{x} - a)^2,$$

where a is any number. This is easily verified by writing

$$\Sigma(x_i - a)^2 = \Sigma[(x_i - \bar{x}) + (\bar{x} - a)]^2$$

and expanding this binomial. A second property has to do with the change in the variance when the numbers x_i are transformed into numbers y_i by a linear change: $x_i = ay_i + b$. We have already seen that $\bar{x} = a\bar{y} + b$, and hence:

$$s_x{}^2 = \frac{1}{n-1} \sum (x_i - \bar{x})^2 = \frac{1}{n-1} \sum (ay_i - a\bar{y})^2 = a^2 s_y{}^2,$$

or

$$s_x = as_y.$$

As in the case of the sample mean, a modified formula is used when one has grouped data. It is as follows:

$$s_x{}^2 = \frac{1}{n-1} \sum_{i=1}^{k} f_i(x_i - \bar{x})^2,$$

where k is the number of class intervals, f_i the frequency of the ith class interval, and $\bar{x}$ is the sample mean as always. The parallel axis theorem is also expressible in terms of a frequency tabulation; in the form most frequently used for computation, it is as follows:

$$(n-1)s_x{}^2 = \sum x_i{}^2 f_i - \frac{(\Sigma x_i f_i)^2}{n}$$

We illustrate with the data in Table 7.2:

x_i	f_i	$y_i = \dfrac{x_i - 31.7}{1.1}$	$f_i y_i{}^2$
27.3	3	−4	48
28.4	7	−3	63
29.5	25	−2	100
30.6	42	−1	42
31.7	56	0	0
32.8	30	1	30
33.9	22	2	88
35.0	11	3	99
36.1	3	4	48
37.2	1	5	25
	200		543

(Computed previously: $\Sigma f_i y_i = -1$)

$$199 s_y{}^2 = \sum_{1}^{10} y_i{}^2 f_i - \frac{1}{200} \left(\sum_{1}^{10} y_i f_i \right)^2$$

$$s_y{}^2 = \frac{1}{199} \left[543 - \frac{1}{200} (-1)^2 \right] = 2.73$$

$$s_x{}^2 = (1.1)^2 s_y{}^2 = 3.30.$$

7.4 Other Statistics

Since any quantity computed using the observed values in a sample is a "statistic," the supply of statistics is endless. We mention here a few which are related to those already discussed.

We have seen that the median of a sample is located by counting halfway over from one end when the data are arranged numerically. One might count a quarter of the way instead—obtaining thereby what are called "quartiles," or more generally, a certain percentage of the way, obtaining "percentiles." Graphically, the thirty-sixth percentile may be found, for example, by starting at .36 on the cumulative relative frequency scale on the cumulative frequency graph, proceeding horizontally to the graph, and then down, reading the thirty-sixth percentile on the horizontal scale.

A measure of dispersion which is occasionally used is the "mean deviation" which is defined as

$$\frac{1}{n} \sum_{i=1}^{n} |x_i - m|,$$

the average of the absolute values of the deviations, where the quantity m is either the sample mean or the sample median (both definitions are used).

Problems

Dial Tension (Grams)	Frequency
6.5	3
7.0	2
7.5	30
8.0	42
8.5	36
9.0	28
9.5	28
10.0	15
10.5	8
11.0	3
11.5	1
12.0	1
12.5	1
13.0	0
13.5	1
14.0	1

[See Problem 7–R1, page 129]

7-13. Calculate the range, variance, and mean deviation (from the mean) for the set of numbers in Problem 7-3 (page 121).

7-14. Estimate the first quartile (twenty-fifth percentile) and the sixty-third percentile of the data in Table 7.2 using the cumulative frequency graph, Figure 7-3 (page 121).

7-15—7-19. Compute the standard deviation for the frequency distributions of Problems 7-1 to 7-5.

Review Problems—Chapter 7

7-R1. A sample of 200 instruments is tested for dial tension. The dial tension is checked manually by a gram gage. The data is presented in the table on page 128.

(a) Compute the arithmetic mean of this frequency distribution.

(b) Compute the variance and standard deviation of this frequency distribution.

(c) Construct the histogram and the cumulative frequency graph for this distribution. (Remark about the effect that "skewness" has upon the shape of the cumulative frequency graph.)

7-R2. The following set of data represents weights (in ounces) of sixty "1-pound" packages of bacon. Describe this data according to the methods of this chapter.

$16\frac{1}{4}$	16	$15\frac{7}{8}$	$16\frac{1}{4}$	$15\frac{7}{8}$
$15\frac{3}{4}$	16	16	17	$16\frac{1}{8}$
$16\frac{1}{8}$	$16\frac{1}{8}$	$15\frac{7}{8}$	$16\frac{1}{4}$	$16\frac{1}{4}$
$15\frac{7}{8}$	16	16	$16\frac{1}{8}$	$16\frac{1}{8}$
$15\frac{7}{8}$	16	$15\frac{7}{8}$	$16\frac{1}{2}$	16
16	$15\frac{7}{8}$	$16\frac{1}{4}$	$16\frac{1}{8}$	$16\frac{1}{8}$
$16\frac{1}{8}$	$16\frac{1}{4}$	$16\frac{1}{4}$	$16\frac{1}{4}$	$16\frac{1}{4}$
$15\frac{7}{8}$	$16\frac{1}{4}$	16	$15\frac{7}{8}$	16
$16\frac{1}{8}$	$16\frac{7}{8}$	$15\frac{7}{8}$	$15\frac{3}{4}$	$15\frac{7}{8}$
$16\frac{1}{4}$	16	$16\frac{1}{2}$	$16\frac{1}{8}$	16
$16\frac{1}{8}$	$16\frac{1}{8}$	$15\frac{7}{8}$	$16\frac{1}{8}$	$16\frac{1}{4}$
$16\frac{1}{4}$	$16\frac{1}{8}$	16	$16\frac{1}{8}$	16

7-R3. The following data giving power consumption (kilowatts per 24 hours), represent the results of twenty-five freezer performance checks after operational tests have been made on the production line.

4.72	4.32	4.61	4.89	4.61
4.57	4.95	4.55	4.70	4.54
4.47	4.90	4.74	4.59	4.35
4.43	4.75	4.83	4.43	4.55
4.46	4.66	4.55	4.54	4.91

(a) Compute the mean of the entire set of data of twenty-five observations.

(b) Compute the mean of each set of five observations.

(c) Compute the mean of the five group means. How does this value compare with the mean that you computed in part (a)?

8/Testing Statistical Hypotheses

8.0 Introduction

In many situations the reason for gathering and analyzing data is a need for objective assistance in deciding on a course of action. Let us consider that either of two courses of action, A or B, is possible. We assume, further, that it would be clear whether A or B is the better action, if only we knew the nature of a certain population—that is, if we knew the probability distribution of a certain random variable. The whole population, or the precise distribution of probability, is usually unattainable. Therefore, we are forced to settle for such information as can be gleaned from a sample and to make our choice between actions A and B on the basis of the sample.

Example 8–a

A political campaign manager wants to decide whether or not to expend some extra effort just before an election. If he knew the proportion of the population of voters who would vote for his candidate, he could easily decide what to do. If this proportion is greater than one-half, he would decide that extra effort is unnecessary, since his candidate is due to win without it. If it is less than one-half, some extra effort is needed in an attempt to swing votes.

Suppose that in a poll of 500 voters, 260 are in favor of his candidate. Should the manager take this as evidence that his candidate will win and act accordingly?

Example 8–b

A critical dimension in a manufactured part is a random variable with standard deviation .005 inch. It is decided that the expected value of this critical dimension should be .140 inch if there is to be an acceptably low number of misfits. A sample of five parts taken from the production line averages .147 inch in the critical dimension. Is this evidence that the "level" has shifted and that corrective action should be taken?

Although the reason for examining the results in a sample is to choose between courses of action, we use the language of "testing statistical hypotheses."

130

Definition: A statistical *hypothesis* is a statement concerning the probability distribution of a random variable.

It is common for *a priori* considerations to suggest that not every conceivable hypothesis should be admitted in a given situation and that some would be ridiculous. Those that are considered possible are referred to as *admissible* hypotheses.

Example 8–c

Suppose that manufactured articles of a given type are classed as either defective or good. We introduce the random variable X which takes on the value 1 if an article is defective and 0 if it is good. It would be quite inappropriate to assume that X is normally distributed. Surely, X is of the Bernoulli type, and the only real question concerns the value of p, the probability of obtaining a defective article. But, again, not all values of p are admitted, since p is a probability and must lie on the range from 0 to 1.

The admissible hypotheses are that X has a Bernoulli distribution with parameter p where p can have any value from 0 to 1.

It is common, as in Example 8–c, to specify hypotheses by giving the *type* of the distribution and the value of a *parameter* of the distribution. In such cases we often identify the hypotheses with the corresponding values of the parameter and neglect to state the distribution type in giving the hypotheses. We say "the hypothesis $p < .2$," for instance, when it is clear from the context that the distribution type is the Bernoulli. We are concerned with "testing" only an assumption concerning p. Other features of the distribution are considered as not under test.

It is convenient to think of a given statistical hypothesis as made up of "elementary" hypotheses. The customary terminology is that of the following definitions.

Definition: A *simple* hypothesis is a complete specification of a probability distribution.

A *composite* hypothesis is any statistical hypothesis which is not a simple hypothesis.

Example 8–d

The statement that X is normally distributed with mean 0 and variance 1 is a simple hypothesis concerning X, since with this information we can write down the specific density function of X. On the other hand the statement that X is normally distributed with mean 0 is composite, since the distribution is not completely defined without a specification of the variance.

The word "composite," in describing an incomplete description of a probability distribution, is appropriate in the following sense. We think of a composite hypothesis as being made up of the collection of all simple hypotheses consistent with it. Thus, for instance, the hypothesis that (X Bernoulli and) $p \leq .2$ is to be thought of as being "composed" of all simple hypotheses of the form $p = p_0$, where p_0 is any single number on the range from 0 to .2. A composite hypothesis is correct if some one of the simple hypotheses which make it up is correct.

8.1 Tests of Hypotheses

Let us assume that we have decided what kinds of populations would make us prefer action A and what kinds action B. We can think of the collection of all admissible simple hypotheses in two piles, which we label H_0 and H_1:

H_0: the set of all simple hypotheses which, if true, would make A the better action.

H_1: the set of all simple hypotheses which, if true, would make B the better action.

The hypothesis H_0 is true, then, if the population is described correctly by some one of the simple hypotheses in the set labeled H_0. The hypothesis H_0 is simple or composite according to whether there is just one or more than one hypothesis in the pile. Similar remarks, of course, apply to H_1.

The hypothesis H_0 is often called "the hypothesis being tested" or "the hypothesis under test," and H_1 "the alternative hypothesis," It is said that we "test H_0 against the alternative H_1." Such terminology, though standard, is asymmetrical. This is unfortunate, since really we are making a decision between two actions; it would thus be more descriptive to say that we are testing to decide between the hypotheses H_0 and H_1.

Definition: A statistical *test* of hypotheses concerning a population is any *rule* which operates to choose for us between two courses of action, on the basis of a sample from the population.

Such a rule or test must prepare us for any contingency—to give us, *before* the sample is obtained, a course of action to follow corresponding to each foreseeable outcome of the sampling. In the simpler tests with which we shall be most concerned, part of the test will be a specification of how large a sample is to be drawn.

In constructing a statistical test, one must first have in mind the two courses of action and then make a decision as to which hypotheses correspond to one action and which to the other. These are subjective processes. Consequently, in statistical theory it is usual to phrase results in terms of the hypotheses rather than in terms of the actions to be taken. When a rule comprising a test is followed, we say: "We accept H_0 (and automatically reject H_1)," if the result of the sampling is such that the rule chooses action A; and "we reject H_0 (and automatically accept H_1)," if the result is such as to choose action B.

Example 8–e

In the case of the campaign manager of Example 8–a, a decision rule might be as follows: Initiate some extra promotional effort if fewer than 260 out of 500 voters polled are in favor of his candidate. Whether this rule is overly cautious or not cautious enough remains to be determined.

Another rule might be to take action if (and only if) more than 400 voters out of the 500 are in favor of his candidate. No one in his right mind would adopt such a rule, but it is none the less a rule. It is not always so clear as to which of two rules is the better.

The rules in Example 8–e are phrased in terms of the number of voters out of 500 which have a certain preference. This number is a random variable, depending as it does on the random sample of voters; it is a statistic. In general, the statistic upon which a test is based is called the *test statistic* or the *test variable*. The rule to be followed in a test can be phrased in terms of the values of this test statistic.

Definition: The range of values of a test statistic which, for a given test, requires rejection of H_0 is called the *critical region* of the test.

It is important to observe that once the test variable is given, *the test defines the critical region and the critical region defines the test.*

Example 8–f

Consider again testing the expected value of the critical dimension of the manufactured part, as in Example 8–b. Consider the following possible rule. Examine a sample of five and calculate the sample mean. If the sample mean falls farther than .003 inch from .140 inch, reject H_0, that there has been no change in expected value from .140 inch. (That is, accept H_1: There has been a change.)

The critical region, which characterizes this rule, is given by the inequality

$$|\bar{x} - .140| > .003.$$

It must be realized that the results of a sample can be misleading. The particular sample on which the decision is to be made might turn out to be quite different in character from the population. Indeed, it can be so different as to lead to a decision to reject H_0 even in cases in which H_0 is true, or to accept H_0 in cases in which H_0 is not true. A statistical test is subject to error in these two ways, called *type I* and *type II* errors, respectively. This terminology is quite arbitrary and does not imply that type I errors are more important than type II errors. In fact, these labels would be reversed simply by interchanging the labels H_0 and H_1, which were also arbitrary designations.

We should naturally be concerned about making either type of error, and in subsequent sections we shall consider probabilities associated with errors of decision.

Since statistical tests are subject to errors, the test cannot *prove* anything about the population. If the rule defining the test tells us to reject H_0, in a given instance, this does not mean that H_0 is necessarily false. Nor does the statistician have to *believe* that H_0 is false. He is asked to *act* as though it were false, taking therewith the accompanying risk of a wrong decision.

Problems

8-1. It is assumed that the two sides of a certain coin are equally likely, but the coin has not been examined to make sure it has heads on one side and tails on the other. It is desired to test the hypothesis H_0 that the coin is a standard one, as produced by the mint. The test is to be based on four tosses of the coin.
   (a) What is the alternative hypothesis? Is it simple or composite?
   (b) What test could be adopted which would never lead one to reject H_0 when the coin is standard? What is the probability that with this test one discovers a two-headed coin?
   (c) Let X denote the number of heads in the four tosses. If the critical region of a test is taken to be $X = 0$ or 4, what is the probability that this test would lead to rejection of H_0 when the coin is actually a standard one?

8-2. Determine in each case whether the hypothesis given is simple or composite:
   (a) A pair of dice is "straight."
   (b) A pair of dice is "crooked."
   (c) $E(X) = 3$.
   (d) X is Poisson with mean 2.
   (e) X is uniformly distributed.
   (f) A coin is biased.

8-3. To test the hypothesis that the expected weight of a box of cereal is 10 ounces, the following test is adopted. The hypothesis is rejected if a carton of forty-eight boxes weighs more than 30.5 or less than 29.5 pounds. What is the probability that the hypothesis is rejected when it is really true, given that the variance of box weights is .5 ounce²?

8.2 Simple H_0 and Simple H_1

The problem of constructing and analyzing statistical tests is relatively straightforward when the hypotheses H_0 and H_1 are both simple.

The probability of any event depends on the assumed probability distribution; hence, the probability of rejecting H_0 depends on what simple hypothesis describes the population. To indicate which hypothesis is used in making a calculation of probability we shall use a subscript on the P. We then define the *size* of the type I error to be

$$\alpha = P_{H_0}(\text{reject } H_0)$$
$$= P_{H_0}(\text{test statistic falls in critical region}).$$

Similarly, the size of the type II error is defined to be

$$\beta = P_{H_1}(\text{accept } H_0)$$
$$= P_{H_1}(\text{test statistic does not fall in critical region}).$$

The probability of making, say, a type I error cannot be calculated in an absolute sense, because we have no way of knowing the likelihood of occurrence of a situation in which H_0 is true. The quantity α represents the probability, *assuming that H_0 is true*, that the test will reject H_0. Similarly, β represents the probability, *assuming that H_1 is true*, that the test will reject H_1.

Different tests, of course, have different α's and β's associated with them, and ideally we should like to choose a test for which *both* α and β are small. We can make $\alpha = 0$ by adopting as the test the rule of never rejecting H_0. However, for this test $\beta = 1$. In general if we try to make one error size small (for a given size sample), the other error size will tend to be large.

Example 8-g

Consider a normal distribution with variance 1. We wish to test

$$H_0: \mu = 0, \quad \text{and} \quad H_1: \mu = 2.$$

Suppose that we take a single observation, X, as test statistic. Intuition suggests a preference for $\mu = 2$ if X is too large, and on this basis we choose $X > K$ as the critical region, for some appropriately chosen value of K.

In Figure 8–1 are shown the density functions of X corresponding to H_0 and H_1, and the areas defining α and β are indicated corresponding to the rejection region $X > K = 1.5$.

This last example shows clearly (referring to Figure 8–1) how α can be made arbitrarily small by adjusting the value of K, and how β increases in

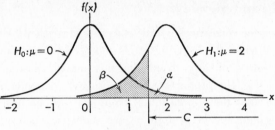

Figure 8-1

the process. To show what can happen when the critical region is not wisely chosen, consider the following example.

Example 8-h

Again testing $\mu = 0$ against $\mu = 2$ in a normal population with variance 1, let us adopt as a critical region $|X| < K$, where X is a single observation, on which the test is based. The probability that X falls in the critical region, assuming H_0 to be correct, can easily be made as small as we please by simply making K small enough. The disastrous effect on β is seen in Figure 8-2 which again shows the densities corresponding to H_0 and H_1.

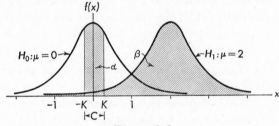

Figure 8-2

In these examples we have seen that trying to make both α and β small is working at cross purposes. It is clear, too, that even if two different tests have the same sized type I errors, their type II error sizes may be quite different. Of two such tests, we should naturally prefer the one with the smaller sized type II error.

The following definition of "best" test is based on the notion that one type of error is more serious than the other; we fix the size of that error and among such tests choose as best the one with the smallest sized error of the other type. By interchanging the labels H_0 and H_1, if necessary, we can always consider the error of type I to be the more serious. To avoid cumbersome expression, let us denote by $(C, n; \alpha, \beta)$ a test with critical region C based on sample size n, whose type I error size is α and whose type II error size is β.

Definition: A test $(C^*, n; \alpha^*, \beta^*)$ is *best* among all tests $(C, n; \alpha, \beta)$ for which $\alpha \leq \alpha^*$, provided that $\beta^* \leq \beta$.

In testing the simple hypotheses

H_0: the population density (or probability) function is $f_0(x)$,
H_1: the population density (or probability) function is $f_1(x)$,

a best test, according to the above definition of "best," can always be constructed. It is given by the critical region

$$\frac{f_1(x_1) \cdots f_1(x_n)}{f_0(x_1) \cdots f_0(x_n)} > K,$$

where $x_1, \ldots, x_n$ is a random sample and K is a constant to be chosen to correspond to a given α. (For a proof of this fact, called the Neyman-Pearson Lemma, see A. M. Mood, *Introduction to the Theory of Statistics*, McGraw-Hill, pp. 249–252.)

Although for samples of given size, fixing α does not allow us to choose β (except as we choose the test with the minimum β), we can often achieve a specified smallness in both α and β by leaving the sample size to be determined.

Example 8–i

Suppose that a random variable X takes on the value 1 with probability p and 0 with probability $1 - p$ and that we wish to test

$$H_0: p = .4 \quad \text{against} \quad H_1: p = .6.$$

Suppose, further, that we should like to have $\alpha = .01$ and $\beta = .10$. Let f denote the frequency of 1's in a sample of n trials. The critical region which is best in the sense of the above definition is readily shown to be of the intuitively reasonable type:

$$C: f > K.$$

Assuming that n will turn out to be large enough for a normal approximation to the distribution of f, we require that

$$\alpha = .01 = P_{.4}(\text{reject } H_0)$$
$$= P_{.4}(f > K) \doteq 1 - \Phi\left(\frac{K + 1/2 - .4n}{\sqrt{.24n}}\right)$$

and

$$\beta = .10 = P_{.6}(\text{accept } H_0)$$
$$= P_{.6}(f \leq K) \doteq \Phi\left(\frac{K + 1/2 - .6n}{\sqrt{.24n}}\right).$$

We refer to Table I, page 253, for values of $\Phi(z)$, and find

$$\frac{K + 1/2 - .4n}{\sqrt{.24n}} = 2.33$$

$$\frac{K + 1/2 - .6n}{\sqrt{.24n}} = 1.28.$$

Solving these equations simultaneously we find $n = 24$ and $K = 15.$†

Problems

8–4. Referring to Example 8–i above, consider the test $f > 52$ based on 100 observations. Compute the corresponding α and β.

8–5. Referring to Problem 8–4, and again using 100 observations, determine K so that the test $f \leq K$ has the same α as in that problem. What is the corresponding β?

8–6. Referring to example 8–i above, determine the sample sizes needed to make $\beta = .05$ and .01, respectively, using the same α (namely, .01) as in that example.

8–7. Show that the best test for the hypotheses in Example 8–i is of the type given there, using the inequality of the "Neyman-Pearson Lemma." [*Hint:* The product $f(x_1) \cdots f(x_n)$ which appears in the numerator and denominator is just $p^f(1 - p)^{n-f}$, where f is the number of 1's in the sample. Use $p = p_1$ for the numerator and $p = p_0$ for the denominator.]

8.3 Power of a Test

When H_0 and H_1 are composite, we do not have (as in the preceding section) uniquely defined error sizes. The probability of rejecting H_0 when it should not be rejected depends upon the probability distribution of the population. If any one of the simple hypotheses making up H_0 is true, H_0 should not be rejected, and the probability of rejection is in general different for these various simple hypotheses in H_0. The variation of the probability of rejection, as a function of which simple hypothesis is assumed correct, is embodied in the power function.

Definition: The *power function* of a statistical test is the probability of rejecting H_0, considered as a function of what simple hypothesis h is assumed to be true:

$$\text{Power function} = P_h(H_0 \text{ is rejected}).$$

(Again the subscript on P indicates the population distribution used to calculate the probability of the indicated event.) In terms of the decision between action A and action B, the value of the power function, correspond-

---

† In practice, charts are available for graphical solution for n and K. See, for example, *Handbook of Industrial Statistics*, by Bowker and Liebermen, Prentice-Hall, 1955.

ng to an assumed population distribution, is the probability that a sample
from such a population would lead to action B when the test rule is followed.

Since the hypothesis H_0 is rejected when the test statistic falls in the
critical region, we have

$$\text{Power function} = P_h(\text{test statistic falls in } C) = P_h(C).$$

Ideally, we should like the probability of rejecting H_0 to be zero when
H_0 should *not* be rejected—i.e., when H_0 is correct; and we should like the
probability of rejecting H_0 to be 1 when H_0 *should* be rejected. Thinking
of the simple hypotheses h as identified with values of a parameter plotted
along a horizontal axis, the ideal power function has the form shown in
Figure 8–3.

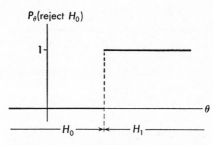

Figure 8–3.   Ideal Power Function

The term "power" stems from the notion that a test has that much
"detecting power"—power to detect that H_0 is false when this is the case.
However, the power function is still defined, and is of interest, for simple
hypotheses which lie in H_0.

A test whose power function is large for simple hypotheses in H_1 is
thought of as a "powerful test"; and one test is considered "more powerful"
than another if its power function is larger than that of the other on H_1, but
is no larger on H_0.

In some fields of application it is more common to discuss the "operating characteristic function" in place of the power function.

Definition: The *operating characteristic function* of a test is the
probability that the test leads to acceptance of H_0, considered as a function
of the particular simple hypothesis which is used in the computation of
probabilities.

The operating characteristic function, or "*OC* function," is simply related
to the power function, since the probabilities of acceptance and rejection of

H_0 must add to unity:

$$OC \text{ function} = P_h(\text{accept } H_0)$$
$$= 1 - P_h(\text{reject } H_0) = 1 - \text{Power function.}$$

If we know one of these functions, we also know the other. The graph of one is just the graph of the other "turned upside down." The ideal operating characteristic function, corresponding to the ideal power function of Figure 8–3, is therefore as shown in Figure 8–4.

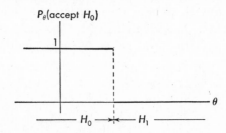

Figure 8–4. Ideal Operating Characteristic

The terms "OC function" and "power function" suggest different kinds of functions. Actually, the asymmetry of terminology is misleading. Which function is the power function and which is the OC function depends on the designations of H_0 and H_1, and these were arbitrary. The power and OC functions for testing H_0 and H_1 would be the OC and power functions, respectively, for testing the same hypotheses but with interchanged labels, H_1 and H_0.

An actual test is not so discriminating as the ideal one pictured in Figure 8–4, since sample information is not perfectly reliable in reflecting population characteristics. In practice, fortunately, such a sharp test is often not required. For cases in which the correct simple hypothesis is near the boundary between H_0 and H_1, it is hard to insist that one action or the other is better.

Suppose, for instance, that we can identify the simple hypotheses with the parameter θ, and consider the values of θ as plotted horizontally. Let θ_0 denote the value of θ which separates H_0 from H_1. If θ is actually quite near θ_0, we are often not much concerned over which action is taken. That is, if the test leads to acceptance of H_0 in a case in which the actual θ is just a *little* ways into H_1, we are indifferent to this error, or at any rate, accept it philosophically.

Let us consider that it is possible to choose a value θ' in H_0 and a value θ'' in H_1, such that for values of θ between θ' and θ'' we are indifferent as to whether or not a correct decision is made. However, we strongly prefer to accept H_0 when θ is farther into H_0 than is θ' and strongly prefer to accept H_1 when θ is farther into H_1 than is θ''. We have thus modified our definition of "ideal," such that the ideal OC function would appear as in Figure 8–5. There we have

$$P_\theta(\text{accept } H_0) = 1, \text{ when } \theta < \theta'$$

and

$$P_\theta(\text{reject } H_0) = 1, \text{ when } \theta > \theta''.$$

In the zone between θ' and θ'' we are not overly concerned about the precise shape of the OC curve, except that perhaps it is desirable that it should decrease on that range.

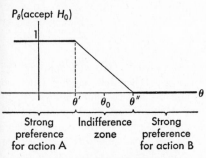

Figure 8–5. **Modified Ideal Operat-** **Figure 8–6. Typical Operating**
ing Characteristic   Characteristic

Even with this modification of what we consider ideal, an actual test will not usually be ideal. Generally, its OC function will look more like the one shown in Figure 8–6. In such a case we might define α as the maximum probability of rejecting H_0 for $\theta < \theta'$ and β as the maximum probability of accepting H_0 for $\theta > \theta''$. These quantities have been marked on the graph.

The α and β shown in Figure 8–6 can both be made as small as we please. On the other hand, imagining the indifference zone to shrink to zero width, the α and β would add to 1, in the limit, and could not both be made as small as we please.

The political campaign manager discussed in Example 8–a would be penalized by losing the election if his test erred one way, even if only a little bit, and would spend an unnecessary amount of money if his test erred the other way. He might not *want* to gamble on losing *either* the election or the money, and this goal requires the ideal operating characteristic of Figure 8–4. Without a 100 per cent sample, however, he is forced to gamble to some extent. Infinitely fine discrimination is not possible with finite samples.

It should be pointed out that, even though we introduce an indifference zone for the purpose of designing a test, we still either reject H_0 or accept H_0 (take action B or action A) depending on the outcome of the test. In Chapter 12 we shall discuss a modification of the test procedure which introduces a kind of indifference zone in the values of the test statistic, with the rule that sampling is continued if the statistic falls in that zone; no decision is then made until it can be a strong decision.

Example 8-j

Again consider the 100 thumbtacks tossed on the table, and let p denote the probability that a single tack lands point up when tossed. The admissible hypotheses correspond to values of p on the range $0 \leq p \leq 1$. Suppose that the hypothesis being tested and the alternative are, respectively,

$$H_0: p \leq .4.$$
$$H_1: p > .4.$$

It seems reasonable that the more tacks out of the 100 which land with point up, the more willing we should be to assume that p is large rather than small. Thus (on these intuitive grounds) we might choose the number f of tacks which fall with point up as the test statistic. The values of f larger than some specified amount would define the critical region. To be specific, let us choose the following critical region: $C: f > 50$. This is, if more than one-half of the 100 tacks land with point up, we accept $p > .4$ in preference to $p \leq .4$.

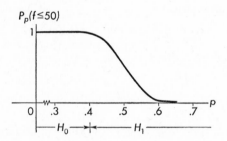

Figure 8-7. OC Function for Example 8-j

The operating characteristic function is now a function of p, since we identify the values of p and the simple admissible hypotheses. The OC function can be written explicitly as follows:

$$OC \text{ function} = P_p(\text{accept } H_0) = \sum_{0}^{50} \binom{100}{k} p^k (1-p)^{100-k}.$$

The graph of the OC function is shown in Figure 8-7. Note that the acceptance probability is high over H_0 and low over H_1, as should be the case.

The *OC* function naturally changes if we change the test—that is, if we change the critical region. It also changes if we change the size of the sample to be used, for a fixed critical region. Effects of these changes are seen in the following examples.

Example 8–k

We return to the thumbtack problem of Example 8–j above. Plotted in Figure 8–8 on a common set of axes are the graphs of the *OC* functions corresponding to three critical regions: $f > 40$, $f > 50$, and $f > 60$ (recall that we toss 100 tacks and that f is the number of tacks which land with point up).

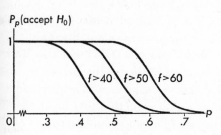

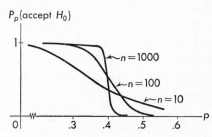

Figure 8–8. *OC* Curves for Various Critical Regions

Figure 8–9. *OC* Curves for Various Sample Sizes

Example 8–l

Suppose now that 1000 tacks are tossed, and consider a critical region of $f > 400$, (corresponding to $f > 40$ when n was 100). The operating characteristic for this test, that for the test $f > 40$, $n = 100$, and that for the test $f > 4$, $n = 10$ are shown in Figure 8–9. The largest sample gives the most discriminating test—that is, the most nearly ideal test.

8.4 Test Procedure Summarized

Although different situations require different treatments of detail, we can give the main points to be observed in a common type of statistical test. It will be noticed that a good deal of planning precedes the data collection in this outline of procedure, whereas in practice a person is often asked to interpret a sheaf of data which has been gathered and presented to him without prior planning. In such a case he will have to spend some time learning about why and how the data was obtained and then try to design tests as though he had seen no data. If there is opportunity to gather more data for tests after they are planned, there is no harm in using data already at hand to aid in planning, if it is "suitable." But in general, a test should not be designed on the basis of the data which is also to be used in the test. (Sometimes one has to do this, and it may be better than doing nothing.)

We have considered only tests which are to be used to choose between one of two actions, and the following procedure is phrased accordingly.†

First it must be determined what the random variable or population is, knowledge of which would enable one to make a decision between the two actions.

It must be decided next what hypotheses H_0 would require one action and what hypotheses H_1 would require the other action, including such assumptions as are not to be tested but are given in a priori manner. Sometimes H_1 might only be as specific as stating that H_0 is false.

Choosing the test statistic and the type of critical region for the test can often be done in the same process, although we have not discussed the method for doing this. What is frequently done is to choose the test statistic to be that statistic commonly used to estimate the parameter in terms of which H_0 and H_1 are given and then to make use of the alternative hypothesis to determine the type of critical region. On the other hand, there are cases in which the hypotheses being tested are not given in terms of one or more parameters, and in which the only tool for selecting the test statistic is intuition; the critical region is then also chosen intuitively.

At this point one obtains a decision, usually arbitrary, as to the sizes of errors (of types I and II) which can be tolerated. He may wish to introduce an indifference zone, if this is practical. The sample size and the precise critical region are then found, and the OC function should be examined in its entirety to make sure the test is adequate.

Data may now be obtained, the value of the test statistic computed, and the decision made according to whether this value falls inside or outside the critical region.

The following summary presents a brief outline of the test procedure.

(1) Choose the random variable and decide on the a priori conditions which are not under test but are considered known.

(2) Determine the hypothesis H_0 together with the alternative hypothesis H_1.

(3) Specify the test statistic.

(4) Either (a) choose the sample size n and the significance level α or (b) choose two values of the parameter and the corresponding α and β and find n.

† The theory of testing hypotheses introduced here will be applied in several of the subsequent chapters. We shall assume, for sinplicity in giving examples and problems in what follows, that correct procedures have been used, without carrying the student through their details in every case.

(5) Determine the critical region.

(6) Take a random sample, calculate the value of the test statistic, and make a decision to accept H_0 or to reject H_0.

It is to be observed that there is much in the way of arbitrariness in the above test procedure. The designation of what is under test, the association of certain simple hypotheses with action A, and the values of α and β (or the critical region and the sample size) are all arbitrary. Some of this is avoided in the theory of decisions, in which one attaches numerical risks to errors and attempts to "rationalize" his behavior by minimizing his total risk in some sense. Unfortunately, even in this more sophisticated theory (which we discuss briefly in Chapter 12), there is arbitrariness in the choice of behavior—that is, in the "sense" in which risk is minimized.

Problems

8–8. In testing $H_0: \mu \leq 0$ against $H_1: \mu > 0$ for a normally distributed variable with variance 1, it is decided to accept H_0 if a single observation drawn (i.e., $n = 1$) is less than .5.
  (a) Determine and sketch the OC function for this test, using Table I, page 253.
  (b) If the range $-.1 < \mu < .1$ is adopted as an "indifference zone," determine the corresponding α and β.

8–9. A batch of ten articles is to be rejected or passed on the basis of the following test. One is drawn and if it is found defective, the batch is rejected; if it is found good, another is drawn. If this second article is defective, the lot is rejected; if it is good, the lot is passed. Determine the operating characteristic for this test, as a function of M, the actual number of defectives in the batch.

8–10. In testing $p = 1/2$ against $p \neq 1/2$ for a Bernoulli population, we reject $p = 1/2$ if no 1's or three 1's occur in three observations. Sketch the OC function for this test.

8.5 Acceptance Sampling

An important application of the theory of testing hypotheses is in the field of acceptance sampling. Certain manufactured articles are to be shipped in "lots," and it is desired that the quality of each lot be ascertained —either by the manufacturer before shipment or by the buyer before acceptance. We consider here only the case in which individual articles may be classed as either *good* or *defective*, although a similar discussion is possible when the quality of an article must be described by a more continuous measure.

Ideally, it would be best to have no defectives in a lot, but it is assumed that a few defectives are permissible if this will save testing the entire lot. A "100 per cent inspection" of a lot is usually quite expensive. Furthermore, because of weaknesses in either human or mechanical inspection, a complete inspection does not necessarily insure a perfect lot. Certainly if testing is at all destructive, complete inspection is not advisable.

Two courses of action are possible—to reject the lot or to pass the lot—and the statistical test is a rule for deciding between these actions on the basis of a *sample* drawn from the lot. The test statistic is taken to be the number of defectives in the sample. The type of rule which suggests itself is one which requires rejection of the lot if the sample contains more than a specified number of defectives. The following notation will be used:

N = lot size.

n = sample size.

X = number of defectives in a sample.

c = "acceptance number" (this many or fewer defectives in the sample requires acceptance of the lot).

M = actual number of defectives in a lot.

The exact distribution of X, the test statistic, depends on the actual number (M) of defectives in the lot. For a given number of defectives in the lot, the distribution is of the hypergeometric type (Section 3.44):

$$P_M(X = k) = P_M(k \text{ defectives among the sample of } n \text{ articles})$$
$$= \frac{\binom{M}{k}\binom{N-M}{n-k}}{\binom{N}{n}}.$$

As discussed in Section 3.45, this hypergeometric formula for probability can be replaced in practice by the binomial formula, when the lot size is much greater than the sample size:

$$P_M(X = k) = \binom{n}{k}\left(\frac{M}{N}\right)^k\left(1 - \frac{M}{N}\right)^{n-k} \qquad (N \gg n),$$

or, if we denote the *lot fraction defective* M/N by p:

$$P_p(X = k) \doteq \binom{n}{k} p^k (1 - p)^{n-k}.$$

If p is "small" and n "large" (but still much smaller than N), we may use the Poisson approximation:

$$P_p(X = k) \doteq e^{-np} \frac{(np)^k}{k!}.$$

The *operating characteristic* for the test defined by a given acceptance number c is usually denoted by L:

$$L(p) = L\left(\frac{M}{N}\right) = P_M(\text{lot is passed})$$

$$= P_M(X \le c) = \sum_{k=0}^{c} P(X = k).$$

In place of defining an H_0 and H_1 with a sharp boundary between them, we fix numbers p_1 and p_2 such that we strongly prefer to accept the lot if the actual lot fraction defective is less than p_1 and strongly prefer to reject the lot if the actual lot fraction defective is greater than p_2. Fixing error sizes at these points determines the operating characteristic:

$$\alpha = \max_{p \le p_1} [1 - L(p)] = 1 - L(p_1)$$

and

$$\beta = \max_{p \ge p_2} L(p) = L(p_2).$$

Since the "producer" is the one most concerned about the size of α, it is sometimes called the "producer's risk"; similarly, β would be termed the "consumer's risk." It should be emphasized that one should really examine the entire operating characteristic rather than consider only α and β at p_1 and p_2 to make sure that the sampling plan gives adequate protection over the range of fraction defective, p.

Example 8–m

Suppose that the lot size is eight, and consider the plan defined by an acceptance number $c = 1$ in a sample of size four. Then

$$L\left(\frac{M}{N}\right) = \sum_{k=0}^{1} P_M(X = k) = \frac{\binom{M}{0}\binom{8-M}{4}}{\binom{8}{4}} + \frac{\binom{M}{1}\binom{8-M}{3}}{\binom{8}{4}}.$$

The values of this operating characteristic function are then as follows:

M	0	1	2	3	4	5	6	7	8
L	1	1	$\frac{55}{70}$	$\frac{35}{70}$	$\frac{17}{70}$	$\frac{5}{70}$	0	0	0

Example 8–n

Consider the more realistic situation of $N = 1000$, $n = 50$, and $c = 2$. Here we have

$$L(p) = \sum_{k=0}^{2} \frac{\binom{M}{0}\binom{1000-M}{50}}{\binom{1000}{50}} \doteq \sum_{k=0}^{2} \binom{50}{k} p^k (1-p)^{50-k} \doteq \sum_{k=0}^{2} e^{-50p} \frac{(50p)^k}{k!},$$

the last approximation being successful only for small p. It is important to observe that the lot size—and therefore the percentage of the lot used in the sample—is not involved in the approximations.

There is plotted in Figure 8–10 the operating characteristic of this test.

Suppose that in conjunction with a sampling plan, the rule is adopted of replacing defective articles located in samples from passed lots with good articles and of giving rejected lots complete inspection, again replacing defectives with good articles. We are then interested in the quality of lots which have been subjected to this procedure. This quality is random,

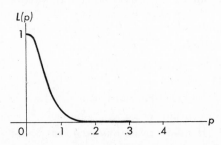

Figure 8–10.   Operating Characteristic for Example 8–n

because of the random number of defectives in the uninspected portion of lots which passed the sampling inspection. Further, the randomness depends on the initial quality of a lot. If we consider that lots are taken from a production process in which there is a certain probability p_o that an article is defective, the sample is, in effect, taken from that process, and

$$P_{p_o}(\text{lot is accepted}) = \sum_{k=0}^{c} \binom{n}{k} p_o{}^k (1 - p_o)^{n-k}.$$

(This is not an approximation.) The expected number of defectives in the untested portion of lots which pass is then just $(N - n)p_o$; the number of defectives in rejected lots is 0 (assuming the rule given above to be followed). Hence, among all lots from the production line, the expected fraction defective is

$$AOQ = \left(1 - \frac{n}{N}\right) p_o P(\text{a lot is accepted}),$$

where AOQ denotes "average outgoing quality." The "average outgoing quality limit" is then defined to be

$$AOQL = \max_{p_o} AOQ.$$

Example 8–o

For $N = 8$, $n = 4$, and $c = 1$ (as in Example 8–m), we have

$$AOQ = \left(1 - \frac{4}{8}\right) p_o \sum_{k=0}^{1} \binom{4}{k} p_o{}^k (1 - p_o)^{n-k},$$

where p_o is the probability that a defective article is produced. This expression is readily seen to have a maximum of 8/81 at $p_o = 1/3$. This maximum value, 8/81, is the *AOQL*. The graph of *AOQ* as a function of p_o is shown in Figure 8–11.

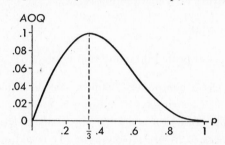

Figure 8–11. Average Outgoing Quality

Problems

8–11. A random sample of 50 items is taken from a lot, and the lot is accepted if the sample contains at most one defective item. Calculate the probability of accepting
  (a) a lot of 10,000 items, 500 of which are defective.
  (b) a lot of 1000 items, 50 of which are defective.
  (c) a lot of 100 items, 5 of which are defective.

8–12. Determine the operating characteristic of the test determined by $n = 4$, $c = 1$, and $N = 10$.

8–13. Plot the operating characteristics, on the same coordinate axes, for each of the following cases:
  (a) $N = 25$, $n = 5$, $c = 0$.
  (b) $N = 100$, $n = 20$, $c = 0$.
  (c) $N = 400$, $n = 80$, $c = 0$.

8–14. Plot the operating characteristics, on the same coordinate axes, for each of the following cases:
  (a) $N = 50$, $n = 20$, $c = 0$.
  (b) $N = 100$, $n = 20$, $c = 0$.
  (c) $N = 400$ $n = 20$, $c = 0$.
  (d) $N = \infty$, $n = 20$, $c = 0$.

8.6 Testing Goodness of Fit

Many widely used statistical tests assume that the population distribution is of a known type. The assumption of normality is quite common, for instance, and one would like to be assured on the basis of a statistical test that such an assumption is reasonable. A "goodness of fit" test is one which is used for the purpose of determining whether an assumed population distribution, or distribution type, is consistent with data obtained from the population.

Consider the problem of testing a specific population distribution. The null hypothesis in this case is, for a continuous variable,

H_0: the population density function is $f(x)$

and for a discrete variable,

H_0: the population probability function is $p(x_i)$,

where $f(x)$ or $p(x_i)$ is a completely defined, specific function. The alternative hypothesis is exceedingly composite, namely, that the population density or probability function is *not* the one given in H_0.

Tests for goodness of fit are most commonly based on the discrepancy between *observed* frequencies of values and *expected* or theoretical frequencies, or on the discrepancy between the "sample distribution function" and the assumed population distribution function. Different tests result from different ways of measuring the discrepancy. In the first section below we present the classical "chi-square" test for goodness of fit and in the second, the Kolmogorov-Smirnov test. Each has its advantages and disadvantages.

8.6.1 The Chi-Square Test

The oldest goodness of fit test (K. Pearson, 1900) is the chi-square test. It is valid only for large samples, but it has the features of being applicable in testing either discrete or continuous distributions and in testing either completely or a partially specified distribution. We treat first the case of testing a completely specified distribution.

A random sample of size n is obtained from the population, and we denote by f_i (as before) the frequency of the value x_i in the sample. If the population is discrete, and defined by the probability function $p(x_i) = P(X = x_i)$, the expected value of f_i is $np(x_i)$. In general, f_i will not exactly equal $np(x_i)$, and the differences $f_i - np(x_i)$ are thought of as related to the extent of departure of the actual population probabilities from $p(x_i)$. To avoid cancellation we square these differences. Weighting them with a factor which is the reciprocal of the expected frequency, and summing, yields the following statistic, whose asymptotic distribution under the null hypothesis is known:

$$\chi^2 = \sum_{1}^{k} \frac{[f_i - np(x_i)]^2}{np(x_i)}.$$

It can be shown that under H_0, and for large samples, this statistic has approximately the chi-square distribution with $k - 1$ "degrees of freedom" (Table II, page 256), where k is the number of distinct possible values. The rejection region is taken to be of the form $\chi^2 > K$.

Example 8–p

To test the equal likelihood of the six faces of a die, it is cast 120 times, with the following resulting frequencies of the six faces: 18, 23, 16, 21, 18, 24. Is the die "straight"?

The expected frequencies are all 20, and the value of χ^2 is readily computed:

$$\chi^2 = \frac{1}{20} [(18 - 20)^2 + (23 - 20)^2 + \cdots + (24 - 20)^2] = 2.5.$$

Reference to Table II, page 256, shows (using $6 - 1 = 5$ degrees of freedom) the rejection limit for $\alpha = .10$ to be about 9.2. Since $2.5 < 9.2$, we accept H_0 (that the six faces are equally likely) at the 10 per cent level.

The number k of distinct values x_i is assumed here to be finite. However, the test can be applied when there are really infinitely many distinct possible values by grouping the values. That is, one can include in one class the infinitely many values having the smallest probabilities, as in Example 8–r below. Indeed, it has been found that the expected frequency of each possible value should not be too small, if the chi-square distribution is to approximate adequately the distribution of the test statistic. A rule of thumb frequently used is to group the values so that each expected frequency is no less than five: $np(x_i) \geq 5$. (This incidentally ensures that k is finite.) This same rule of thumb applies to the expected frequencies of the class intervals when we consider below the continuous case. It is to be observed that, in any case where grouping is done, we are really testing the probabilities corresponding to the grouped values, and not the original probabilities.

Let us consider next a continuous distribution and the problem of testing the hypothesis

H_0: the population density function is $f(x)$.

In order to make a comparison with observed frequencies, which have been recorded for some arbitrary set of class intervals, it is appropriate to discretize the population in terms of those class intervals and write

$$p_i = P(X \text{ falls in the } i\text{th class interval}).$$

This would be computed in terms of whatever probability distribution is assumed. If H_0 is correct,

$$p_i = \int_{S_i} f(x) \, dx = \int_{x_i}^{x_{i+1}} f(x) \, dx = F(x_{i+1}) - F(x_i),$$

where S_i denotes the ith class interval, with endpoints x_i and x_{i+1}, and $F(x)$ is the population distribution function corresponding to $f(x)$. The expected frequency of occurrence of values in S_i is now np_i, and we compute the statistic

$$\chi^2 = \sum_{i=1}^{k} \frac{(f_i - np_i)^2}{np_i}.$$

Again, under H_0, this has asymptotically the chi-square distribution with $k - 1$ degrees of freedom. It must be realized, however, that we are not really testing $f(x)$, but rather the probabilities p_i, which could arise from various $f(x)$'s, so long as the areas over the class intervals agree.

Example 8-q

Taking a set of eighty of the observations in Table 7–1, we obtain the frequency distribution given in the following table. Suppose that it is desired to test the hypothesis that the population from which the data are taken is normal with mean 32 and standard deviation 1.8. Using Table I, page 253 expected frequencies can be computed under this H_0. For example,

$$p_3 = P(29.75 < X < 31.25) = \Phi \left(\frac{29.75 - 32}{1.8} \right) - \Phi \left(\frac{31.25 - 32}{1.8} \right)$$
$$\doteq .2327,$$

and $np_3 = 80 \times .2327 \doteq 18.6$.

Class Interval	Frequency	Probability	Expected Frequency
26.75–28.25	2	.0166	1.33
28.25–29.75	1	.087	6.96
29.75–31.25	16	.233	18.6
31.25–32.75	27	.323	25.9
32.75–34.25	19	.233	18.6
34.25–35.75	11	.087	6.96
35.75–37.25	4	.0166	1.33

After grouping so that the first interval is $x < 29.75$ and the last is $x > 34.24$, the statistic χ^2 is found to be about 9.1, which exceeds the rejection limit of 7.78 at the 10 per cent level, but not the rejection limit of 9.49 at the 5 per cent level. (The number of degrees of freedom is one less than five, the number of class intervals after regrouping.) The regrouping is done in accordance with the rule of thumb that np_i should be at least five in order for the approximating chi-square distribution to be applicable.

Suppose now that we wish to test, not a specific distribution, but whether or not a population has a distribution which is among a given family of distributions:

H_0: the population density is $f(x, \theta)$,

where θ denotes one or more parameters. Now we cannot compute the class interval probabilities without specifying θ. If θ is specified on the basis of previously obtained data, we can proceed with the test as described above using new data—which is a test for $f(x, \theta)$ with that value of θ so obtained.

If the parameters θ are estimated from the data which is to be used in testing the given H_0, it turns out, fortunately, that the statistic χ^2 again has the chi-square distribution asymptotically (under H_0), but with a smaller number of degrees of freedom. This is true provided that the estimate of θ used is of a certain "good" type (what is called asymptotically efficient and asymptotically normal). The reduced number of degrees of freedom is $k - 1 - j$, where j denotes the number of estimated parameters. (This asymptotic distribution of χ^2 requires, we point out, that the estimation of parameters be carried out on the basis of the same classification of data as is to be used in the test.) As an example, it is true that for a normal population the sample mean and sample variance are "good" estimates of population mean and population variance, so that in testing normality, the number of degrees of freedom is $k - 1 - 2 = k - 3$.

Example 8–r

Consider the following data† from a discrete population suspected to be of the Poisson type:

x_i	0	1	2	3 or 4
f_i	109	65	22	4

(The grouping of 3 and 4 is in anticipation of the requirement that $np_i \geq 5$.) The sample mean here is .62 and is of the appropriate type for estimating the parameter m

† This classical set of data gives the number of men per annum killed by the kick of a horse in certain Prussian army corps over the period 1875–94. It was first analyzed by von Bortkiewicz (1898).

in the Poisson formula: $e^{-m}(m^k/k!)$. Using $m = .62$ we obtain the following expected frequencies:

x_i	0	1	2	3 or 4 or more
p_i	107.6	66.7	20.6	5.1

The value of χ^2 is then found to be about .4, considerably less than the rejection limit (2 degrees of freedom: $4 - 1 - 1$) for even a 30 per cent level. We accept the Poisson distribution.

In Example 8–q we have applied the chi-square test to the normal case, as is traditional, but we should mention that this application to a continuous case is not so happy as might be desired. The hypothesis being tested is that certain class intervals have given expected frequencies, but it does not take into account the fact that the values of the random variable in question, and hence the class intervals, have a natural order which is an important aspect of normality.

8.6.2 The Kolmogorov–Smirnov Statistic

The test to be discussed here has the advantage of being applicable even for small samples, but it has the disadvantages that it is strictly appropriate only in the case of a continuous distribution and is not (in its present form) adaptable to testing a distribution *type*, as was the chi-square test. The test is based on the statistic

$$D_n = \max_{-\infty < x < \infty} |F_n(x) - F(x)|,$$

where $F(x)$ is the specific population distribution function being tested, and $F_n(x)$ is the "sample distribution function":

$$F_n(x) = \sum_{x_i \leq x} \frac{f_i}{n}.$$

(This would be the probability distribution function corresponding to a lump of probability in the amount $1/n$ at each observed value.) The term "max" refers to the maximum, over the range of values of x, of the differences indicated, although to be mathematically correct, the term "least upper bound" is sometimes more appropriate.

The quantity D_n is, indeed, a statistic, since the function $F_n(x)$ is computed from the sample. Both the asymptotic (large sample) and finite sample distributions of D_n are independent of $F(x)$ and are available in tables. Table VIIa, page 261, gives some of the percentiles of D_n for certain sample sizes. The critical region used is $D_n > K$. This is taken on intuitive grounds, although estimates of the power of this test indicate that it is a good test.

Example 8–s

Consider the ten observations: 31.0, 31.4, 33.3, 33.4, 33.5, 33.7, 34.4, 34.9, 36.2, 37, which happen to be the first two groups of five in Table 7.1. The sample distribution of this sample is sketched in Figure 8–12, along with the normal distribution whose mean is 32 and whose standard deviation is 1.8. The maximum deviation

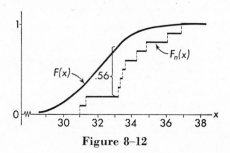

Figure 8–12

appears to be about .56. From Table VIIa we read that the ninety-fifth percentile of the distribution of D_n is .409, and we reject the hypothesis that the population is normal with mean 32 and standard deviation 1.8 at the 5 per cent level.

The power of the Kolmogorov-Smirnov test for a given alternative hypothesis is the probability of rejecting H_0 in favor of that alternative, assuming the alternative to be true. For the (simple) alternative hypothesis h_1, the power is

$$P_{h_1}(\text{reject } H_0) = P_{h_1}(D_n > K),$$

where K is the critical value of D_n corresponding to the given level. This power is not known for every conceivable alternative hypothesis, but a lower bound for the power has been obtained in terms of the maximum distance between the distributions corresponding to H_0 and the alternative being considered. The "distance" between distribution functions $F(x)$ and $F_1(x)$ is defined as follows:

$$\Delta = \max_{-\infty < x < \infty} |F_1(x) - F(x)|.$$

The graphs in Figure 8–13 show the lower bound plotted as a function of Δ for the levels .05 and .01.

The Kolmogorov-Smirnov test is often used in the case of a discrete population, even though the tables employed are obtained under the assumption of a continuous population distribution. This is because it has been found that such practice is on the "safe" side, in the sense that the actual

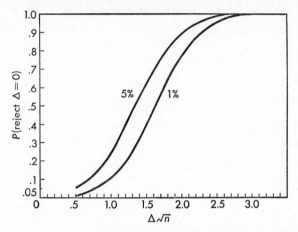

Figure 8–13. Lower Bounds for the Power of the K-S Test
Reproduced from "The Kolmogorov-Smirnov Test for Goodness of Fit," by F.J. Massey, Jr., *Journal of the American Statistical Association*, **46** (1951), 68–78.

significance level of the resulting test is no bigger than the one assumed in using the tables.

Example 8–t

Four coins are tossed 160 times with the following results:

Number of heads	0	1	2	3	4
Frequency	10	33	61	43	13
Cumulative frequency	10	43	104	147	160

The distribution function we should probably want to test is the binomial one corresponding to the number of successes in four independent trials, with probability 1/2 of success in a single trial. The step heights above the horizontal axis for this distribution function are proportional to 10, 50, 110, 150, 160. The maximum discrepancy between this theoretical distribution function and the empirical one given above is $7/160 \doteq .044$. Comparing this with the 20 per cent acceptance limit from Table VIIa, page 261, namely:

$$\frac{1.07}{\sqrt{160}} \doteq .085,$$

we are led to accept the given binomial distribution at the 20 per cent level.

Although in the above example the values of the random variable involved are inherent in the experiment, there are many cases in which an experiment has a finite set of outcomes which do not have numbers naturally assigned to them. The coding or assignment of numbers to outcomes is quite arbitrary in such cases. For example, we have frequently called heads 1 and tails 0, but we could have just as properly called tails 1 and heads 0. The sample distribution functions corresponding to these two assignments would be different, for most samples. The maximum deviations corresponding to the two assignments might lead to different actions—accepting the assumed value of p in one case, and rejecting it in the other.

Example 8-u

Taking the frequencies of Example 8-p for the faces 1, 2, 3, 4, 5, 6, of a die, the sample distribution function has step heights proportional to 0, 18, 41, 57, 78, 96, 120, as compared with the step heights of the H_0 distribution, which are proportional to 0, 20, 40, 60, 80, 100, 120. The maximum discrepancy is $4/120 \doteq .033$, which is smaller than the 10 per cent rejection limit from Table VIIa, $1.22/\sqrt{120} = .111$. Thus, H_0 is accepted.

Suppose, however, that we use the following code: one dot = 2, two dots = 5, three dots = 1, four dots = 4, five dots = 3, and six dots = 6. Using the same sample of 120 tosses as above, we find that the sample distribution function now has step heights above the horizontal proportional to 16, 34, 52, 73, 96, 120. The maximum departure from the H_0 distribution function is now $8/120 \doteq .067$, considerably closer to the rejection limit than previously, even though the same experimental results have been used.

It should be clear in such cases as these, in which we are really interested only in the probabilities of the individual outcomes, and not in the distribution function corresponding to an arbitrary assignment of values to outcomes, that the Kolmogorov-Smirnov test is not appropriate.

Problems

8-15. Suppose that a coin falls heads 230 times in 400 tosses. Test for $p = 1 - p = 1/2$ at the 1 per cent level, using the chi-square test.

8-16. Consider the data in the following table:

x_i	-2.5	-2	-1.5	-1	$-.5$	0	.5	1.0	1.5	2.0
f_i	1	3	5	10	17	19	19	12	7	7

(a) Use this data in testing that the population is normal with mean 0 and variance 1, using the chi-square test at the 10 per cent level.

(b) Use this data in testing normality of the population by means of the chi-square test at the 10 per cent level.

8-17. Using the data of Problem 7-1(a) (page 121), test the hypothesis that the probabilities of the various numbers are equal.

8-18. Apply the Kolmogorov-Smirnov test at the 10 per cent level (that the population is normal with mean 0 and variance 1) to the data in Problem 8–15(a), using first the code 1 for heads and 0 for tails, and then the code 0 for heads and 1 for tails.

8–19. Compute D_n for the data of Problem 8–14. How does this compare with the 1 per cent rejection limit for D_n determined from Table VIIa?

8.7 Tests for Randomness

In discussing estimating and testing in previous chapters, it has been assumed that the sample used for the purpose was a random sample. The theory quoted leans strongly on this assumption that the sample observations are independent and identically distributed, each with the distribution of the population. The phenomenon yielding the data will be said to be in statistical control if a random sample can be obtained.

It often happens, however, that in the process of gathering data, the "population" changes in one or more of its characteristics so that the observations are not from the same population. It is also possible that dependence is introduced between the sample observations. In such cases we have not only the question as to the validity of our processes of estimating, say, the population mean, but also the question: Is there a population? Before plowing blindly ahead into the drifts of estimation and testing, it is often wise to test the data gathering process to determine if we may reasonably accept the assumption that the sample obtained is a random sample. Briefly put, we should test H_0: The process is in statistical control.

In this section we shall describe certain tests of this hypothesis based on what are called runs. These tests are sometimes referred to as tests for randomness, since a succession of observations comprising a random sample is sometimes called a sequence of "random numbers." The notion of "randomness" is that as each observation is made, the pattern of potential values is the same, and each observation is totally independent of any other observation. But observe that we cannot possibly test for control or randomness unless we keep track of the observations *in the order in which they are made*.

Run tests are based on the notion that if observations are random, there should not be any trends, but rather erratic bouncing back and forth. To be sure, even a *regular* bouncing back and forth would not be considered random, but periodic. We shall discuss two types of runs, namely, runs above and below the median and runs up and down. These tests will be described as being applied to the sample observations, to test shifts in level. However, if we wish to group the observations into small chunks, keeping the *order* of these "rational subgroups" intact, we can test for a shift in "level of *variability*" by applying the run tests to the *ranges* of the chunks.

8.7.1 Runs Above and Below the Median

We consider a random sample $X_1, X_2, \ldots, X_n$, where the observations are listed in the order obtained. Suppose we then note, for each observation, whether it is above or below the median of the sample. Marking down an a for above and a b for below, we obtain thereby a sequence of a's and b's, such as this:

$$a, b, a, a, a, b, b, a, b, a, b, b.$$

We say that each string of a's or b's, uninterrupted by the other letter, is a *run*. Thus, in the above sequence of a's and b's, we have the following runs:

$$a \quad b \quad a, a, a \quad b, b \quad a \quad b \quad a \quad b, b,$$

a total of eight.

When the sample *is* actually a random sample, the number of runs above and below the sample median is a random variable. The distribution of this discrete, random variable under H_0 (the population is in control) has been studied, and it is known that the mean and variance of the distribution of the total number of runs r are as follows:

$$E(r) = \frac{n+2}{2}, \qquad \text{var } r = \frac{n}{4}\left(1 - \frac{1}{n-1}\right).$$

Actually, these formulas are exact only if (1) the total number of observations is even, so that there are as many observations above as below the sample median and (2) the population is truly continuous, so that the probability of several observations *at* the median value is zero. We return to this point presently.

It also happens that (under H_0) the total number of runs is asymptotically normally distributed and that therefore the normal distribution function may be used as an approximation to the distribution of r for "large n." In practice, "large" may be taken to mean greater than twenty-five. This asymptotic property, and the formulas for mean and variance of r above, hold no matter what the distribution of the population, so long as it is a population (and is continuous). The number of runs is a "distribution-free" statistic.

For large samples, then, the percentiles of the r distribution may be approximated, using those of the normal distribution. We have

$$P(r \leq r_p) = p \doteq \Phi\left(\frac{r_p + \frac{1}{2} - \frac{n+2}{2}}{\sqrt{\frac{n(n-2)}{4(n-1)}}}\right),$$

and hence

$$r_p = \frac{1}{2}\left(n + 1 + z_p\sqrt{\frac{n(n-2)}{n-1}}\right) \doteq \frac{1}{2}(n + 1 + z_p\sqrt{n-1}),$$

where z_p is the $100p$ percentile of the standard normal distribution.

Having settled on a test statistic and determined the distribution of this statistic under H_0 (the sample is a random sample), it remains to determine the type of critical region to employ. This depends on the alternative hypothesis. If we assume that the successive observations are actually from populations with similar distributions but with a slowly shifting mean, we would expect intuitively to find fewer runs, the earlier observations tending to be a's, for example, and the later ones b's. In such a case, we take $r < K$ as the type of critical region. If the number of runs is excessively large, this suggests a systematic shifting back and forth from one observation to the next, on either side of the median. If, then, we are testing against a shifting population mean, we probably should use $r < K$, but if we have no better idea as to the alternative other than that it is the opposite of H_0 (that is, the sample is not a random sample), perhaps the critical region to take would be $|r - E(r)| > K$.

Example 8–v

Suppose that we are testing randomness against the alternative of a shifting level, using a sample of size 50. Suppose that in the sample there are twenty runs. Would this be cause for rejecting randomness at the 10 per cent level?

Taking $r < K$ as the type of critical region, we find the tenth percentile of the r distribution under H_0 to be

$$r_{.10} = \frac{1}{2}(50 + 1 - 1.28\sqrt{49}) \doteq 21,$$

and so we reject the hypothesis of randomness.

We have two loose ends. First, if the number of sample observations is not even, but is large enough for the normal approximation, the results used above are practically correct, and we use them. Second, if there are sample values at the median of the sample, which only can happen when we "discretize" the results by rounding off (as we must do!), we must arbitrarily assign an a or b. This is sometimes done in such a way as to decrease the total number of runs (especially if we are using $r < K$ as a critical region) and sometimes done by the toss of a coin (that is, randomly).

8.7.2 Runs Up and Down

Again we consider a set of n observations, $X_1, \ldots, X_n$, listed in the order obtained. We now write down either $+$ or $-$ between each pair of successive observations, depending on whether the latter one is greater or less (respectively) than the earlier one. Again, for randomness to be accepted, we should want a *moderate* number of runs, counting runs of $+$'s and $-$'s in the same way as we counted runs above and below the median. Too few runs would suggest a slowly varying level and too many would suggest a systematic variation—perhaps a dependence of one observation on the preceding pair.

Again we might have ties, with actual, rounded-off data, and these may be broken by chance or so as to make rejection of randomness more likely.

In the case of runs up and down the total number of runs r is again asymptotically normally distributed, under the assumption of randomness, with mean and variance given by

$$E(r) = \frac{1}{3}(2n - 1), \qquad \text{var } r = \frac{1}{90}(16n - 29).$$

Construction of a test for randomness ($n > 20$) based on runs up and down parallels that based on runs above and below the median.

Example 8–w

Consider the following thirty observations (taken from a table of what are called "random sampling numbers"; they *should* be random):

> 15, 77, 01, 64, 69, 69, 58, 40, 81, 16, 60, 20, 00, 84, 22
> 28, 26, 46, 66, 36, 86, 66, 17, 34, 49, 85, 40, 51, 40, 10.

These yield the following sequence of signs:

$$+ - + + \; ? \; - - + - + - - - + -$$
$$+ - + + - + - - - + + + - + - - \; .$$

There are twenty runs here, counting the tie (?) *either* as $+$ or $-$. Now for $n = 30$, $E(r) = 59/3$, and var $r = 451/90 = 5.1$. If we take the critical region to be $r < K$, a choice of $\alpha = .20$ would yield a K of $59/3 - .84\sqrt{5.1} \doteq 17.8$. We accept randomness, since $20 > 17.8$.

Problems

8–20. Apply the run tests to the data of Table 7.1 on page 116, first, assuming that the data was recorded left to right and second, assuming that the data was recorded top to bottom, in the order of occurrence.

8–21. Apply the run tests to the data in Problem 7–4 (page 121), given that the data was recorded, as it was obtained, in columns.

9/Testing and Estimating Location

9.0 Introduction

Perhaps the parameter of greatest interest in describing a probability distribution is its expectation, μ. This measures (when it exists, and it usually does in practice) the "location" or "center of gravity" of the distribution, or the "level" of the population random variable. In the present chapter, we shall consider the problem of estimating the expectation and of testing hypotheses concerning the expectation on the basis of information contained in a sample from the population.

Because it is the center of gravity of the *sample* distribution, the sample mean $\bar{X}$ suggests itself as the statistic most likely to be useful in connection with the expectation. It happens, indeed, that $\bar{X}$ is usually an excellent choice. However, we should realize that it is but one of many reasonable statistics which might be useful—to name three: the sample median, the average of the smallest and largest observations, and the average of the first and third sample quartiles. For all we know, without further study, any one of these three might be better than $\bar{X}$ for getting at μ in some cases.

We shall consider mainly the estimation of μ using $\bar{X}$ and the testing of hypotheses concerning μ using $\bar{X}$ as test statistic. Other statistics, for estimating μ and for testing the population median, will be treated briefly towards the end of the chapter.

9.1 The Sample Mean As an Estimate of μ

Since it depends on sample observations, the sample mean is a random variable. This implies, among other things, that the mean of a single sample can have any of a host of values and will probably not be equal to μ. Even if it were equal to μ, this would be so unexpected that we should never know it—unless, of course, we knew the population mean to start with.

162

We ask, then: If the mean of a sample is not equal to μ, how close to μ is it apt to be? To answer this we need to know the probability distribution of $\bar{X}$.

The expected value of the random variable $\bar{X}$ is easily computed. Using the additive property of the expectation, we have

$$E(\bar{X}) = E\left[\frac{1}{n}(X_1 + \cdots + X_n)\right] = \frac{1}{n}[E(X_1) + \cdots + E(X_n)] = \mu.$$

Thus, the center of the distribution of $\bar{X}$ is at the center of the distribution of X—it is μ, the parameter we should like to estimate. However, this is small comfort, since any *single* value of $\bar{X}$ can still be "miles off." The real question concerns the reliability or repeatability of $\bar{X}$, and this has to do with the *dispersion* of values of $\bar{X}$ about the center value.

We have measured dispersion in a probability distribution by means of the variance. Given a random sample $X_1, \ldots, X_n$, from a population with variance σ^2, we have

$$\text{var}(\bar{X}) = \text{var}\left(\frac{1}{n}\Sigma X_i\right) = \frac{1}{n^2}(\text{var } X_1 + \cdots + \text{var } X_n) = \frac{\sigma^2}{n}.$$

(Independence of the sample observations permits taking the sum of the variances for the variance of the sum; and var $X_i = \sigma^2$ for each observation since each observation has the distribution of the population.) Hence, the variability in $\bar{X}$ as measured by its variance *decreases as n increases*. In fact, var $\bar{X}$ approaches zero as n becomes infinite. This means that the variance of $\bar{X}$ can be made arbitrarily small by taking a sufficiently large sample. The larger the sample, the smaller the sample to sample fluctuation in sample means.

If we can take large samples, then, it appears that the mean of a given sample should be an excellent approximation to the population mean. The probability distribution of $\bar{X}$ gets narrower and narrower as $n \to \infty$, with all of the probability being lumped at μ in the limit. We know, too, from the Central Limit Theorem, that the shape of the distribution of $\bar{X}$ tends to that of the normal distribution. These phenomena are observed in the following example.

Example 9–a

Consider a random variable X whose distribution is that shown in Figure 9–1, marked "$n = 1$." (This happens to be the chi-square distribution with one degree of freedom.) Consider a random sample of n observations on this random variable. The density functions for $\bar{X}$ corresponding to $n = 3, 6, 10, 50,$ and 100 are shown in the same figure. The population mean is 1.

The approach of the distribution of $\bar{X}$ to that of a "constant random variable" (zero variance) is expressed in the following "law of large numbers":

$$\lim_{n \to \infty} P(|\bar{X} - \mu| > \epsilon) = 0, \qquad \text{given any} \qquad \epsilon > 0.$$

It is said that "$\bar{X}$ approaches μ in probability," to describe this relation.†

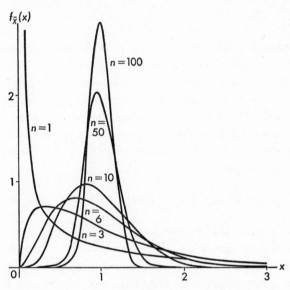

Figure 9–1. Illustration of the Effect of Sample Size on the Distribution of $\bar{X}$

Example 9–b

Consider a Bernoulli population: two possible values, 1 and 0, with probabilities p and $1 - p$, respectively. The expected value is equal to p. Therefore, the sample mean converges in probability to p. But the mean of a sample from such a population is simply the relative frequency of 1's, f/n. Thus, for any $\epsilon > 0$,

$$\lim_{n \to \infty} P\left(\left|\frac{f}{n} - p\right| > \epsilon\right) = 0.$$

In other words, the relative frequency of occurrence of any event converges in

† The relation can be proved using the "Tchebychev inequality" (page 52). It is often called the "weak" law of large numbers, to distinguish it from the "strong law of large numbers," which states:

$$P(\lim_{n \to \infty} \bar{X} = \mu) = 1.$$

Although mathematically a stronger statement, this strong law is more sophisticated, and its role in statistics is somewhat hidden.

probability to the probability of that event. This important result of probability theory is a principal reason why the theory is accepted as the foundation for statistics.

Example 9–c

It is found that the scores on a certain test can be assumed normally distributed with mean 72 and standard deviation 10. What is the probability that in a group of 100 scores, the average score differs from 72 by more than three points?

The sample mean $\bar{X}$ is normal if the population is normal. The expected value of $\bar{X}$ is the population mean, 72, and the standard deviation of $\bar{X}$ is

$$\sigma_{\bar{X}} = \frac{\sigma}{\sqrt{n}} = \frac{10}{\sqrt{100}} = 1.$$

Therefore, using Table I, page 253.

$$P(|\bar{X} - 72| > 3) = 2\Phi\left(\frac{-3}{1}\right) = .0026$$

Problems

9–1. Let X be a random variable with mean 100 and variance 25. Determine the probability that $|\bar{X} - 100| > 1$
   (a) if $\bar{X}$ is the mean of a sample of size 25.
   (b) if $\bar{X}$ is the mean of a sample of size 100.
9–2. Referring to Problem 9–1, determine a sample size, n such that
   (a) $P(|\bar{X} - 100| > .5) \leq .01$.
   (b) $P(|\bar{X} - 100| > .5) \leq .001$.

9.2 Large Sample Confidence Limits for μ

The sample mean is commonly used to give an estimate of a population mean, but it is too often given without any indication as to accuracy. Such indication can be given by an "interval estimate," which we proceed to describe.

Suppose that $X_1, \ldots, X_n$ are the observations in a random sample from a population X with unknown expectation μ, but whose variance σ^2 is assumed to be known (that σ^2 is known is, actually, an uncommon situation). Then if either (1) the population is normal or (2) the sample is large, the distribution of $\bar{X}$ may be considered normal with expectation μ and variance σ^2/n. (This is an approximation if the population is not normal, but is exact if the population is normal.) Hence, in these two cases we may write such approximate equalities as, for instance,

$$P\left(|\bar{X} - \mu| < 1.96\,\frac{\sigma}{\sqrt{n}}\right) \doteq .95, \text{ (large } n, \text{ or normal population)},$$

since we find from the table of normal distribution function values that about

5 per cent of the area under a normal density curve is divided equally between the "tails" outside the range from $\mu - 1.96\sigma$ to $\mu + 1.96\sigma$.

The inequality in the above equation may also be written as

$$|\mu - \bar{X}| < 1.96 \frac{\sigma}{\sqrt{n}},$$

or, equivalently,

$$-1.96 \frac{\sigma}{\sqrt{n}} < \mu - \bar{X} < +1.96 \frac{\sigma}{\sqrt{n}}.$$

Adding $\bar{X}$ to all members of this extended inequality, we obtain

$$\bar{X} - 1.96 \frac{\sigma}{\sqrt{n}} < \mu < \bar{X} + 1.96 \frac{\sigma}{\sqrt{n}}.$$

Since this inequality is equivalent to the one given in the initial probability equation, the probability that it holds is the same, 95 per cent:

$$P\left(\bar{X} - 1.96 \frac{\sigma}{\sqrt{n}} < \mu < \bar{X} + 1.96 \frac{\sigma}{\sqrt{n}}\right) \doteq .95.$$

A word of explanation: μ is a *constant*, with no chance aspect to it whatever! The P refers to the thing that is random inside the brackets, and that is $\bar{X}$. The interval

$$\bar{X} - 1.96 \frac{\sigma}{\sqrt{n}} \qquad \text{to} \qquad \bar{X} + 1.96 \frac{\sigma}{\sqrt{n}}$$

has, then, *random endpoints*. It is a random interval. And the probability is about .95 that in a given case this random interval will "cover" or include within it the value μ. The interval is called a 95 per cent *confidence interval*, or a confidence interval corresponding to a confidence coefficient of .95. The endpoints of the interval are called *confidence limits*. They depend on the particular sample used in their computation.

The procedure in a given case is as follows: (1) Obtain a sample, (2) compute the sample mean, and from it (3) compute the endpoints of the confidence interval as given above. If this happens to be one of the expected 95 per cent of the times when the random interval covers μ, then the computed confidence interval includes μ within it. Actually, of course, it either does include μ or it does not. One would never know.

Confidence coefficients other than .95 are used, of course, and the multiplier 1.96 must be modified accordingly. Some commonly used confidence coefficients γ and corresponding multipliers k_γ are given in the following table:

γ	k_γ
.99	2.57
.9545	2.00
.95	1.96
.90	1.64

The general relationship is

$$1 - \gamma = 2(1 - \Phi(k_\gamma)).$$

If the population variance is not known, it is commonly estimated in large samples by computing the sample variance, $s_x{}^2$. Thus, the approximate confidence limits are (95 per cent):

$$\bar{X} \pm 1.96 \frac{s_x}{\sqrt{n}}.$$

A modification for "small" samples from a normal population will be given in Section 9.5. The estimation of σ^2 by $s_x{}^2$ will be discussed more in detail in Chapter 10.

Example 9–d

The mean of the 200 viscosity measurements given in Table 7.1, page 116, was computed on page 124 to be 31.7. We were not given the population variance, but the sample variance was found to be 3.3 (page 127). Using these numbers, we can construct an approximate confidence interval for the expected value of the population. Taking .90 (arbitrarily) as the confidence coefficient, the 90 per cent confidence limits for μ are found to be

$$31.7 \pm 1.64 \frac{\sqrt{3.3}}{\sqrt{200}} = 31.7 \pm .21.$$

Problems

9–3. A group of 30 out of 500 freshman men have an average height of 5 feet 10 inches, with standard deviation 2 inches. Determine an approximate 95 per cent confidence interval for the average height of the 500 freshmen.

9–4. A series of measurements of a certain dimension of twenty-five parts has a mean of 2.3 and a standard deviation of .1. Assuming that the "actual" dimension is the mean, μ, of the population of possible dimensions, construct a confidence interval for μ

(a) Using a 99 per cent confidence coefficient.

(b) Using a 95 per cent confidence coefficient.

9–5. If it is known from long experience that the variability in a certain method of determining the concentration of a chemical in solution is indicated by a standard deviation of .005 gram per cubic centimeter, determine the number of measurements necessary to obtain a 99 per cent confidence interval for concentration which is only .001 gram per cubic centimeter wide.

9–6. Verify the entries in the table of values of k_γ.

9.3 Confidence Limits for p

We have seen many instances in which the population being sampled is of the Bernoulli type—a random variable X which takes on only two values, 1 and 0, with probabilities p and $q = 1 - p$, respectively. In such a case, $E(X) = p$, and we may set up a confidence interval for this expected value as described in the preceding section. Corresponding to a confidence coefficient γ, the approximate confidence limits for p, assuming n large, are

$$\bar{X} \pm k_\gamma \frac{s_x}{\sqrt{n}},$$

where in this instance, $s_x{}^2$ is simply related to $\bar{X}$:

$$s_x{}^2 = \frac{n}{n-1} \bar{X}(1 - \bar{X}) \doteq \bar{X}(1 - \bar{X}).$$

Hence, we may write the above confidence limits in the form

$$\bar{X} \pm k_\gamma \sqrt{\frac{\bar{X}(1 - \bar{X})}{n}}.$$

The sample variance was used in these limits as a substitute for the population variance, assuming the latter to be unknown. In the case at hand, however, we observe that the population variance is dependent on the parameter being estimated : $\sigma^2 = p(1 - p)$. In such a case, the inequality

$$|p - \bar{X}| < k_\gamma \frac{\sigma}{\sqrt{n}} = k_\gamma \sqrt{\frac{p(1 - p)}{n}}$$

can be solved for p, yielding the following confidence limits for p (we write k in place of k_γ for convenience):

$$\frac{1}{1 + k^2/n} \left(\bar{X} + \frac{k^2}{2n} \pm k \sqrt{\frac{\bar{X}(1 - \bar{X})}{n} + \frac{k^2}{4n^2}} \right).$$

These limits are still only approximate, however, since the relation between k_γ and γ is determined assuming that X is *normally* distributed, which is only approximately true.

(We notice that if n is quite large, the confidence limits as determined in this way reduce to the expressions given earlier, where we simply substituted the sample variance for the population variance.)

A similar technique may be employed whenever the population variance is expressible in terms of the population mean, although the inequality involved may be harder to solve than the quadratic solved above.

Example 9–e

A certain treatment is found effective in sixteen out of twenty-five cases. Construct an approximate 99 per cent confidence interval for the probability that it will be effective in a given case.

Letting 1 denote "effective" and 0 denote "not effective," we have a Bernoulli population, with the desired probability p as the parameter. The sample size is twenty-five, and the sample mean is $\bar{X} = 16/25 = .64$. Approximate confidence limits are (using the simpler formula)

$$.64 \pm 2.57 \sqrt{\frac{.64(.36)}{25}} \doteq .64 \pm .25.$$

The corresponding confidence interval is then $.39 < p < .89$.

This sample size is not particularly large, and it is of interest to use the more complicated formula for comparison; the result is the interval $.28 < p < .95$, which suggests that perhaps the simpler formula was not good enough in this case. It would have worked better if the sample size were, say, 100 or greater.

Problems

9–7. Out of 200 identical thumtacks tossed on a table, 140 are found to have landed with point up. Dertemine a 90 per cent confidence interval and a 99 per cent confidence interval for the probability that a single tack lands with point up.

9–8. Out of 40 identical thumb-tacks tossed on a table, 28 are found to have landed with point up. Determine a 90 per cent confidence interval for the probability that a single tack lands with point up.

9–9. Ten out of a certain sample of 100 articles produced in a certain process are found to have defects. Construct a 95 per cent confidence interval for the probability that a single article produced in the process is defective.

9–10. Referring to Example 9–e, compare the results using the simple and the more complicated formulas for confidence limits, if the experiment had included 100 cases, with effectiveness found in 64.

9–11. A geiger counter records 120 counts in a certain one-minute period. Construct a 95 per cent confidence interval for λ, the average number of counts in a one-second period. [*Hint:* Let X denote the total number of counts in a one-minute period. This is assumed to have the Poisson distribution, with $\mu = \sigma^2 = 60\lambda$. For this large value of λt the Poisson distribution is nearly normal, and therefore

$$P(|X - 60\lambda| < 1.96 \sqrt{60\lambda}) \doteq .95.$$

Solve the inequality here for λ, and thereby obtain the desired (approximate) confidence limits.]

9.4 Testing Hypotheses on μ

Let us now shift the point of view from that of estimating the expected value μ to that of testing to determine whether a specified value μ_0 is reasonable in view of the results of a sample. The test statistic used will be the sample mean.

The hypothesis that $\mu = \mu_0$ is generally not a simple hypothesis. It is simple only in cases in which the admissible hypotheses are of a type whose distributions are completely determined by specification of the expectation. Even if we assume the population variance to be known, the hypothesis $\mu = \mu_0$ is composite unless the expectation and variance together determine the population distribution. However, because of the Central Limit Theorem, the test statistic $\bar{X}$ is asymptotically normal (μ, σ^2) no matter what the population distribution. This means that it is possible to answer probability questions concerning the mean of a large sample given only the population mean and variance.

In this section we shall consider tests for μ in cases in which the population variance σ^2 is assumed to be known. Except for the case of a normal population, the samples will be assumed large enough for application of the Central Limit Theorem. The small sample case with unknown variance will be considered (for normal populations only) in the next section.

No matter what the precise hypotheses concerning μ are, the operating characteristic function of the test will depend only on the critical region of the test. We shall consider "one-sided" critical regions and "two-sided" critical regions and show how each is appropriate in a certain case.

9.4.1 One-Sided Tests

In choosing between $\mu = \mu_0$ and $\mu = \mu_1$, it is reasonable that we should prefer to accept the larger μ for large values of $\bar{X}$ and that we should prefer the smaller μ for small values of $\bar{X}$. We therefore adopt the critical region $\bar{X} > K$ for testing

$$H_0: \mu = \mu_0 \text{ and } H_1: \mu = \mu_1,$$

where $\mu_1 > \mu_0$. Indeed, the critical region $\bar{X} > K$ would be reasonable for any hypotheses such that the values of μ in H_0 lie to the left of those in H_1

as in the following cases:

$$H_0: \mu = \mu_0 \text{ and } H_1: \mu > \mu_0,$$

or

$$H_0: \mu \leq \mu_0 \text{ and } H_1: \mu > \mu_0.$$

(Clearly, if the μ values in H_0 lie to the *right* of those in H_1, the test $\bar{X} < K$ would be appropriate—again a one-sided critical region.)

The operating characteristic function of the test $\bar{X} > K$ is defined by the probability that $\bar{X}$ fails to exceed K. For large samples, or for a normal population, the operating characteristic is a function of μ, the actual population mean:

$$OC \text{ function} = P_\mu(\text{accept } H_0)$$
$$= P_\mu(\bar{X} < K) = \Phi\left(\frac{K - \mu}{\sigma/\sqrt{n}}\right),$$

where the population variance is known. The symbol $\Phi(z)$ denotes the standard normal distribution function (Table I, page 253). The graph of this OC function for a typical case is shown in Figure 9–2. (In this case it

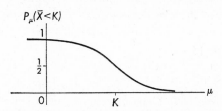

Figure 9–2. Operating Characteristic for a One-Sided Test

happens to be a normal distribution curve reversed, as is seen from the above equation.)

It is clear from the graph that as long as the values of μ in H_0 are smaller than those in H_1, the probability of acceptance will be higher on H_0 than on H_1, which is as it should be.

The effects of n and K on the operating characteristic function should be observed. The curve is "centered" at $\mu = K$. Changing K has the effect of shifting the OC curve to the right or to the left. The sample size determines the sampling variability in $\bar{X}$. An increase in n steepens the descent, or "squares up" the OC curve, so that it approaches the ideal operating characteristic as $n \to \infty$.

If the sample size n is given, the *steepness* of the curve is thereby given. Setting a significance level α then fixes the operating characteristic *horizontally*, thereby determining K. It also fixes β, however defined.

Example 9-f

Suppose we wish to test $H_0: \mu = 0$ against $H_1: \mu = 2$, with $\sigma^2 = 1$, based on a sample of size 100, and it is decided that the probability of rejecting H_0 when H_0 is true should be only .01. This fixes the critical region as follows:

$$.01 = P_0(\bar{X} < K)$$
$$= 1 - \Phi\left(\frac{K - 0}{1/\sqrt{100}}\right) = \Phi\left(\frac{0 - K}{1/\sqrt{100}}\right)$$

Using Table I we find the first percentile of the standard normal distribution to be

$$z_{.01} = -2.33.$$

Hence,

$$-10K = -2.33, \quad \text{or} \quad K = .233.$$

But then

$$\beta = P_2(\bar{X} < K) = \Phi\left(\frac{K - 2}{1/\sqrt{100}}\right) = \Phi(-17.67) \doteq 0.$$

The test can also be specified by giving the protection desired in the form of an α, or probability of rejecting H_0 when a certain μ' is the population mean, and a β, or probability of accepting H_1 when a certain μ'' ($\mu'' > \mu'$) is the population mean. These fix the K and the sample size, as seen in the following example.

Example 9-g

A certain type of light bulb is reputed to have a life of 1000 hours. Actually the life is a random variable with an approximately normal distribution with $\sigma = 200$ hours. It is desired to test $H_0: \mu = 1000$ against $H_1: \mu < 1000$, using the mean life in a sample of n bulbs, with a critical region $C: \bar{X} < K$.

The decision is made that if the mean life is actually 800 hours but H_0 is accepted, there will be too many complaints and that if the mean life is actually 1050 hours, rejection of H_0 would be extremely annoying. Setting $\alpha = \beta = .05$ (arbitrarily), we then find

$$\alpha = .05 = P_{1050}(\text{reject } H_0) = P_{1050}(\bar{X} < K) = \Phi\left(\frac{K - 1050}{200/\sqrt{n}}\right),$$
$$\beta = .05 = P_{800}(\text{accept } H_0) = P_{800}(\bar{X} > K) = 1 - \Phi\left(\frac{K - 800}{200/\sqrt{n}}\right).$$

Referring to Table I we have

$$-1.65 = \frac{K - 1050}{200/\sqrt{n}} = \frac{800 - K}{200/\sqrt{n}},$$

from which it is easily deduced that $K = 925$ hours, and $n = 7$. The test then is to take a sample of size seven, and if $\bar{X} < 925$ hours, reject H_0.

This critical region is commonly expressed in terms of the standardized test statistic

$$Z = \frac{\bar{X} - 1050}{\sigma/\sqrt{n}}.$$

The critical value $\bar{X} = 925$ corresponds to

$$Z = \frac{925 - 1050}{200/\sqrt{7}} = -1.65,$$

which is the fifth percentile of the Z distribution. The test then consists in calculating Z from the $\bar{X}$ of a given sample, and rejecting H_0 if $Z < -1.65$.

9.4.2 Two-Sided Tests

In testing $\mu = \mu_0$ against the alternative $\mu \neq \mu_0$, it is natural to reject μ_0 in favor of a different value if the mean of a sample is excessively far from

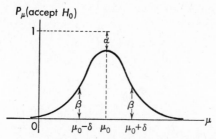

Figure 9–3. Operating Characteristic for a Two-Sided Test

μ_0, on *either* side. That is, we adopt the critical region

$$|\bar{X} - \mu_0| > K.$$

The operating characteristic function corresponding to this critical region can be computed (again given σ^2) if we assume either a normal population or a sample size large enough so that $\bar{X}$ may be considered normally distributed. It is

OC function $= P_\mu(\text{accept } H_0)$

$$= P_\mu(|\bar{X} - \mu_0| < K) = \Phi\left(\frac{\mu_0 + K - \mu}{\sigma/\sqrt{n}}\right) - \Phi\left(\frac{\mu_0 - K - \mu}{\sigma/\sqrt{n}}\right).$$

Considered as a function of μ for a fixed critical region and fixed sample size, this is the operating characteristic function. Its graph will resemble that shown in Figure 9–3. Note that this test is unbiased—the largest probability of accepting H_0 is at H_0.

The significance level would normally be taken as the probability of rejection when H_0 is true:

$$\alpha = P_{\mu_0}(\text{reject } H_0)$$

$$= P_{\mu_0}(|\bar{X} - \mu_0| > K) = 2\left[1 - \Phi\left(\frac{K}{\sigma/\sqrt{n}}\right)\right] = 2\Phi\left(\frac{-K}{\sigma/\sqrt{n}}\right).$$

If we wish to introduce a zone of indifference about μ_0, we may define β as the probability of accepting H_0 (the operating characteristic) at some $\mu_0 + \delta$ (or at $\mu_0 - \delta$, which gives the same result).

Example 9-h

A manufactured part is to fit other parts, and a certain critical dimension is designed to be 2 inches. The variability in manufacturing is indicated by a variance of .0025 in.^{2}. It is decided, say, that if the expected dimension does not differ from 2 inches by more than .02 inch, the number of misfits will not be too great.

Picking $\alpha = .05$, and $\beta = .1$, what rejection limits and sample size are required? We have the following two equations:

$$\alpha = .05 = 2\Phi\left(\frac{-K}{.05/\sqrt{n}}\right)$$

$$\beta = .1 = P_{\mu_0 + .02}(|\bar{X} - \mu_0| < K)$$

$$= \Phi\left(\frac{K - .02}{.05/\sqrt{n}}\right) + \Phi\left(\frac{K + .02}{.05/\sqrt{n}}\right) - 1.$$

These can be solved by trial and error, with the aid of Table I, with the result that

$$\frac{.02}{.05/\sqrt{n}} = 3.24,$$

so that $n \doteq 66$. To verify this, let us suppose that we are given the sample size $n = 66$, and the significance level, $\alpha = .05$. Then

$$.05 = 2\Phi\left(\frac{-K}{.05/\sqrt{66}}\right), \text{ whence } K = 1.96\frac{.05}{\sqrt{66}} = .012.$$

But then

$$\beta = P_{\mu_0 + .02}(\text{accept } H_0)$$

$$= \Phi\left(\frac{-.008}{.05/\sqrt{66}}\right) + \Phi\left(\frac{.032}{.05/\sqrt{66}}\right) - 1 = .097.$$

Let us next show how a confidence interval may be used in a test. We have seen previously how the inequality in such a statement as

$$P(|\bar{X} - \mu| < 1.96\sigma_{\bar{X}}) \doteq .95 \qquad (\text{large } n)$$

may be rewritten in the form

$$\bar{X} - 1.96\sigma_{\bar{X}} < \mu < \bar{X} + 1.96\sigma_{\bar{X}}.$$

This inequality has then the probability .95 also, and the interval defined by it is a 95 per cent confidence interval for μ. That is, before a sample is drawn and $\bar{X}$ is determined, the probability is .95 that the interval computed from $\bar{X}$ will include the actual fixed value of μ.

Consider again the hypothesis H_0: $\mu = \mu_0$, with the two-sided alternative $\mu \neq \mu_0$. (Assume as above that σ is given, the same for both H_0 and H_1.) Suppose we adopt as a test that H_0 will be rejected if μ_0 does not lie in the confidence interval—that is, if

$$|\mu_0 - \bar{X}| > 1.96\sigma_{\bar{X}}.$$

But this is equivalent to saying that $\bar{X}$ falls farther from μ_0 than a certain amount, which is just the two-sided test used previously. The confidence coefficient, .95, is precisely $1 - \alpha$, where α is the significance level of the test.

(If we wished to test against a one-sided alternative, we should have to construct a one-sided confidence interval to show the relationship.)

Example 9–i

Consider again the dimension of a part treated in Example 9–h. We want to test H_0: $\mu = 2$ against H_1: $\mu \neq 2$. If $\bar{X} = 2.04$ for a given day's sample of fifty, the corresponding 95 per cent confidence interval has the limits

$$2.04 \pm 1.96\,\frac{.05}{\sqrt{50}}$$

This interval, from 2.026 to 2.054, does not include 2, and thus we reject $\mu = 2$ at the 5 per cent level.

Problems

9–12. The sixty weights given in Problem 7–R2, page 129, were obtained to test the hypothesis that the expected weight is 16 ounces. Given that the mean of this sample is 16.115, should the hypothesis be accepted at the 10 per cent level? (Notice that it should first be decided whether a one-sided or two-sided test is appropriate.) Determine the probability that with the test used the population mean could be 16.1 without being detected. Use the sample standard deviation .243 in place of σ.

9–13. It is desired to test H_0: $\lambda t = 1$ against H_1: $\lambda t = 2$ assuming that a population is of the Poisson type with parameter λt. Using the mean of a sample as the basis of the test, determine the rejection region and sample size corresponding to $\alpha = \beta = .01$. (Proceed as though the sample size were large enough for a normal approximation and then notice that it turns out to be so.)

9–14. Noticing that when a certain pair of dice are thrown, 7's and 11's seem to come up an unusually large number of times, a man decides to conduct a test and throws the dice 162 times. If he adopts a significance level of .20, what should be the critical region, in terms of the number of 7's and 11's in the 162 throws?

9–15. Articles taken from a production line are classed as good or defective. Let p denote the probability that a defective piece is produced. It is decided to fix .05 as the probability both of acting to stop production when $p = .1$ and of acting to allow production to continue when $p = .2$. What size sample should be taken and what maximum number of defectives in the sample should be allowed to achieve this aim?

9–16. Referring to Example 9–g, compute the probability that H_0 is rejected when $\mu = 1000$, using the sample size and critical region determined in that example.

9.5 Small Sample Modification

In testing hypotheses concerning the expected value, we often assumed that, because of the large sample size used, the unknown population variance may be replaced by the sample variance. That is, instead of

$$z = \frac{\bar{x} - \mu}{\sigma/\sqrt{n}}$$

one uses

$$t = \frac{\bar{x} - \mu}{s_x/\sqrt{n}},$$

assuming that t is distributed approximately as a standard normal random variable. For small samples, however, the denominator in t cannot successfully be considered constant (it is a *random* variable), and the normal distribution does not apply, even though the population, and hence $\bar{X}$, be normally distributed.

In general, the ratio of any standard normal variable to the positive square root of an independent chi-square variable divided by its number of degrees of freedom has a distribution—called the t distribution—dependent only on that number of degrees of freedom. It is an exercise in calculus (but a nontrivial one) to show that the density function of such a t distribution, corresponding to ν degrees of freedom, is as follows:

$$f(x, \nu) = (\text{const.})(1 + t^2/\nu)^{-(\nu+1)/2},$$

where the constant multiplier is chosen to make the integral of $f(x, \nu)$ equal to 1.

In particular, *when the population is normal*, the quantity we have named t above can be written in the following form:

$$t = \sqrt{n}\,\frac{\bar{x} - \mu}{s_x} = \frac{\dfrac{\bar{x} - \mu}{\sigma/\sqrt{n}}}{\sqrt{\dfrac{1}{n-1}\dfrac{(n-1)s_x^2}{\sigma^2}}},$$

where the numerator on the right is a standard normal variable, and

$(n - 1)s_x^2/\sigma^2$ has the chi-square distribution, as will be discussed in section 10.2.2. Thus, the quantity t has the t distribution with $n - 1$ degrees of freedom.

The t distribution is tabulated in Table III, page 257. In this table we can find, for example, the percentiles $t_{.025}$ and $t_{.975}$, such that

$$P(t_{.025} < t < t_{.975}) = .95.$$

Then (substituting the expression for t in terms of $\bar{X}$),

$$P\left\{\bar{X} + (t_{.025})\frac{s_x}{\sqrt{n}} < \mu < \bar{X} + (t_{.975})\frac{s_x}{\sqrt{n}}\right\} = .95,$$

and we have a 95 per cent confidence interval for μ.

For a general confidence coefficient γ the multipliers to use in the confidence limits are the percentiles $t_{\alpha/2}$ and $t_{1-\alpha/2}$, where $\alpha = 1 - \gamma$.

To test the hypothesis H_0: $\mu = \mu_0$ either against H_1: $\mu > \mu_0$ or against H_1: $\mu \neq \mu_0$, we employ the statistic

$$t = \sqrt{n}\left(\frac{\bar{X} - \mu_0}{s_x}\right).$$

This has the t distribution (with $n - 1$ degrees of freedom) under H_0. The critical region will be of the form

$$C: t > t_{1-\alpha}, \quad \text{for} \quad H_1: \mu > \mu_0,$$

or

$$C: |t| > t_{1-\alpha/2}, \quad \text{for} \quad H_1: \alpha \neq \mu_0,$$

where α is the arbitrarily set significance level.

Example 9–j

The first twenty of the measurements of viscosity in Table 7.1, page 116, have a mean $\bar{X} = 33.5$ and a variance $s_x^2 = 3.36$. The 95 per cent confidence interval (assuming a *normal* population) constructed using the t distribution is then

$$33.5 \pm \frac{1.83}{\sqrt{20}} \times 2.09,$$

which has a width of about 1.71. (The 2.09 was obtained from the t table; it is the 97.5 percentile of the t distribution with parameter 19.) If we had followed the earlier scheme of approximating the standard deviation of the population with that of the sample, but using the multiplier 1.96 based on a normal distribution, the width of the confidence interval would be

$$\frac{2 \times 1.83}{\sqrt{20}} \times 1.96$$

or about 1.61, which is narrower than is justified.

Example 9-k

In Example 9-g we considered testing the expected life of a light bulb of a certain type, using a sample size of seven to test $H_0: \mu = 1000$ against $H_0: \mu < 1000$, assuming a normal distribution with standard deviation 200 hours. The critical region was $\bar{X} < 925$, and this provided a protection given by an α of .05 at $\mu = 1050$ and a β of .05 at $\mu = 800$. The test statistic could have been taken as

$$Z = \frac{\bar{X} - 1050}{200/\sqrt{7}},$$

with a rejection region given by $Z < -1.65$. Now let us suppose that 200 hours is the *sample* standard deviation (with σ^2 unknown). We then use

$$t = \frac{\bar{X} - 1050}{s_x/\sqrt{7}}$$

as our test statistic. If we use $C: t < -1.65$ as the critical region, we have (interpolating in Table III, page 257)

$$\alpha = P_{1050}(t < -1.65) \doteq .075.$$

To compute β, we need

$$P_{800}\left(\frac{\bar{X} - 1050}{s_x/\sqrt{7}} < -1.65\right),$$

and because the quantity t does *not* have the t distribution when $\mu = 800$, we cannot complete the calculation. The distribution required here is called the "noncentral t distribution," and extensive tables are available. Determination of the operating characteristic function would also require these tables of the more general t distribution. Such operating characteristic curves are available, for example, in *Handbook of Industrial Statistics*, by Bowker and Lieberman.

Problems

9–17. In testing $H_0: \mu = 2$ against $H_1: \mu \neq 2$ in a normal population, a sample of size fifteen yields $\bar{X} = 2.14$ and $s_x = .36$. Should H_0 be accepted at the 5 per cent level?

9–18. Assuming the data given is a random sample from a normal population, construct a 90 per cent confidence interval for μ.

3.79	3.53	3.59	3.83	3.75
3.53	3.71	3.35	3.84	3.90
3.85	3.89	3.69	3.59	3.67
3.57	3.85	3.77	3.49	3.63

9–19. If the data in Problem 9–18 had been obtained to test $H_0: \mu = 3.5$ against $\mu > 3.5$, would you accept H_0 at the 10 per cent level? Construct the corresponding one-sided confidence interval.

9.6 Control Charts for $\bar{X}$

In Section 8.7 we discussed the concept of control and presented some tests for control against the alternative of a shift in level. (This shift in level, we remarked, could be a shift in level of variability, by applying the tests to ranges or standard deviations of subsamples.) In this section we introduce a tool which is commonly used for detecting that a process is out of control soon after the shift occurs. It is usually assumed that a shift in level is the result of "assignable causes" and that as soon as the shift is detected, action is taken to remove these causes.

In a physical operation we think of chance causes as the large bundle of small influences which determine the particular outcome that we happen to obtain. When the operation is in control, we use the language that there exists a *constant* system of chance causes—constant, that is, over successive observations. The purpose of the *control chart* is to detect when assignable causes perturb the chance cause system.

We may plot a sequence of observed values on a control chart. Or, values of $\bar{X}$, computed from subgroups of, say, two to ten observations, may be plotted in the order in which they occur. We identify the vertical axis with the measured characteristic and the horizontal axis with the observation number or sample number. Certain horizontal lines, called control lines, are drawn on the chart.

The control chart is simply a *graphical* method of testing for significance; if the plotted characteristic happens to be too large, say, we reject the hypothesis of no change in the population, i.e., we reject the hypothesis that the system is still in control. It will be seen that the control limits correspond to boundaries of a certain critical region.

There are two types of situations in which control charts are useful: (1) We wish to detect lack of control when the distribution is specified. We have experienced a process which has been in control for a sufficiently long period of time to "know" that sort of process with which we are dealing. Parameters are assigned values on the basis of this long history. These values may be considered as "standards." (2) We wish to detect lack of control when the distribution is *not* specified in advance. Here we must use current information from the process to estimate the process parameters and to establish criteria for determining whether statistical control exists. We now consider these two types of problems.

In the following examples, we shall present data obtained by actually drawing chips, with replacement and mixing. Three sets of chips were used, numbers being marked on the chips according to the following table of frequencies.   The frequencies were picked† so that the distributions are approximately normal, with parameters μ and σ as shown in the table.

	A	B	C
12			1
11			1
10			1
9			3
8			5
7		1	8
6		3	12
5	1	10	16
4	3	23	20
3	10	39	22
2	23	48	23
1	39	39	22
0	48	23	20
−1	39	10	16
−2	23	3	12
−3	10	1	8
−4	3		5
−5	1		3
−6			1
−7			1
−8			1
−9			
−10			
Totals	200	200	201
μ	0	2	2
σ	1.715	1.715	3.5

Example 9–1

We assume that a system is known to have been in control and that the appropriate distribution is the one simulated by frequency A above.   The parameters of this distribution, $\mu = 0$ and $\sigma = 1.715$, are used to construct control limits for testing future control as follows; the statistic used is the mean of samples of size five:

† These approximate distributions were devised by H. Working and E.G. Olds; cf. *Manual for an Introduction to Statistical Methods of Quality Control in Industry*, Office of Production Research and Development, War Production Board, April, 1944.

$\bar{X}$ Control Chart

Center Line $\qquad\qquad\qquad E(\bar{X}) = \mu = 0$

Upper Control Limit $E(\bar{X}) + \dfrac{3\sigma}{\sqrt{n}} = 0 + \dfrac{3 \times 1.715}{\sqrt{5}} = 2.30$

Lower Control Limit $E(\bar{X}) - \dfrac{3\sigma}{\sqrt{n}} = 0 - \dfrac{3 \times 1.715}{\sqrt{5}} = -2.30.$

(The constants in these limits will be discussed below.) Drawing twenty samples of five each from a bowl of chips marked according to frequency distribution A above, the sample means were computed and plotted on the graph in Figure 9–4. The samples were taken one chip at a time, with replacement and thorough mixing after each drawing, so we have here a population which is as much in control physically as we could ever expect to achieve. The chart in Figure 9–4 shows, then, some typical

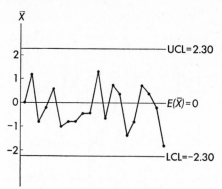

Figure 9–4

results when a system is actually under statistical control. Notice that the points remain well within the control limits and that therefore no action to investigate assignable causes would have been warranted at any point in the sampling process. (We observe, too, that the fluctuations appear to be random, rather than systematic.)

The constants used in computing the control limits in the above example come about as follows. First, the sample size comes from a consideration of OC curves, to provide adequate protection in catching given shifts in process level or variability. At any rate, this is how we should like to think of determining n; but in practice one works with two charts simultaneously, and the same n may not be quite the best for both, and so one compromises. The usual compromise is a sample size of from two to ten.

The constant "3" in the $\bar{X}$ limits corresponds to an α of .0026 if the original population is normal. However, the "3" has become almost standard and is often used regardless of the underlying distribution—as a starting point, at least, although it may turn out that in certain instances these limits require modification for the chart to be of practical value, as shown by experience. The control limits as thus calculated are called "three-sigma limits."

Example 9–m

Again we assume that a system is known to be in control, this time being represented by frequency distribution B above, approximating a normal distribution with mean 2 and standard deviation 1.715. On the control chart in Figure 9–5, center lines and control limits have been determined as described in the preceding example. Forty samples of five were drawn (one chip at a time), the first twenty from population B, the next ten from population A, and the remaining ten from population C.

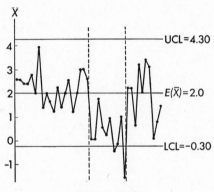

Figure 9–5

Observe that the first twenty points again keep within the control limits. However, among the samples numbered twenty-one through thirty (from A), there is evidence of a shift in mean or level to a lower value. In the last ten samples, the mean appears to be centered again at 2 (as it should be, since the sample was drawn from C).

Problems

9–20. A process is known to have been in statistical control with expected value $\mu = 15$ and standard deviation $\sigma = 3.5$. Samples of size eight each are taken in order to test for continued statistical control.

    (a) What are the center line and the control limits for the $\bar{X}$ control chart?

    (b) Suppose that the process shifts to the value of $\mu = 16$ but that the standard deviation does not change. What is the chance of catching this process shift on the first sample after the change in level? Construct the OC curve for this test.

    (c) Referring to part (b), what is the chance of catching the process shift on the first or second sample? Construct the OC curve for this test.

9–21. Make up 201 slips of paper marked with the numbers $-8, -7, \ldots , 12$ in accordance with the frequencies given for "Distribution C" on page 180. Construct control lines based on samples of size five, and on the assumption that the process is in control, described by "Distribution A." Obtain twenty samples of size five by drawing (with replacement and mixing) from the prepared slips, and plot the means on the control chart.

9.7 The Sample Median As an Estimate of μ

The sample median is simpler by far to compute than the sample mean. Can we use the sample median to estimate the center of a population?

It can be shown that for large samples the sample median is approximately normal, with expected value equal to the population median m and standard deviation equal to $(2f(m)\sqrt{n})^{-1}$, where $f(x)$ is the population density. Hence as the sample size becomes infinite, the distribution of the sample median narrows down on the population median (in much the same manner that the limit in probability of the sample mean is the population mean, cf. page 164).

Surely, then, it is reasonable to use the sample median to estimate the population median. Moreover, if the population distribution happens to be such that the median and expected value coincide, the sample median can be used to estimate the expected value, or population mean. The median and expected value of a probability distribution will coincide if the distribution is symmetrical about the expected value, as is the case in a normal distribution.

The median of a sample from a normal population, then, can be used as an estimate of the parameter μ of the population. But the question arises: How good is the median in comparison with the sample mean?

To obtain a comparison, recall that in obtaining an interval estimate, the width of the confidence interval was found proportional to the standard deviation of the statistic used in the estimation. Hence, if we use the sample mean, the confidence interval width is proportional to $\sigma/\sqrt{n}$. And if we use the sample median, the interval width is proportional to

$$\frac{1}{2f(\mu)\sqrt{n}} = \frac{\sigma}{\sqrt{n}} \cdot \sqrt{\frac{\pi}{2}}.$$

For a given sample size, then, the confidence interval based on the sample median is $\sqrt{\pi/2} = 1.2533$ times as wide as the confidence interval based on the sample mean. Or, for confidence intervals of the *same* width, the sample size required using the sample median is about 57 per cent greater than the size required using the sample mean. Choosing between the two estimates then reduces to a matter of economics: Which is cheaper, increasing the sample size or computing the arithmetic mean? In some cases the answer could be the former, and in other cases the latter.

Example 9–n

The median of the 200 viscosity measurements in Table 7.2, page 118, is about 31.6. Using the sample standard deviation of 1.82 as the population standard deviation, the 95 per cent confidence limits for μ (assuming a normal population) are

$$31.6 \pm 1.96 \times \frac{1.82}{\sqrt{200}} \sqrt{\frac{\pi}{2}} = 31.7 \pm .32.$$

(Compare this result with that obtained using the sample mean, in Example 9–d, page 167.)

Problems

9–22. Construct a test of $H_0: \mu = 0$ against $H_1: \mu = 1$ assuming a normal population with $\sigma^2 = 2$, using the sample median as the test statistic, and using $\alpha = .05$, $\beta = .1$.

9–23. Consider the population with density function $(1/b)e^{-x/b}$, $x \geq 0$.
  (a) Determine the distribution function and from it the population median in terms of the parameter b.
  (b) Compute the standard deviation of the distribution of the sample median (assuming a large sample).
  (c) Construct a confidence interval for the parameter b on the basis of the sample median.
  (d) Carry out the computations for obtaining the confidence interval in the particular case of the data in the following table, giving the life in hours of 390 electron tubes:

Life	Frequency
0– 10	91
11– 20	70
21– 30	54
31– 40	43
41– 50	33
51– 60	26
61– 70	20
71– 80	16
81– 90	12
91–100	9
101–110	5
111–120	3
121–130	4
131–140	3
141–150	1

9.8 The Population Median

The median of a probability distribution is a parameter which (along with the expectation) measures or describes the location of the distribution. It will exist in cases in which the expectation does not exist. For a continuous random variable, the median is that number m such that

$$P(X > m) = P(X < m) = \frac{1}{2}.$$

Suppose that it is desired to test the hypothesis that $m = m_0$. If this value of X is actually the median, we should expect approximately half of the observations in a random sample to lie on either side of it. This suggests taking the number of sample observations in excess of m_0 as a test statistic. Under the hypothesis H_0, that $m = m_0$, $P(X - m_0 > 0) = 1/2$, and therefore the number of observations exceeding m_0 has the binomial distribution with $p = 1/2$.

What type of critical region to use depends again on the alternative we have in mind. If the alternative is $m \neq m_0$, we should reject H_0 for either too many or too few observations in excess of m_0. If it is $m > m_0$, we use a one-sided test, and reject H_0 if there are too few observations in excess of m_0. Since specifying a value $m = m_1$ does not define the probability $P(X > m_0)$, we cannot compute the power corresponding to that alternative. For a class of alternatives such that $P(X > m_0) = p$, which means that m_0 is the $100p$ percentile (rather than the fiftieth), the power is readily computed using the binomial distribution with that value of p. For sufficiently large samples, of course, the normal approximation is applicable.

Example 9–o

Consider testing $m = 32$ against $m \neq 32$, using a sample of twenty observations. Suppose that it is decided to reject $m = 32$ if more than fifteen or less than five observations fall above 32. If $m = 32$, this critical region has the probability (size of the type I error):

$$\left[\binom{20}{0} + \cdots + \binom{20}{4} + \binom{20}{16} + \cdots + \binom{20}{20} \right] \left(\frac{1}{2} \right)^{20} \doteq .012$$

Given the following twenty observations:

$$37.0\ 31.4\ 34.4\ 33.3\ 34.9\ 31.6\ 31.6\ 31.3\ 34.6\ 32.6$$
$$36.2\ 31.0\ 33.5\ 33.7\ 33.4\ 34.4\ 32.1\ 33.3\ 32.7\ 31.5,$$

we construct the following pattern of signs, $+$ if an observation exceeds 32, and $-$ if it is less than 32:

$$+ - + + + - - - + +$$
$$+ - + + + + + + + -.$$

There are fourteen plus signs, which is not enough for rejection of H_0 at the significance level .012.

A confidence interval for the population median can be constructed as follows. Let $X_{(1)}, \ldots, X_{(n)}$ denote the observations in a random sample arranged in *numerical* order (rather than in the order drawn). Then if $r < s$,

$$P(X_{(r)} < m < X_{(s)}) = P(\text{exactly } r \text{ or } r + 1 \text{ or } \ldots \text{ or } s - 1 \text{ observations are } \leq m)$$

$$= \sum_{k=r}^{s-1} \binom{n}{k} \left(\frac{1}{2}\right)^n.$$

Thus, the random interval from the rth observation to the sth, in numerical order, is a confidence interval for m with confidence coefficient given by the above sum of binomial probabilities.

Example 9–p

In the case of twenty observations, the interval from the fourth to the sixteenth observation in order will include m with probability .991, according to the calculation in the preceding example. For the twenty observations given in that example, $X_{(4)} = 31.5$, and $X_{(16)} = 34.6$. These are 99.1 per cent confidence limits.

Problems

9–24. In a table of "random normal numbers" taken from a population with expectation 2 and variance 1, 88 out of 150 entries are found to be larger than 2. Would you accept $\mu = 2$ on this basis? (*Note:* For a normal population, the mean and median coincide.)

9–25. In testing $H_0: m = 20$ against $H_1: m > 20$, we adopt the rule that if more than eight out of ten observations are larger than twenty, H_0 is rejected.
   (a) Compute α.
   (b) Compute the probability that if $P(X > 20) = 2/3$, H_0 is accepted.

9–26. Determine the probability that m is included between the fortieth and sixtieth observations, in numerical order, of a random sample of 100 observations.

10/Estimating and Testing Variability

10.0 Introduction

It is often necessary to measure the inherent variability of a given random variable. If the variability is great, a given observation is not as reliable as it would be if the variability were small. Also, we have seen that the variability in the population is reflected in variability in the sample mean. Indeed, the variability in a given population played an important role when we constructed confidence intervals and tested statistical hypotheses concerning the expected value.

Population variability can sometimes be crudely indicated by the range of possible values—the largest possible value minus the smallest—but in many cases this range is infinite. More common is the population variance, σ^2, whose appropriateness for describing variability was discussed in Chapter 3, page 52. In this chapter we shall consider the estimation of σ^2 and the testing of hypotheses concerning σ^2.

In Chapter 7 the sample variance and sample range were introduced as measures of dispersion of the numbers making up the sample. Assuming that dispersion of the observations in a sample reflects a variability in the population from which the sample is taken, it is natural to use the sample variance and sample range as estimates of population variability.

The variance and range of a sample are statistics—random variables computed from the observations of a random sample. As with all statistics, these *vary* from sample to sample and consequently cannot accurately give a *fixed* population parameter. However, we can at least know the pattern of variation of each statistic; this is the information contained in the probability distribution of the statistic. In order to estimate σ^2 and test hypotheses on σ^2, we must know the *distributions* of the statistics to be used in the estimation and testing.

10.1 Properties of the Sample Variance

Consider a population represented by a random variable X with expected value μ and variance σ^2. A random sample of size n is drawn, $X_1, \ldots, X_n$, and the sum of squared deviations about the sample mean is computed:

$$(n - 1)s_x^2 = \sum_{i=1}^{n} (X_i - \bar{X})^2.$$

We have used capital X's to indicate that we are thinking of this as a random variable, in terms of all possible outcomes and a probability distribution. This statistic has an expected value which we now calculate.

According to the "parallel axis theorem" (page 52), taking $a = \mu$, we have

$$(n - 1)s_x^2 = \sum_{i=1}^{n} (X_i - \mu)^2 - n(\bar{X} - \mu)^2.$$

Taking the expected value on both sides, we obtain

$$(n - 1)E(s_x^2) = \sum_{i=1}^{n} E[(X_i - \mu)^2] - nE[(\bar{X} - \mu)^2]$$

$$= \sum_{i=1}^{n} \sigma^2 - n\frac{\sigma^2}{n} = (n - 1)\sigma^2,$$

and hence

$$E(s_x^2) = \sigma^2.$$

The statistic s_x^2 thus has a probability distribution "centered" at σ^2. Had we used the division constant n in place of $n - 1$ in defining the sample variance, we should have found

$$E\left(\frac{1}{n} \sum (X_i - \bar{X})^2\right) = E\left(\frac{n-1}{n} s_x^2\right) = \frac{n-1}{n} \sigma^2.$$

A statistic whose expectation is different from the population parameter being estimated is called a "biased" estimate of that parameter. Thus, the quantity $\tilde{s}_x^2 = (1/n)\Sigma(X_i - \bar{X})^2$ is biased as an estimate of σ^2. Contrary to the unpleasant implications of the word "bias," a biased estimate is not necessarily bad. Indeed, in the case of a normal population, the estimate $\tilde{s}_x^2$ is actually slightly better than s_x^2 when they are compared on the basis of their mean square deviations about σ^2. For large samples these estimates are practically equal—the biased form $\tilde{s}_x{}^2$ is "asymptotically unbiased." We should certainly want bias to disappear in large samples; and if an estimate should be biased even for large samples, it is proper and customary to remove the bias with a correction factor.

The question of bias is really not important in assessing the value of an estimator. What counts is whether a single value of the estimator is apt to come anywhere near the parameter being estimated. Bias can be small simply because of cancellation of positive and negative deviations of the estimator from the parameter, without the deviations' being small in magnitude.

Whether successive values of a random variable are consistently near their expectation is indicated by the size of the variance. Therefore, we are interested in the variance of the statistic $s_x{}^2$. A calculation somewhat more involved (but no more profound) than that of the expectation of $s_x{}^2$ shows that whenever the population fourth moment exists,

$$\operatorname{var} s_x{}^2 = \frac{n}{n-1} \left(\frac{E[(X - \mu)^4] - \sigma^4}{n - 1} \right) + o\left(\frac{1}{n}\right),$$

where $o(1/n)$ denotes terms which are negligible in comparison with the first term for large values of n. We see that as n becomes infinite, the variance of $s_x{}^2$ tends to zero, and we have a situation similar to that which obtained in the case of estimating μ by $\bar{X}$. The sample variance approaches the population variance "in probability," in the terminology introduced in Section 9.1.

In the particular case of a *normal* population, the higher population moments can be expressed in terms of σ^2, and the above expression for variance reduces to the following:

$$\operatorname{var} s_x{}^2 = \frac{2\sigma^4}{n - 1} \qquad \text{(normal population)}.$$

The actual probability distribution of the statistic $s_x{}^2$ is not simple for small samples and depends essentially on the population distribution. It is discussed in a subsequent section for the case of a normal population. The asymptotic distribution, however, is simple; it is possible to show, using the Central Limit Theorem, that $s_x{}^2$ (and, in fact, any sample moment about the sample mean) is asymptotically *normally* distributed. Although this is true, we point out that the Central Limit Theorem cannot be applied to the sum in $s_x{}^2$ directly, since all of the terms in the sum involve $\bar{X}$ and are not independent random variables.

10.2 Confidence Intervals Based on s_x^2.

The principle used in constructing confidence intervals for the population mean can be employed here to yield confidence intervals for σ^2. The technique is to write out a probability statement concerning the statistic being used, in terms of the unknown parameter being estimated, and involving no other unknown parameter, if this is possible. The inequality whose probability is given is then "inverted" or "solved" to yield an inequality with the unknown parameter in the middle and functions of the statistic on either side. The latter become the confidence limits.

This procedure is possible when we know the distribution of a statistic; and, according to the discussion of the previous section, the large sample distribution of s_x^2 is known to be normal. The small sample distribution is also known when the population is normal, and we also consider the construction of a confidence interval in this case.

10.2.1 Large Sample Case

In view of the large sample properties of s_x^2 discussed above, we can write

$$P\left(|s_x^2 - \sigma^2| < k_\gamma \sqrt{\frac{\mu_4 - \sigma^4}{n}}\right) \doteq \gamma, \qquad \text{(large } n)$$

where μ_4 is the population fourth moment about the mean. The relation between the specified confidence coefficient γ and the multiplier k_γ is (as in Chapter 9) provided by the normal distribution (see Table Ib, page 255).

Clearly, if the population fourth moment about μ, called μ_4 above, is known, the inequality can be solved for σ^2 to yield a confidence interval. If this fourth moment is not known, an approximate confidence interval could be obtained by replacing it by the fourth sample moment about $\bar{X}$, but the accuracy sacrificed thereby is not easily determined.

Let us consider, rather, that the population is normal, in which case the variance of s_x^2 is $2\sigma^4/(n-1)$. Then we can write

$$P\left(|s_x^2 - \sigma^2| < k_\gamma \sqrt{\frac{2\sigma^4}{n-1}}\right) \doteq \gamma.$$

Solving the inequality in parentheses, which is linear in σ^2, we find the equivalent inequality:

$$\frac{s_x^2}{1 + k_\gamma \sqrt{2/(n-1)}} < \sigma^2 < \frac{s_x^2}{1 - k_\gamma \sqrt{2/(n-1)}}.$$

The extreme members of this inequality are the confidence limits for σ^2 corresponding to the confidence coefficient γ.

Example 10-a

The 200 observations in Table 7.1 were found to have a variance $s_x{}^2 = 3.30$. An approximate 99 per cent confidence interval for σ^2, assuming the population to be normal, has the limits

$$\frac{3.30}{1 \pm 2.57 \sqrt{\dfrac{2}{199}}}.$$

The interval is then $2.62 < \sigma^2 < 4.44$.

10.2.2 Small Sample Case

When the underlying random variable is *normally* distributed, the variance $s_x{}^2$ of the observations in a random sample has a probability distribution simply related to the chi-square distribution, whose density is given in Table 4.1 (page 83) and whose percentiles are tabulated in Table II, page 256. It can be shown that the quantity

$$\frac{(n-1)s_x{}^2}{\sigma^2} = \sum_{i=1}^{n} \left(\frac{X_i - \bar{X}}{\sigma} \right)^2$$

is distributed as the sum of squares of $n - 1$ independent, standard normal variables—that is, it has (by definition of "chi-square") the chi-square distribution with $n - 1$ degrees of freedom.

(If we had used μ in place of $\bar{X}$ in computing the sum of squared deviations, each term in the sum would have been the square of a standard normal variable, and the sum would have had the chi-square distribution with n degrees of freedom. We say that "one degree of freedom has been used up in estimating μ.")

Consider a sample of size n, and let $\chi^2{}_{.05}$ and $\chi^2{}_{.95}$ denote the fifth and ninety-fifth percentiles, respectively, of the chi-square distribution with $n - 1$ degrees of freedom, as shown in Figure 10–1. By definition of these percentiles, we have

$$P\left\{ \chi^2{}_{.05} < \frac{(n-1)s_x{}^2}{\sigma^2} < \chi^2{}_{.95} \right\} = .90.$$

The inequality here is easily solved for σ^2, and the resulting equivalent inequality has the same probability:

$$P\left\{\frac{(n-1)s_x{}^2}{\chi^2{}_{.95}} < \sigma^2 < \frac{(n-1)s_x{}^2}{\chi^2{}_{.05}}\right\} = .90.$$

This defines a 90 per cent confidence interval for σ^2.

Examination of a table of values of the chi-square distribution function shows that percentiles are given only up to 30 degrees of freedom. This is because the chi-square distribution is asymptotically normal. The mean

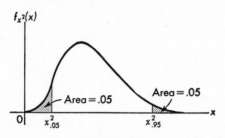

Figure 10–1

and variance of this asymptotic distribution, denoting the number of degrees of freedom by ν, are ν and 2ν, respectively. The standardized variable

$$Z = \frac{\chi^2 - \nu}{\sqrt{2\nu}}$$

is therefore approximately the standard normal variable. Percentiles of χ^2 can then be obtained from those of Z as follows. For any given probability p,

$$p = P(\chi^2 < \chi_p{}^2) = P\left\{\frac{\chi^2 - \nu}{\sqrt{2\nu}} < \frac{\chi_p{}^2 - \nu}{\sqrt{2\nu}}\right\}$$
$$= P\left\{Z < \frac{\chi_p{}^2 - \nu}{\sqrt{2\nu}}\right\},$$

and hence, if z_p denotes the $100p$ percentile of the standard normal distribution,

$$z_p \doteq \frac{\chi_p{}^2 - \nu}{\sqrt{2\nu}},$$

or, upon solving for $\chi_p{}^2$:

$$\chi_p{}^2 \doteq \sqrt{2\nu}z_p + \nu.$$

Now, it happens that an approximation which is somewhat better for the smaller values of ν (and just as good for the larger ones) is obtained by using the variable

$$\sqrt{2\chi^2} - \sqrt{2\nu - 1},$$

which is also asymptotically a standard normal variable. Proceeding as above, we obtain the approximation:

$$\chi_p^2 \doteq \frac{1}{2}(z_p + \sqrt{2\nu - 1})^2.$$

Example 10–b

For $\nu = 30$, and $p = .95$, we find from Table I, page 253, that $z_{.95} = 1.65$, and using the last formula above,

$$\chi^2_{.95} \doteq \frac{1}{2}(1.65 + \sqrt{59})^2 = 43.5.$$

The earlier approximation gives 41.5, and the actual value (from Table II, page 256) is 43.8.

Example 10–c

Let us again use the data in Table 7.1, as in Example 10–a above, to construct a 99 per cent confidence interval for σ^2, assuming a normal population.

With $\nu = n - 1 = 199$, the .5 and 99.5 percentiles of σ^2 are found (as described above) to be 150 and 253. The confidence interval is then

$$\frac{199 \times 3.30}{253} < \sigma^2 < \frac{199 \times 3.30}{150},$$

or from 2.59 to 4.38. This interval is very nearly that obtained in Example 10–a, assuming s_x^2 to be normal.

For $\nu \leq 30$, of course, Table II gives the percentiles. It should be noticed that the smaller the sample size, the wider the confidence interval, as intuition would suggest.

Example 10–d

Suppose that $s_x^2 = 3.30$ in a sample of size twenty. The percentiles corresponding to a confidence coefficient of .98 (at $\nu = 19$) are 7.63 and 36.2, so that a 98 per cent confidence interval is

$$\frac{19 \times 3.30}{36.2} < \sigma^2 < \frac{19 \times 3.30}{7.63},$$

or $1.73 < \sigma^2 < 8.23$. This is considerably wider than that based on a sample of 200, in the preceding example, even though the confidence coefficient is smaller.

10.2.3 Estimating a Variance Common to Several Populations

It is sometimes desired to estimate the variability in a certain measuring process on the basis of several samples. However, the expectations of the distributions from which the samples have been drawn may be quite different.

To be specific, let us assume k *normal* populations, $X_1, \ldots, X_k$, and that we have a sample from each:

$$X_{11}, X_{12}, \ldots, X_{1n_1} \quad \text{from } X_1$$
$$X_{21}, X_{22}, \ldots, X_{2n_2} \quad \text{from } X_2$$
$$\cdots \cdots \cdots \cdots \cdots \cdots \cdots \cdots$$
$$X_{k1}, X_{k2}, \ldots, X_{kn_k} \quad \text{from } X_k.$$

We assume further that the variances of these populations are the same, σ^2, but that the expectations (or "levels") may be different. Since the levels may be different, the "sample variance" obtained after pooling all the data together would not necessarily measure the quantity of interest. Indeed, this collection of all of the data need not even be a sample from *a* population.

Each sample provides, in its s_x^2, an estimate of σ^2. However, the reliability of each such estimate is related to the size n_i of the sample used; and it would be desirable to pool the information to make use of the fact that we really have $n_1 + n_2 + \cdots + n_k$ pieces of data, with possibly that much greater reliability. The natural method of pooling the data would be to average the sample variances; this works if the samples are all of the same size. When such is not the case, the following average, in which the terms are weighted according to sample sizes, is found appropriate:

$$s^2 = \frac{\displaystyle\sum_1^k \sum_1^{n_i} (x_{ij} - \bar{x}_i)^2}{n - k} = \frac{\displaystyle\sum_{i=1}^k (n_i - 1)s_i^2}{n - k}$$

Here n denotes the sum $n_1 + \cdots + n_k$, and $\bar{x}_i$ and s_i^2 are the mean and variance, respectively, of the ith sample.

Because $E[(n_i - 1)s_i^2] = (n_i - 1)\sigma^2$, it follows that

$$E(s^2) = \frac{1}{n - k} \sum_1^k (n_i - 1)\sigma^2 = \sigma^2.$$

This says that s^2 is an unbiased estimate of σ^2. Further, since each quantity $(n_i - 1)s_i^2/\sigma^2$ has the chi-square distribution, with $n_i - 1$ degrees of freedom, their sum $(n - k)s^2/\sigma^2$ has the chi-square distribution with $\Sigma(n_i - 1) = n - k$ degrees of freedom. This is a consequence of the fact that the chi-square property is additive over independent summands, as mentioned in Chapter 5.

Example 10–e

Suppose that the following three sets of observations are obtained from three normal populations whose variances are known to be equal.

Sample	Mean	$(x_{ij} - \bar{x}_i)^2$
11, 9, 13, 11	11	8
25, 28, 31, 27, 30, 33	29	42
19, 23, 19, 21, 20	20.4	11.2

Total sum of
squared deviations: 61.2

The point estimate of σ^2 is then

$$s^2 = \frac{61.2}{15 - 3} \doteq 5.1.$$

An interval estimate is given by the following 90 per cent confidence interval for σ^2:

$$\frac{61.2}{\chi^2_{.95}} < \sigma^2 < \frac{61.2}{\chi^2_{.05}}$$

or

$$2.91 < \sigma^2 < 11.7.$$

10.3 Hypotheses About the Variance of a Normal Population

As in testing hypotheses concerning the expectation, we consider one-sided and two-sided tests. A one-sided test of the type defined by the critical region $C: s_x^2 > K$ would be appropriate for testing, say,

$$H_0: X \text{ is normal with } \sigma^2 \leq \sigma_0^2,$$
$$H_1: X \text{ is normal with } \sigma^2 > \sigma_0^2.$$

The operating characteristic of this test is obtainable from the chi-square distribution as follows:

$$OC \text{ function} = P_{\sigma^2}(s_x^2 < K) = P_{\sigma^2}\left\{ \frac{(n-1)s_x^2}{\sigma^2} < \frac{(n-1)K}{\sigma^2} \right\}$$
$$= F_{\chi^2}\left(\frac{(n-1)K}{\sigma^2} \right)$$

Example 10–f

Consider a sample of size twenty, and the rejection region $s_x^2 > 5$. The operating characteristic function is then

$$OC \text{ function} = F_{\chi^2}\left(\frac{95}{\sigma^2} \right),$$

which is shown in Figure 10–2. From this graph one can read, for instance, the probability that H_0 is rejected when actually $\sigma^2 = 8$:

$$P_{\sigma^2=8}(s_x^2 > 5) \doteq .86.$$

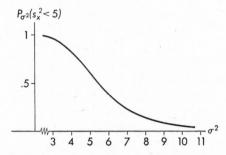

Figure 10–2. Operating Characteristic for Example 10–f

For testing a particular value σ_0^2 against the alternative $\sigma^2 \neq \sigma_0^2$, a two-sided test is appropriate. The rule of accepting σ_0^2 if it is contained in the (two-sided) confidence interval for σ^2, constructed from a given sample, is a two-sided test.

Example 10–g

Suppose that it is desired to test $\sigma^2 = 4$ at the 10 per cent significance level, against the alternative $\sigma^2 \neq 4$, on the basis of a sample of size twenty-five. The 90 per cent confidence interval for σ^2 is given by the following inequality:

$$\frac{24s_x^2}{36.4} < \sigma^2 < \frac{24s_x^2}{13.8}.$$

If the variance of a certain sample turns out to be $s_x^2 = 6$, this interval is $3.96 < \sigma^2 < 10.4$, which includes $\sigma^2 = 4$. Thus, $H_0(\sigma^2 = 4)$ would be accepted. The operating characteristic for the test is expressible in terms of the chi-square distribution:

$$
\begin{aligned}
OC \text{ function} &= P_{\sigma^2}(H_0 \text{ is accepted}) \\
&= P_{\sigma^2}(\text{the confidence interval includes } 4) \\
&= P_{\sigma^2}\left(\frac{24}{36.4} < \frac{4}{s_x^2} < \frac{24}{13.8}\right) \\
&= P_{\sigma^2}\left(13.8\,\frac{4}{\sigma^2} < \frac{24s_x^2}{\sigma^2} < 36.4\,\frac{4}{\sigma^2}\right) \\
&= F_{\chi^2}\left(\frac{146}{\sigma^2}\right) - F_{\chi^2}\left(\frac{55.2}{\sigma^2}\right).
\end{aligned}
$$

Problems

10–1. Outside diameters of seventy "identical" parts are given in the frequency table as follows.

Diameter (Inches)	Frequency
1.0950	2
1.0945	2
1.0940	9
1.0935	15
1.0930	26
1.0925	10
1.0920	6

Assuming a normal population, construct a 90 per cent confidence interval for σ^2 using both the chi-square interval on page 192 and the normal approximation interval on page 190.

10–2. Using the data of the preceding problem, test $\sigma^2 = 25 \times 10^{-8}$ inches^2 against $\sigma^2 > 25 \times 10^{-8}$ inches^2 at the 20 per cent significance level.

10–3. Sketch the OC function for the test whose critical region is given by $s_x^2 > 7$, given that the sample size is thirty.

10–4. The tensile strength (in 1000 pounds per inches^2) of coupons of a certain metal is assumed normally distributed. Test the hypothesis $H_0: \sigma^2 = 2$ against H_1: $\sigma^2 > 2$ at the 20 per cent level, given the five observations 56, 58, 54, 57, 54. Would you reach the same conclusion at the 5 per cent level? What is an 80 per cent confidence interval for σ^2 using the given data? Determine a 95 per cent interval estimate of mean tensile strength.

10–5. Triplicate ash determinations were made by several control laboratories. Moistures were reported so that results could be adjusted to a common basis.

Laboratory	Ash Determination	Laboratory	Ash Determination
I	.393 .390 .391	VI	.415 .415 .409
II	.402 .407 .407	VII	.413 .413 .413
III	.412 .408 .411	VIII	.413 .413 .416
IV	.378 .383 .380	IX	.404 .394 .404
V	.404 .400 .403	X	.412 .409 .409

There is reason to believe that the laboratories are equally reliable in their reporting even though they might not agree on the level of ash content. Consider the data given in the table at the bottom of page 197 and determine a pooled estimate of the common variance together with a 90 per cent confidence interval.

10.4 Range of a Sample from a Normal Population

The distribution of the sample range is not simple in any case. In the case of a normal population, however, the distribution of the range has been extensively studied and tabulated. In particular, one finds tabulated the distribution of what is called the standardized range W:

$$W = \frac{R}{\sigma}.$$

(This use of the word "standardized" is somewhat different from our previous use.) This modified range has the properties

$$E(W) = \frac{1}{\sigma} E(R), \quad \text{and} \quad \text{var } W = \frac{1}{\sigma^2} \text{var } R.$$

Rearranging these slightly we have

$$E(R) = a_n\sigma, \quad \text{and} \quad \text{var } R = b_n^2\sigma^2,$$

where a_n and b_n^2 are the expected value and variance of the standardized range W, respectively, n being the sample size. The quantities a_n and b_n are given in Table V, page 260, as are values of the distribution function of W.

10.4.1 The Small Sample Case

A confidence interval for σ can be constructed as follows. Let us denote by w_p the $100p$ percentile of the distribution of W. We have then, for instance,

$$P(\sigma w_{.025} < R < \sigma w_{.975}) = .95.$$

Solving the inequality for σ yields the confidence limits corresponding to the 5 per cent level:

$$\left(\frac{R}{w_{.975}}, \frac{R}{w_{.025}} \right).$$

Example 10–h

Taking the first twenty observations in Table 7.1, we find the range to be 7. Using this, together with the percentiles $w_{.025}$ and $w_{.975}$ (assuming, of course, that the population is normal!) we have the 95 per cent confidence interval

$$\frac{7}{5.30} < \sigma < \frac{7}{2.45}$$

or
$$1.32 < \sigma < 2.86.$$

The point estimate of σ is given by R/a_n, which in this case is $7/3.74 = 1.87$.

For purposes of comparison, we mention that the variance of the same data is 3.82, giving a 95 per cent confidence interval of

$$2.21 < \sigma^2 < 8.15.$$

Because as the sample size increases, the sample range becomes less and less efficient in comparison with the sample variance as an estimate of population variability, the sample range is not ordinarily used for the purpose when the sample is bigger than, say, fifteen to twenty. However, in the case of quite large samples, another approach based on a computation of ranges is often used. This will be discussed in the next section.

Hypotheses concerning σ^2 (for a normal population) can of course be tested using the sample range. The one-sided critical region $R > K$ would again be appropriate for cases in which the values of σ^2 in H_0 are to the left of those in H_1. The operating characteristic can be determined from the distribution of W, the standardized range introduced above:

$$OC \text{ function} = P_\sigma(\text{accept } H_0) = P_\sigma(R < K)$$
$$= P_\sigma\left(\frac{R}{\sigma} < \frac{K}{\sigma}\right) = F_W\left(\frac{K}{\sigma}\right).$$

Example 10–i

The operating characteristic for the test $R > 6$ is plotted as a function of σ^2 in Figure 10–3, corresponding to a sample size of ten. Plotted on the same coordinate

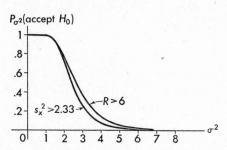

Figure 10–3. Operating Characteristics for Example 10–i

axes is the operating characteristic for the test $s_x^2 > 2.33$. The probability of accepting H_0 when $\sigma^2 = 1.63$ is .90 for both tests, but it will be observed that the OC curve for the test based on sample variance is somewhat lower ("more powerful") for larger values of σ^2.

10.4.2 Average of Several Ranges

Suppose we have a rather large sample and break it up into k samples of n in each (ignoring the leftovers, if any). Let the ranges be denoted by $R_1, R_2, \ldots, R_k$, and define

$$\bar{R} = \frac{1}{k} (R_1 + \cdots + R_k).$$

This quantity, even though more complicated than R, is still easier to compute than the sample variance and turns out to do a rather good job of estimating the population standard deviation—better than R, but not quite so good as s_x^2. Of course, both R and $\bar{R}$ must be corrected for bias.

We work again with a normal population. The mean and variance of R are simple to compute in terms of the mean and variance of the standardized range, a_n and b_n^2, introduced earlier:

$$E(\bar{R}) = \frac{1}{k} \sum_1^k E(R_j) = a_n \sigma,$$

$$\text{var } \bar{R} = \frac{1}{k^2} \sum_1^k \text{var } R_j = \frac{b_n^2}{k} \sigma^2.$$

Note that the sample size to use in determining the a and b^2 is n, not nk. These quantities are not enough to compute probabilities or determine confidence intervals, but we notice that $\bar{R}$ is a sum of independent, identically distributed random variables and is therefore asymptotically normally distributed! Exploiting this fact, we can construct confidence intervals in the usual fashion, the general form being as follows:

$$P \left\{ \frac{\bar{R}}{a_n + z_2(b_n/\sqrt{k})} < \sigma < \frac{\bar{R}}{a_n + z_1(b_n/\sqrt{k})} \right\} = P(z_1 < z < z_2) = 1 - \alpha,$$

where z is the standard normal variable, and z_1 and z_2 are percentiles, usually $z_{\alpha/2}$ and $z_{1-\alpha/2}$, chosen so that this probability equals the desired confidence coefficient, $1 - \alpha$.

Example 10–j

Taking the data of Table 7.1 once more, we find that dividing it into forty groups of five ($k = 40$, $n = 5$) yields an $\bar{R}$ of 3.06. The proper divisor for $n = 5$ is found from the table to be 2.326, giving 1.32 as the estimate of σ. The confidence interval corresponding to a 95 per cent confidence coefficient using $z_{.025}$ and $z_{.975}$ is

$$1.05 < \sigma < 1.25.$$

Dividing the same data into twenty-five groups of eight, we find an $\bar{R}$ of 3.936, and a corresponding estimate 1.38 of σ, with the confidence interval (95 per cent):

$$1.09 < \sigma < 1.28.$$

The above method of estimating σ is quite appropriate when data comes naturally in k packets of n each, the packets being samples from populations with the same σ but with possibly different levels. This kind of problem was treated earlier using a pooled variance, and the $\bar{R}$ computation may be thought of as pooling the ranges.

10.4.3 Control Chart for the Sample Range

A control chart for the sample range is often kept in conjunction with the sample mean control chart, discussed in Section 9.6. Although a change in the variability of a random quantity resulting from a production process is detected ultimately in the $\bar{X}$ chart, the combination of $\bar{X}$ and R charts is more effective.

Example 10–k

As in Example 9–l, we assume that a system is known to have been in control, with a normal distribution, and $\mu = 0, \sigma = 1.715$. The control chart constants are computed as follows:

R Control Chart

Center Line	$E(R) = d_2\sigma =$	$2.326 \times 1.715 = 3.99$
Upper Control Limit	$D_2\sigma =$	$4.918 \times 1.715 = 8.43$
Lower Control Limit	$D_1\sigma =$	$0 \times 1.715 = 0$

The constant d_2 is just $E(R/\sigma)$ as discussed in Section 10.41; it is tabulated in Table VI, page 260. The constants D_1 and D_2 involve ingredients, for the range, corresponding to the 3 used for $\bar{X}$; they are also given in Table VI.

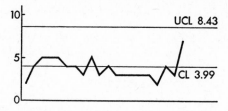

Figure 10–4.   Control Chart for Example 10–k

The control chart for R shown in Figure 10–4 is the one plotted from the same sample as was used in Example 9–l. Notice that the points remain within the control limits.

In the following example, we show how a control chart may be used in checking randomness, or control, in a situation in which it is not known whether the process in question is under control. If the parameters are not known, we cannot construct control lines as previously, but must get them from the data, after enough is on hand for the results to be approximately meaningful. We do not use the control chart to go after assignable causes as they come up, inasmuch as the control limits are put in after the data is obtained.

Example 10–1

We again use twenty samples of five from population A, but do not assume that the population characteristics are known. In fact, we do not know whether a

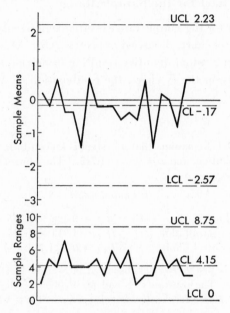

Figure 10–5. $\bar{X}$ anb R Control Charts for Example 10–1

population exists. We have then twenty means and twenty ranges. The "grand average" of the sample means is the over-all average, denoted by $\bar{\bar{X}}$:

$$\bar{\bar{X}} = \frac{1}{20} \Sigma \bar{X}_i,$$

where $\bar{X}_i$ is the mean of the ith sample. This over-all average is used as a center line on the $\bar{X}$ chart. The average sample range, $\bar{R}$, is used as a measure of variability. The computations of center lines and control limits are as follows:

$\bar{X}$ Control Chart

Center Line: $\bar{\bar{X}}$ $= -.17$
Upper Control Limit: $\bar{\bar{X}} + A_2\bar{R} = -.17 + .577 \times 4.15 = 2.23$
Lower Control Limit: $\bar{\bar{X}} - A_2\bar{R} = -.17 - .577 \times 4.15 = -2.57$

R Control Chart

Center Line: $\bar{R}$ = 4.15
Upper Control Limit: $D_4\bar{R}$ = 2.115 × 4.15 = 8.75
Lower Control Limit: $D_3\bar{R}$ = 0 × 4.15 = 0

The twenty samples shown on the chart give no reason to believe that there are "assignable causes" to be rooted out. However, if the first twenty samples indicated the process to be out of control, an attempt should be made to free the process of the assignable causes. Then new data can be obtained and revised control limits determined. The values of $\bar{X}$ and R are plotted in the control charts in Figure 10–5.

Problems

10–6. Estimate σ using $\bar{R}$, based on the data given in Problem 10–5.

10–7. Refer to the data given in Problem 10–5. Estimate the population standard deviation common to the different laboratories using $\bar{R}$. Determine the 90 per cent confidence limits for the standard deviation.

10–8. While determining the flow characteristics of oil through an aircraft valve, the inlet oil temperature is measured in degrees Fahrenheit. Consider the following nine readings: 99, 93, 99, 97, 90, 96, 93, 88, 89. Eestimate the population standard deviation using the sample range. Compare this value with the sample standard deviation. Construct 90 per cent confidence limits for σ (a) based on R and (b) based on the sample variance. (Assume a normal population.)

10–9. Determine the probability that σ^2 = 6 is accepted when actually σ^2 = 12, if the test used is to reject σ^2 = 6 when $\bar{R}$ > 8.5, using twenty samples of size seven. Determine also α for this test.

10–10. A process is known to have been in statistical control with expected value μ = 15 and standard deviation σ = 3.5. Samples of size eight each are taken in order to test for continued statistical control. What are the center line and the control limits for the R control chart?

10–11. Consider the following six subgroups of four observations each taken in sequence. The data were obtained by measuring the power consumption of a unit and are given in kilowatt hours per 24 hours. No standards have been determined for the process.

3.79	3.53	3.59	3.83	3.75	3.73
3.53	3.71	3.35	3.84	3.90	3.82
3.85	3.89	3.69	3.59	3.67	3.75
3.57	3.85	3.77	3.49	3.63	3.65

(a) Estimate the expected value of the power consumption.
(b) Determine the control limits for the $\bar{X}$ control chart.
(c) Determine the control limits for the R control chart.
(d) Remark about the statistical control from the above data.
(e) Test randomness using a run test.

11/Comparison of Two Populations

11.0 Introduction

The following questions indicate a type of problem one often meets: Does a population of smokers have greater susceptibility of a given type than a population of nonsmokers? Does fertilizer A work better than fertilizer B on the average? Does a certain new piece of equipment produce bar stock with greater variation in dimensions than the old? Are men better drivers than women? Do the batches of peanut butter from one manufacturer exhibit generally more oil separation than those of another? Does one method of measuring the concentration of a chemical have more inherent variability than another?

These problems involve comparing two populations, one action being appropriate if they can be considered the same population, and another action appropriate if there is some difference, or if some change has taken place from one population to the other.

Interest may center on the difference in location or centering, as measured by the expected value or median, or in variability or repeatability, as measured by the variance. There may be interest in other differences, of course, but level and variability changes are important in most problems of this type.

We shall consider in this chapter (1), a variant of the Kolmogorov-Smirnov test, for testing deviations between two population distribution functions; (2) tests for a difference in population locations; and (3) a test for a difference in population variabilities.

11.1 Comparing Two Population Distribution Functions

Consider the independent random variables X_1 and X_2, with associated distribution functions $F_1(x)$ and $F_2(x)$, and assume that we have random

204

samples from each, n_1 observations from X_1 and n_2 observations from X_2. Denote the sample distribution functions (see Section 8.6.2) by $F_{n_1}(x)$ and $F_{n_2}(x)$, respectively.

It would be expected that because of random sampling fluctuations, the sample distributions would differ, even if the population distributions were identical. On the other hand, too great a discrepancy might be taken as grounds for rejecting the hypothesis that the populations are identical.

We consider, then, the statistic D defined as

$$D = \max_{-\infty < x < \infty} |F_{n_2}(x) - F_{n_1}(x)|.$$

The Smirnov test consists in rejecting the hypothesis that $F_1(x) = F_2(x)$ if for a given pair of samples, the value of D turns out to exceed a specified critical value (depending on the desired significance level of the test). Table VIIb, page 262, gives critical values corresponding to various levels of significance (i.e., values of α).

Strictly, the population distributions should be of the continuous type, but again (as in Section 8.6.2) using the test in the discrete case does not increase the effective significance level of the test. In recording data from a continuous population (and in regrouping the data, if this is done) a person is forced to "discretize" or round off; essentially, then, he tests class interval probabilities, which is a discrete problem.

Example 11–a

Consider the two sets of data given in the frequency tabulations below. The maximum absolute difference in cumulative relative frequencies is .1, and the 5 per

X_i	Frequencies		Cumulative Frequencies	
	Sample 1	Sample 2	Sample 1	Sample 2
0	5	6	5	6
1	9	2	14	8
2	4	5	18	13
3	5	7	23	20
4	7	8	30	28
5	2	4	32	32
6	8	4	40	36
7	4	9	44	45
8	9	6	53	51
9	7	9	60	60
	$n_1 = 60$	$n_2 = 60$		

cent critical value of D from Table VIIb is about .25. Thus, we accept the hypothesis that $F_1(x) = F_2(x)$ at the 5 per cent significance level.

Problems

11-1. Construct frequency tabulations for each of the two sets of 100 numbers obtained by dividing the data of Table 7.1 (page 116) horizontally at the middle of the table. Apply the Smirnov test discussed in the above section to test the hypothesis that the two samples of 100 came from the same population.

11-2. Use the Smirnov test to compare the populations from which the data of Problems 7-1(a) and 7-1(b) were obtained.

11.2 Comparison of Locations

Consider again the independent random variables X_1 and X_2, which we now wish to compare with respect to their location parameters. The comparison is to be based on a random sample of size n_1 from X_1 and a random sample of size n_2 from X_2.

If the location parameter is the expected value, the null hypothesis most commonly considered is that $\mu_1 = \mu_2$, where $\mu_1 = E(X_1)$ and $\mu_2 = E(X_2)$. The most sweeping alternative is simply that $\mu_1 \neq \mu_2$, although we might be interested, in some instances, in one-sided alternatives such as $\mu_1 < \mu_2$. The type of test to use, of course, depends on the alternatives admitted.

In addition to the testing problem, one might also wish to estimate the discrepancy between the populations, in terms of $\mu_2 - \mu_1$, for instance. In the first section below we consider the problems of estimating this difference, and of testing hypotheses about it, using the sample means as statistics. Subsequent sections give some "nonparametric" tests for the hypothesis of no difference in population locations.

11.2.1 Tests Using Sample Means

Let $\bar{X}_1$ and $\bar{X}_2$ be means of samples of sizes n_1 and n_2 from X_1 and X_2, respectively. Recalling our experience in estimating an expectation using the sample mean, it is reasonable that we should use $\bar{X}_2 - \bar{X}_1$ in attacking the difference $\mu_2 - \mu_1 = \Delta\mu$. Let us consider the sampling distribution of the difference in sample means, $\bar{X}_2 - \bar{X}_1 = \Delta\bar{X}$.

The mean and variance of $\Delta\bar{X}$ are easily computed. The mean is

$$E(\Delta\bar{X}) = E(\bar{X}_2) - E(\bar{X}_1) = \mu_2 - \mu_1 = \Delta\mu.$$

We see, then, that in the language introduced in the preceding chapter, $\Delta\bar{X}$ is unbiased in its estimation of $\Delta\mu$. The variance of $\Delta\bar{X}$ is easily computed using the additive property of the variance operation over sums of independent variables; it is perfectly natural and useful to assume that the observations from X_1 and those from X_2 are all mutually independent, so that $\bar{X}_1$ and $\bar{X}_2$ are independent.   We find, then,

$$\text{var } (\Delta\bar{X}) = \text{var } \bar{X}_2 + \text{var } (-\bar{X}_1) = \frac{{\sigma_2}^2}{n_2} + \frac{{\sigma_1}^2}{n_1}.$$

(The reader should convince himself intuitively that the plus sign is correct, rather than a minus sign.)

As to the probability distribution of $\Delta\bar{X}$, we have two important cases—the large sample distribution and the small sample distribution when the populations are normal.

When n_1 and n_2 are large, the distributions of $\bar{X}_1$ and $\bar{X}_2$ are (by the Central Limit Theorem, page 96) approximately normal; and, of course, $-\bar{X}_2$ is then also approximately normally distributed.   Hence, the difference $\Delta\bar{X}$, which may be written as the sum $\bar{X}_2 + (-\bar{X}_1)$ of two nearly normal variables, is nearly normal.   The parameters of the distribution are those given above for $\Delta\bar{X}$ which hold in general.

The word "approximately" can be omitted from the discussion above if the underlying populations are themselves normal; in this case the sample means and their difference are *exactly* normal, even for small samples.

Example 11–b

Consider a shearing pin with a hexagonal head.   A metallurgist wishes to compare the Rockwell hardness readings taken on the shank of the pin with those on the hexagonal head.   He finds that the average and standard deviation of fifty readings on the shank are 41.63 and 1.8, respectively.   Also, the average and standard deviation of fifty readings taken on the head are 40.67 and 2.0, respectively. Assuming that hardness readings are normally distributed, test the difference of the means.

We are testing the hypothesis $H_0: \mu_1 = \mu_2$, against the alternative hypothesis $H_1: \mu_1 \neq \mu_2$.   The test statistic to be used is

$$Z = \frac{\bar{X}_2 - \bar{X}_1}{\sqrt{\dfrac{{\sigma_1}^2}{n_1} + \dfrac{{\sigma_2}^2}{n_2}}},$$

which is a standard normal variable if H_0 is correct.   The critical region corresponding to a level of 5 per cent is $|Z| > 1.96$.   Actually, we do not know the population variances; but assuming the samples are sufficiently large that we get useful results by approximating the population variances by sample variances, we can compute the value of Z for the particular samples given, obtaining $z = 2.51$. Since this exceeds 1.96, we reject H_0.

Example 11-c

To determine whether a fertilizer is effective, 100 plants out of 1000 are left unfertilized. Of the 100, 53 are found to have satisfactory growth, and out of the 900 fertilized plants, 783 are found satisfactory. Is the fertilizer effective?

We assume that the word effective implies effectively better and that we wish to test, therefore, the hypotheses H_0: $p_1 \leq p_2$ and H_1: $p_1 > p_2$, where p_1 and p_2 are the probabilities of satisfactory growth, with and without fertilizer, respectively. We use the test statistic

$$Z = \frac{\bar{X}_1 - \bar{X}_2}{\sqrt{\frac{(p_1 q_1)}{n_1} + \frac{(p_2 q_2)}{n_2}}}$$

and set up a critical region of the type $Z > K$, corresponding to a level, say, of 10 per cent. That is, the probability that $Z > K$, when $p_1 = p_2$, is to be .10; hence, $K = 1.65$. Of course, again we do not know the population variances $(p_i q_i)/n_i$. But we assume that we can approximate them using the sample estimates of p_i, namely, $\bar{X}_i$. The sample calculations give $z = 6.65$, and we reject the hypothesis H_0.

When the sample sizes are not large enough to use the Central Limit Theorem, we must know the precise population distributions in order to construct the distribution of $\bar{X}_2 - \bar{X}_1$, and we have no right to use sample variances to estimate population variances in the confidence intervals as we have done above. If the populations can be considered normal, the appropriate tool is again the t distribution, introduced for small sample interval estimation of the mean in Section 9.5.

There are two situations that we should consider, namely, (1) to make a test concerning the means of two normal distributions assuming that the variances are equal and (2) to make a test concerning the means of two normal distributions with unequal variances. We shall briefly discuss the first situation.

We choose as the hypotheses H_0 and H_1 to be tested, say,

$$H_0: \mu_1 \geq \mu_2 \text{ and } H_1: \mu_1 < \mu_2.$$

Next we choose the test statistic

$$t = \frac{\bar{X}_1 - \bar{X}_2}{s \sqrt{\frac{1}{n_1} + \frac{1}{n_2}}}$$

where s^2 is the "pooled variance":

$$s^2 = \frac{n_1 s_1{}^2 + n_2 s_2{}^2}{n_1 + n_2 - 2}$$

If we consider that n and α are given, we construct the appropriate critical region of the type $t < K$ using the t distribution for $n_1 + n_2 - 2$ degrees of freedom. We then carry out the test, by evaluating the statistic, and accept or reject H_0.

Example 11–d

Suppose that raw data from two samples give the statistics in the following table:

Sample	n_i	$\bar{x}_i$	s_i^2	$n_i s_i^2$
1	10	23.5	4.3	43.0
2	15	19.2	5.1	76.5

The populations are assumed to be normal and to have equal variances.
   To test equality of means, we compute t:

$$t = \frac{23.5 - 19.2}{s \sqrt{1/10 + 1/15}},$$

where

$$s^2 = \frac{1}{23}(43.0 + 76.5) = 5.2.$$

We find $t = 4.66$, which is well within the rejection region $|t| > 2.07$ corresponding to a 5 per cent significance level.

Problems

11–3. Two analysts each make fifty independent determinations of the melting point of a certain chemical. The sample mean and variance of the readings found by analyst I are, respectively, 73.6 and 10 while the sample mean and variance found by analyst II are, respectively, 72.4 and 8. It is argued that there is a tendency for analyst I to get higher results. What is your conclusion? If you conclude that the analysts differ, determine the 90 per cent confidence limits for the difference.

11–4. We are interested in replacing wire B by wire A if the resistance per unit length is not significantly decreased. The data shown in table on page 210 were presented as the results of twenty tests on each wire.
   (a) If we know that the standard deviations of the two testing procedures are both .0017 ohms, what is your recommendation?
   (b) Construct the OC curve for your test.
   (c) If we assume that the two standard deviations are unknown (but equal) would you change your recommendation?
   (d) Construct the 95 per cent confidence limits for the difference. (Does the value 0 lie between these limits?)

Wire A	Wire B
.051 (ohms)	.054
.047	.051
.049	.052
.048	.051
.048	.051
.049	.055
.049	.049
.049	.049
.049	.051
.051	.052
.049	.057
.051	.051
.053	.054
.050	.051
.053	.052
.047	.052
.049	.050
.050	.052
.051	.052
.049	.048

11.2.2 The Sign Test

If two random variables X_1 and X_2 have *identical* continuous distributions, the probability that an observation from one exceeds an observation from the other is one-half:

$$H_0: P(X_2 > X_1) = \frac{1}{2}.$$

More generally, this probability is not one-half, but some other number between 0 and 1, say, p. In any event, the distribution of the number of times the observation of X_2 exceeds the observation of X_1 in n pairs of observations is binomially distributed (n, p), with expected value np.

Consider then the random samples (of equal size):

$$x_{11}, x_{12}, \ldots, x_{1n} \quad \text{from } X_1,$$

and

$$x_{21}, x_{22}, \ldots, x_{2n} \quad \text{from } X_2.$$

If we record a plus sign $(+)$ when $x_{2i} > x_{1i}$ and a minus sign $(-)$ when $x_{2i} < x_{1i}$, the number of plus signs obtained is the number of times an observation from one population exceeds an observation from the other and is binomial (n, p). Under H_0, $p = 1/2$.

(The sign test can be used also, clearly, to test $P(X_2 > X_1 + k) = 1/2$, by the simple expedient of considering the differences $X_2 - X_1 - k$ in assigning plus or minus.)

Testing H_0 is then equivalent to testing $p = 1/2$ in a Bernoulli population, using the sample sum (i.e., the number of plus signs) as the test statistic, a problem we have discussed in considerable detail in Chapter 8. In particular, the proportion of plus signs can be used as an estimate of $P(X_2 > X_1)$. It is important to notice, however, that this equivalence is independent of the type of distribution of X_1 and X_2. The test is then what is called "distribution free" or "nonparametric."

This sign test is closely related to the sign test used in testing a given value of the population median (Section 9.9), in that both reduce to testing $p = 1/2$ in a Bernoulli population.

Example 11-e

Examining the data in Table 7.1, page 116, considering the first twenty observations and the last twenty observations as coming from possibly different populations, we find nineteen plus signs in twenty differences, as shown in the table on page 212. If the alternative to $p = P(X_2 > X_1) = 1/2$ is that $p < 1/2$, the appropriate test is to reject $p = 1/2$ if there are "too few" plus signs. We see that

$$P_{p=1/2} \text{ (fewer than 6 plus signs)}$$

$$\doteq \Phi\left(\frac{5.5 - 10}{\sqrt{5}}\right) \doteq .022,$$

and hence we reject $p = 1/2$ at the 2.2 per cent level, in favor of $p < 1/2$.

Application of the sign test requires a pairing of the data and remains valid so long as the comparisons are independent and $P(X_2 > X_1)$ remains fixed. Such is the case if, as in the above example, the observations are paired as they are obtained—the first observation from X_1 with the first from X_2, and so on.

The sign test is applicable, too, in a case in which X_1 and X_2 may not have fixed distributions at each observation, but in which $P(X_2 > X_1)$ remains fixed (and the comparisons are independent). For example, if pipes of two different alloys are to be compared as to corrosion resistance, one might bury $2n$ pipes in pairs—such that the extraneous factors are the same for the pipes in a pair, but possibly different from pair to pair. The data are then a series of n differences ΔX_i (or signs of differences, if no quantitative measure is used). If the ΔX's can be considered normally distributed, a t test would be in order, but with only $n - 1$ degrees of freedom (as opposed to the $2n - 2$ degrees of freedom when samples from X_1 and X_2 are available separately).

x_{1i}	x_{2i}	Sign of $x_{2i} - x_{1i}$
37.0	31.0	−
31.4	31.3	−
34.4	30.7	−
33.3	32.8	−
34.9	30.6	−
36.2	30.0	−
31.0	29.5	−
33.5	30.8	−
33.7	31.3	−
33.4	31.3	−
34.8	29.2	−
30.8	29.0	−
32.9	31.6	−
34.3	31.4	−
33.3	30.6	−
34.5	32.5	−
30.0	30.3	+
32.8	32.7	−
35.9	30.7	−
32.4	31.7	−

When applicable, a t test is generally more efficient than a sign test. However, the sign test is much easier to apply, and it is sometimes valid where a t test is not, namely, in cases in which the underlying variables are not normal—or perhaps not even numerical variables.

Although if the population distributions are continuous, the probability of a "tie" $(X_1 = X_2)$ is zero, ties occur in practice because of round off. Alternative procedures for treating ties are to assign half of them plus and half minus, to toss a coin in each case, or to ignore them. The best of these procedures turns out to be the last—ignore the ties and base the test on only those pairs of observations in which there is a difference.

With this rule as to the treatment of ties, there is no harm in allowing the populations to be discrete. An important case of this type is that in which one does not measure the individuals from each population, but only compares them, recording + if one is better than the other, − if the other is bettter han the one, and 0 if they are equal. If the populations are equivalent, the probability of $+$ is equal to the probability of $-$, although not necessarily equal to 1/2. On the other hand, if we ignore ties, it is the conditional probability (given a difference) which counts, and the conditional probabilities of $+$ and $-$ would be each 1/2.

Example 11–f

Two dozen tomatoes of variety A and two dozen of variety B are selected at random and compared in pairs as to the quality (pulpiness, taste, etc.). Suppose that there are six ties and that variety A scores higher than variety B in thirteen of the remaining eighteen pairs. The probability of five or fewer minus signs or five or fewer plus signs is (using the binomial formula) about .096. Hence, the given result would call for rejection of equality of the varieties at the 10 per cent significance level, against the alternative that there is a difference. If the alternative had been that variety A is of better quality than variety B, a one-sided test would be appropriate; and the test which calls for rejection of equal qualities when thirteen or more plus signs out of eighteen occur has an α of .048.

11.2.3 The Median Test

Another *distribution-free* test for a difference in locations is the *median test*. The observations from the two samples are arranged in numerical order, and the test statistic is the number m_1 of observations from the sample from X_1 which are to the left of the combined median. If there are "too few" of the X_1 observations to the left of this median, we should assume that the distribution of X_1 is shifted to the right of that of X_2 in preference to the null hypothesis that they are identical.

The interpretation of "too few" again requires a knowledge of the distribution of the test statistic under the hypothesis H_0. Suppose we denote the sample sizes by n_1 and n_2 (from X_1 and X_2 respectively), and let $n_1 + n_2 = n$ be an even number. The over-all median is obtained by arranging the n numbers from both sets according to magnitude and dividing the list into equal parts, $n/2$ numbers on each side of the median.

Suppose that in the arranging process we keep the numbers tagged with the original subscript indicating the order in which the observations were obtained. It happens that *if the null hypothesis H_0 is correct*, all distinct arrangements of subscripts are equally likely when the observations are arranged numerically. If this is so, probabilities can be computed as in Chapter 1. In particular, the probability that m_1 observations from X_1 are to the left of the over-all median is just the number of arrangements of the subscripts for which this is true divided by the total possible number of arrangements. The total possible number of arrangements is the number of arrangements of n things, namely, $n!$ The number of these in which m_1

observations from X_1 are to the left of the median is

$$\binom{n_1}{m_1}\binom{n_2}{m_2} \cdot \frac{n}{2}! \left(n - \frac{n}{2}\right)!,$$

where m_2 is the number of observations from X_2 to the left of the median, equal to $n/2 - m_1$. Dividing, we have

$$P_{H_0} (m_1 \text{ observations from } X_1 \text{ to the left of the median}) = \frac{\binom{n_1}{m_1}\binom{n_2}{m_2}}{\binom{n}{m_1 + m_2}}.$$

Thus, if H_0 is correct, n_1 has a hypergeometric distribution, with mean $n_1/2$ and variance $(n_1 n_2)/(4[n - 1])$. If one has access to tables of the hypergeometric distribution, the type I error can be discussed numerically; actually, this hypergeometric distribution is approximately normal if (as a rule of thumb) $(n_1 n_2)/(4[n - 1]) > 9$, which simplifies the table work.

Example 11–g

Consider again the data used in Example 11–e; we write out the data again, this time putting observations in numerical order as shown in the table on page 215. There are four observations from sample 2 above the median. The probability of seven or fewer observations to one side of the median is

$$\sum_{k=0}^{7} \frac{\binom{20}{k}\binom{20}{20 - k}}{\binom{40}{20}} \doteq .056$$

and, similarly, the probability of six or fewer to one side is about .013. Thus, we reject equality of locations of the populations from which the samples are drawn, at the 5 per cent significance level. (The values of probabilities given here can be computed without difficulty with the aid of a table of logarithms of factorials.)

11.2.4 The Wilcoxon-Mann-Whitney Test

Consider once more independent random samples,

$$x_1, x_2, \ldots, x_m \qquad \text{from } X$$

and

$$y_1, y_2, \ldots, y_n \qquad \text{from } Y,$$

obtained for testing the null hypothesis:

$$H_0: \text{The distributions of } X \text{ and } Y \text{ are identical.}$$

Sample 1	Sample 2	
37.0		
36.2		
35.9		
34.9		
34.8		
34.5		
34.4		
34.3		
33.7		
33.5		
33.4		
33.3, 33.3		
32.9		
32.8	32.8	
	32.7	
	32.5	
32.4		
	31.7	

—————————————————————————— Over-all Median

Sample 1	Sample 2	
	31.6	
31.4	31.4	
	31.3, 31.3, 31.3	
31.0	31.0	
30.8	30.8	
	30.7, 30.7	
	30.6, 30.6	
	30.3	
30.0	30.0	
	29.5	
	29.2	
	29.0	

Suppose that the sample observations are ordered numerically, yielding a sequence of x's and y's (dropping the subscripts) such as the following:

$$x, y, x, y, y, x, x, y, x.$$

For each y, we count one "inversion" for each x which precedes that y in the sequence, and let U denote the total number of such inversions for the y's. Putting it in another way, for each pair of observations x_i and y_j, we let

$$z_{ij} = \begin{cases} 1, \text{ if } x_i < y_j, \\ 0, \text{ if } x_i > y_j, \end{cases}$$

and let

$$U = \sum_{j=1}^{n} \sum_{i=1}^{m} z_{ij}.$$

Under the null hypothesis, z_{ij} is a Bernoulli variable with $p = 1/2$, and hence

$$E(U) = E\left(\sum_{j} \sum_{i} z_{ij}\right) = \sum_{j} \sum_{i} E(z_{ij}) = \frac{mn}{2}.$$

Since the z_{ij} are not independent, the variance is somewhat (but not much) harder to compute; the result is this:

$$\text{var } U = \frac{mn}{12}(m + n + 1).$$

It can be shown, further, that U is asymptotically normal with these parameters.

Knowing the value of U is equivalent to knowing the "rank sums." Let the observations be assigned ranks, according to where they fall in the numerical arrangement of the observations from the two samples—the smallest being assigned rank 1, the next smallest rank 2, etc. If the rank of the smallest y is r_1, there are $r_1 - 1$ corresponding inversions; if the rank of the next smallest y is r_2, there are $r_2 - 2$ corresponding inversions; and so on. Hence,

$$U = (r_1 - 1) + \cdots + (r_n - n) = \sum_{j=1}^{n} r_j - \frac{n(n+1)}{2}.$$

Calling the sum of the ranks of the y's R_y, we have then

$$R_y = U_y + \frac{n(n+1)}{2},$$

where we have used U_y to denote the number of inversions for the y's. Similarly, of course,

$$R_x = U_x + \frac{m(m+1)}{2}.$$

We notice that

$$E(R_x) = E(U_x) + \frac{m(m+1)}{2} = \frac{mn + m(m+1)}{2},$$

and that var R_x = var U_x.

If the alternative hypothesis is that the X and Y distributions are not identical, the null hypothesis is rejected if U_y (or R_y, or U_x, or R_x) is either too large or too small. If the X distribution is to the right of the Y distribution, the X values tend to appear to the right of the Y values, and U_x is then large; for such an alternative we reject H_0 if U_x exceeds a value depending on the significance level. These tests are especially sensitive to differences in *location*, as opposed to differences in variability.

Table VIII, page 263, gives rejection limits for sample sizes up to 10. They are given as lower rejection limits, so that, for example, if H_1 is that the X distribution is to the right of the Y distribution (which would tend to make U_x large), we use U_y rejecting H_0 if U_y is less than or equal to the indicated rejection limit. The same table can be used to obtain two-sided rejection limits, the upper limit being mn minus the lower rejection limit, provided the level is doubled.

The statistic U (either U_x or U_y) is asymptotically normal, and the probability distribution of the standardized statistic (with a continuity correction thrown in)

$$Z = \frac{U + 1/2 - mn/2}{mn(m + n + 1)/12}$$

is approximately the standard normal distribution for large m and n. At the point where Table VIII leaves off the approximation is only fair, and a better approximation† to $P(U \leq u)$ is given by

$$\Phi(z) - \frac{m^2 + n^2 + mn + m + n}{20mn(m + n + 1)} \phi^{(3)}(z),$$

where $\Phi(z)$ is given in Table I, $\phi^{(3)}(z)$ is the third derivative‡ of the standard normal density, and z comes from u in the same way as Z is given in terms of U above.

Because of round off, ties can occur (in ordering the x and y values) even though the populations of interest are continuous. It is customary to use a randomization process in such cases—pick an order at random from the possible ones. The effect of this is involved, and it will not be discussed here.

Example 11–h

If five observations are taken from X and four observations from Y, we see from Table VIII that (for *either* U_x or U_y)

† See "Significance Probabilities of the Wilcoxon Test," *Annals of Math. Stat.*, XXVI (1955), 301–312, by E. Fix and J.L. Hodges, Jr.

‡ Available, for instance, in the *Mathematical Tables from Handbook of Chemistry and Physics*, Chemical Rubber Publishing Co.

$$P_{H_0}(2 < U < 18) = .936.$$

Thus, the rejection region $U \geq 18$ or $U \leq 2$ has a corresponding type I error size of $\alpha = 6.4$ per cent.

Consider the two sets of observations:

$$10,\ 15,\ 13,\ 17,\ 8, \qquad \text{(from } X)$$

and

$$16,\ 12,\ 9,\ 11 \qquad \text{(from } Y).$$

Putting these nine numbers in order, we have the combined sequence

$$8,\ 9,\ 10,\ 11,\ 12,\ 13,\ 15,\ 16,\ 17,$$

or, to keep track of which numbers came from X and which from Y:

$$x,\ y,\ x,\ y,\ y,\ x,\ x,\ y,\ x.$$

There are $1 + 3 + 3 + 4 = 11$ inversions of the x's, and the rank sum of the x's is $1 + 3 + 6 + 7 + 9 = 26 = 11 + 5 \times 6/2$. Since the number of inversions of the x's is between two and eighteen, we accept the null hypothesis of no difference in population locations.

Example 11-i

From the tabulation in Example 11-g we can easily compute the number of inversions for the observations from sample one. It is about 354, depending on how "ties" are broken. The expected number is

$$\frac{mn}{2} = \frac{20 \times 20}{2} = 200,$$

and the variance is

$$\frac{mn}{12}(m + n + 1) = \frac{400}{12} \times 41 \doteq (37)^2.$$

Thus, 354 corresponds to the value

$$\frac{354 - 200}{37} = \frac{154}{37} \doteq 4$$

of an approximately standard normal variable. The value 4 calls for the rejection of equality of locations, even for a .1 per cent significance level.

It should be evident by now that the set of data in Table 7.1 is subject to question, if it is claimed to represent a sample of 200 from a single population. It fails to pass run tests for randomness and seems to show a definite shift in level from the first to the second half of the data. Furthermore, when the data are exhibited as in Example 11-e, the shift is so obvious as to make a statistical test almost unnecessary.

It is comforting to know, of course, that a statistical test will confirm the "obvious." In addition to handling *less* obvious situations, however, the tests presented here have the value of leading us to examine the data in such a way as to make obvious what might not otherwise be so obvious. When considering *only* the histogram for the data in Table 7.1, we do not suspect the subsequently shown shift in level. Had a control chart been kept as the data were taken, it would have recorded the shift in level graphically.

Problems

11–5. Consider the data given in Problem 11–4. What recommendation would you give if you used the sign test? If you used the median test? If you used the Wilcoxon test?

11–6. Two sets of data are given below. Test the hypothesis that there has been no change in the center of the population at a 10 per cent significance level. Use all three of the nonparametric tests.

A. +4, +1, +6, −1, −1, −1, −2, +3, −4, +4, −1, 0, +6, 0, −2, 0, +5, −2, 0, −3, −3, −1, −3, 0, −2, 0, −2, −7, −4, −1, −2, +1, +3, +3, +1, +1, −5, +6, +2, +1

B. +2, −3, +1, 0, −2, −10, +2, +1, 0, −4, +6, 0, −10, −1, +1, −5, −3, −3, −3, 0, +1, −1, −5, +3, 0, −1, +3, 0, +4, +5, −2, 0, −1, +4, −2, +1, −9, +1, +4, +1

11–7. The set of twenty observations below was obtained from the same process from which those labeled *A* in Problem 11–6 were obtained. Test the hypothesis that there has not been a shift in population center, after the first forty observations,
(a) using the median test.
(b) using the sign test.
(c) using the Mann-Whitney Test.

3, −1, 6, −7, 1, 1, 3, −8, 3, 3, 1, 9, −4, 1, 0, 1, 2, 5, 6, −1

11.3 Comparison of Variances

We consider now the problem of testing the null hypothesis

$$H_0: \sigma_1{}^2 = \sigma_2{}^2,$$

against an alternative hypothesis yet to be specified. We have two populations X_1 and X_2, with samples from each, and $\sigma_1{}^2$ and $\sigma_2{}^2$ are the population variances. Having used the sample variance in testing hypotheses concerning σ^2 and in estimating σ^2 for a single population, it is natural to base the test of H_0 here on a comparison of variances of the samples from the two populations.

There is no unique way of comparing variances, but the obvious ones are to compute the difference in sample variances or to compute the ratio of the sample variances. Assuming independence of the two samples, the sample variances would be independent; and we could therefore construct a large sample test for $\sigma_1^2 - \sigma_2^2$ based on $s_1^2 - s_2^2$, since this difference in sample variances is an asymptotically normally distributed statistic. It is more common, however, for the *ratio* of the variances to be used as a basis of comparison.

This is because the ratio is independent of scale, provided that the same scale is used for both populations, and because the distribution of the ratio under H_0 is found in at least one important case, discussed below, to be independent of any population parameters.

If we are to use the ratio $F = s_1^2/s_2^2$ as a test statistic, it is necessary to know the probability distribution of this random variable. For the important case in which *both populations are normal*, this distribution has been studied and tabulated. In this normal case the ratio F is seen to be the ratio of two independent random variables, each a chi-square variable divided by its number of degrees of freedom—provided that the two population variances are equal, that is, $\sigma_1^2 = \sigma_2^2 = \sigma^2$. For, we can write F as follows:

$$F = \frac{s_1^2}{s_2^2} = \frac{\dfrac{1}{n_1 - 1} \cdot \dfrac{(n_1 - 1)s_1^2}{\sigma^2}}{\dfrac{1}{n_2 - 1} \cdot \dfrac{(n_2 - 1)s_2^2}{\sigma^2}}.$$

The number of degrees of freedom in the numerator and denominator of this ratio are parameters of its distribution, called the F distribution in honor of R.A. Fisher, who pioneered its many uses. The density of the distribution corresponding to r and s degrees of freedom (in numerator and denominator, respectively) can be shown to be as follows:

$$f(x; r, s) = (\text{const.}) \frac{x^{r/2-1}}{(1 + rx/s)^{(r+s)/2}},$$

the constant being determined in the usual way, to make the total probability assigned equal to one. Tables IVa and IVb give the ninety-fifth and ninety-ninth percentiles of the F distribution for various combinations of degrees of freedom.

It will be noticed that tables of F percentiles give only the higher percentiles (90, 95, or 99 per cent), whereas for a two-sided test we would also need to know the lower percentiles (10, 5, or 1 per cent). For example,

$$.05 = P(F < F_{.05}) = 1 - P(F > {}_{.05}) = 1 - P\left(\frac{1}{F} < \frac{1}{F_{.05}}\right),$$

and hence

$$P\left(\frac{1}{F} < \frac{1}{F_{.05}}\right) = .95.$$

This tells us that $1/F_{.05}$ happens to be the ninety-fifth percentile of the distribution of $1/F$. But $1/F$ is a random variable of the *same type* as F, except that the numerator and denominator degrees of freedom are reversed. Thus, to determine $F_{.05}$, we locate the ninety-fifth percentile of the F distribution with the degrees of freedom reversed from those in the initially given F and take its reciprocal.

The F distribution has the advantage of being applicable even for small samples, but has the disadvantage that a normal distribution is assumed for each population.

We shall examine the problem of testing the equality of two variances, then, only in the case of normal populations, so that the F distribution is applicable. In testing $H_0: \sigma_1^2/\sigma_2^2 = 1$, we use the sample analogue s_1^2/s_2^2. The type of critical region depends on the alternative to H_0. If the alternative is one-sided, say, $\sigma_1^2 > \sigma_2^2$, it is natural to take a one-sided critical region, rejecting H_0 if the ratio of sample variances is too much greater than 1. If the alternative is two-sided: $\sigma_2^2 \neq \sigma_1^2$, we should reject H_0 either if s_1^2/s_2^2 is too large or if it is too small.

Example 11–j

Two methods of performing a certain task are to be compared. The results are assumed to be normal random variables, with possibly different variances for the two methods. We wish to test $\sigma_1^2 = \sigma_2^2$ against the two-sided alternative $\sigma_1^2 \neq \sigma_2^2$. The test statistic is the variance ratio $F = s_1^2/s_2^2$, obtained from samples of sizes $n_1 = 13$ and $n_2 = 7$. We decide to accept equality of population variances if the test statistic falls within the range $F_{.05} < F < F_{.95}$. The level of this test is 10 per cent, since under the null hypothesis the ratio F has the F distribution, and therefore

$$P_{H_0}(F_{.05} < F < F_{.95}) = .95 - .05 = .90.$$

The probability of rejection under H_0 is then .10.

The percentiles needed in this test are obtained from Table IVa, page 258, using 12 and 6 degrees of freedom (in numerator and denominator, respectively), so that the acceptance region is

$$\frac{1}{3.00} < F < 4.00.$$

Suppose that data is obtained, and that the results are summarized as follows:

$$\bar{x}_1 = 73.6, \ s_1^2 = 6.2, \ n_1 = 13,$$
$$\bar{x}_2 = 61.0 \ s_2^2 = 8.8, \ n_2 = 7.$$

The statistic F is then $6.2/8.8 = .704$, which falls within the acceptance region determined above; on the basis of this experiment we accept equality of variances at the 10 per cent level.

The power of a test based on the variance ratio F would be the probability that F falls in the critical region of the test, calculated using the probability distribution of F under a specified alternative to H_0. Alternatives can be indexed according to the value of σ_1^2/σ_2^2, and the distribution of F depends only on this ratio (in addition to the sample sizes). Operating characteristics for one- and two-sided tests based on F are given in *Handbook of Industrial Statistics*, by Bowker and Lieberman.

Problems

11–8. Consider that two samples of ten and sixteen observations, respectively, have variances $s_1^2 = .3888$ and $s_2^2 = 2.25$. At a 5 per cent significance level would you accept the hypothesis $H_0: \sigma_1^2 \leq \sigma_2^2$?

11–9. Would you recommend that the methods of testing the resistance of wire A and wire B given in Problem 11–5 have equal variances? State your recommendation on the basis of a 10 per cent level of significance.

11–10. A control laboratory is interested in whether two methods of analysis are equally reliable.

    (a) Does the following data substantiate the assumption of equal variances for the two methods?

    (b) Use the sign test to determine whether there is a significant difference in expected values of the two methods of analysis

Determinations in Per Cent Nickel

Aqueous: 4.27, 4.32, 4.29, 4.30, 4.31, 4.30, 4.30, 4.32, 4.28, 4.32.

Alcoholic: 4.28, 4.32, 4.32, 4.29, 4.31, 4.35, 4.29, 4.32, 4.33, 4.28, 4.37, 4.38, 4.28, 4.32.

12/Some Further Topics

12.0 Introduction

In this chapter we shall indicate some additional important types of statistical problems and methods, which are really beyond the scope of this book. Indeed, volumes have been devoted to the discussion of each topic we shall consider. As a matter of fact, entire volumes have been devoted to other important topics in statistics which we shall not consider (multivariate analysis, sampling methods, bioassay—to name a few).

Rather than soar descriptively far above a topic, for the purpose of giving a view of the whole field, we have chosen to dig into a typical, fundamental problem or two, in each case.

12.1 Sequential Testing

Anyone who conducts a test such as we have been considering in the preceding chapters will undoubtedly be uneasy about making a decision based on the outcome of the test when the test variable falls quite near the boundary between the acceptance and rejection regions. A natural inclination is to gather more data, hoping that the more precise tool of a larger sample will give a more clear-cut decision.

Why not, then, conduct a test as each sample observation is obtained? Perhaps in the process it will be clear very soon what decision is the proper one, thereby eliminating the need for the larger sample. These ideas have been developed extensively in the theory of sequential tests. The basic idea is that certain limits are chosen, A and B, such that whenever the test statistic falls *outside* the interval from A to B, a decision is made—one action being taken if it falls below A, and the other if it falls above B. When the test variable falls *within* the interval A to B, *no* decision is made, and another observation is obtained. We think of the interval from A to B as being a region in which we are not willing to commit ourselves to a decision. The theory says that the sampling is bound to stop sooner or later.

The advantage of such sequential tests is that in general they require less sampling on the average. The sample size is not predetermined; it is, in fact, a random variable. But the *expected* sample size is usually less than that needed for a test based on a fixed sample size with comparable detecting power.

We shall not consider sequential analysis in great detail, but give here two procedures; first, that used in testing the following simple hypotheses on the mean of a Bernoulli population ($X = 1$ with probability p, and $X = 0$ with probability $1 - p$):

$$H_0: p = p_0,$$
$$H_1: p = p_1.$$

The test variable used in this case at the nth stage is

$$\lambda_n = \left(\frac{p_1}{p_0}\right)^{s_n} \left(\frac{1 - p_1}{1 - p_0}\right)^{f_n},$$

where quantities s_n and f_n are the number of successes (probability p) and the number of failures (probability $1 - p$), respectively, up through the nth trial. (*Note:* $s_n + f_n = n$.) The limits A and B are given approximately in terms of α and β by the equations

$$A = \frac{\beta}{1 - \alpha}, \quad B = \frac{1 - \beta}{\alpha}.$$

Example 12–a

Suppose that successive observations are obtained by tossing a coin, with p the probability of getting heads. Let H_0 be $p = .5$, and H_1 be $p = .7$. If we adopt the error sizes $\alpha = .05$ and $\beta = .10$, the limits are $A = 2/19$ and $B = 18$. Suppose, now, that we actually toss a coin, with the following results: $H, T, T, H, H, H, T, T, H, H,$ $T, T, T, H, H, T, T, T, H, H.$ The ratio p_1/p_0 is 1.4, and $(1 - p_1)/(1 - p_0)$ is .6. Computing, we find

$$\lambda_1 = 1.4, \lambda_2 = .84, \lambda_3 = .504, \lambda_4 = .706, \text{ etc.}$$

(Each λ_k is obtained by multiplying the preceding one by 1.4 if the kth trial is heads, and by .6 if the kth trial is tails.) Finally, at the eighteenth trial, we find $\lambda_{18} \doteq .09$, which is less than A. Thus we accept $p = .5$ in preference to $p_1 = .7$. (The remaining two trials are not used and would not have been carried out.) Perhaps it is interesting to compute that if the coin had had two heads, $p = .7$ would be chosen at the ninth toss.

In general, the quantity λ_n is defined as follows:

$$\lambda_n = \frac{f_1(x_1)f_1(x_2) \cdots f_1(x_n)}{f_0(x_1)f_0(x_2) \cdots f_0(x_n)},$$

where f_0 and f_1 are the density functions, in the continuous case, or the probability functions, in the discrete case, corresponding to simple hypotheses H_0 and H_1. (If the hypotheses are composite, but indexed by a parameter θ, we can often reduce the test to simple hypotheses, as discussed in Chapter 8, by introducing the indifference zone and taking as $H_0: \theta = \theta'$ and as $H_1: \theta = \theta''$.) Because of the products and quotient involved, it is convenient to use logarithms, changing the operations to those of addition and subtraction.

For the hypotheses that a population is normal with known variance σ^2 and

$$H_0: \mu = \mu_0,$$
$$H_1: \mu = \mu_1, \ (\mu_1 > \mu_0)$$

the inequality to be used, obtained by computing and rearranging $\log A < \log \lambda_n < \log B$, is as follows (logs are to the base e and written ln):

$$\frac{\sigma^2}{\mu_1 - \mu_0} \ln \frac{\beta}{1 - \alpha} + \frac{n}{2}(\mu_0 + \mu_1) < \sum_1^n x_i < \frac{\sigma^2}{\mu_1 - \mu_0} \ln \frac{1 - \beta}{\alpha} + \frac{n}{2}(\mu_0 + \mu_1).$$

As functions of n, these rejection and acceptance limits are linear. If the sample sum gets larger than the upper one, we reject H_0, and if it gets smaller than the lower one, we accept H_0.

Example 12–b

If we take $\alpha = .05$ and $\beta = .1$ in testing $\mu = 0$ against $\mu = 1$, with $\sigma^2 = 1$, the inequality for continuing sampling is

$$-2.26 + \frac{n}{2} < \sum_1^n x_i < 2.89 + \frac{n}{2}.$$

These acceptance and rejection limits for the sample sum are plotted in Figure 12–1, together with a typical actual test, shown terminating with a decision to accept $\mu = 0$ at the thirteenth observation.

Operating characteristic and average sample number curves for sequential tests are discussed by A. Wald in his pioneering book, *Sequential Analysis*, John Wiley & Sons, 1947.

Problems

12-1. Toss a coin until the test given in Example 12–a selects between $p = .5$ and $p = .7$.

12-2. Construct a sequential test like that in Example 12–a but using $p = .5$ and $p = .1$ as H_0 and H_1, respectively, and with $\alpha = \beta = .2$. Carry out the test by tossing a coin until a decision is reached. Carry out the test by tossing a die, counting 1 and 2 as "success" (associated with the probability p).

12-3. Construct the rejection and acceptance lines for the sample sum (as in Example 12–b) for testing $H_0: \mu = -1$ against $H_1: \mu = 1$ with given variance $\sigma^2 = .25$, and $\alpha = \beta = .1$.

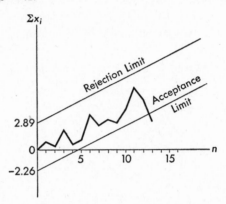

Figure 12–1. A Typical Sequential Test (Example 12–b)

12.2 Regression

Suppose that we are examining the (isothermal) relation between pressure and temperature in a fixed volume of gas. Theory tells us that they are linearly related. However, when we measure pressures p_i corresponding to several temperatures T_i the points (p_i, T_i) do not fall on a straight line. Perhaps we reason that, although we are measuring temperature extremely accurately, our method of measuring pressure is subject to relatively wide statistical fluctuations. Thus, even though pressure and temperature are linearly related, the measured pressure and temperature may not be so because of a random element in the measured pressure. We think of the measured pressure, then, as an actual pressure plus a random error with expected value zero. The problem is this: How can we extract the correct linear relationship from data which do not fall on a line? Another problem which could be considered is whether or not we are justified in assuming a linear relationship between the quantities involved.

These problems have features which occur in a variety of situations, studied under the general heading of "regression" problems. We have here several random variables (the measured pressures) indexed according to values of a controlled or systematic variable (temperature), although often the controlled variable is controlled only in a relative sense.† We are interested in the functional relation between the expectation of the random variable (the actual pressure) and the controlled variable (temperature). We sometimes wish to "confirm" that the relationship is, say, linear (as in this example), or some other given type of functional relation—according to theoretical considerations. And sometimes it is desired to determine the coefficients in the functional relation, given its type (the constant of proportionality in $p = kT$).

A fundamental requirement of data for such tests is that more than one value of the controlled variable be used. With this there are two possibilities, which give different amounts of information: We may have just *one* determination of the random quantity corresponding to each value of the controlled variable, or we may have *several* values of the random quantity at each index value. The latter situation will not be discussed here.

We adopt the notation x for the controlled variable, and $x_1, x_2, \ldots, x_k$ for the particular values used in the experiment. (These are *not* random in our model.) The random quantity we denote by Y_x, letting $y_1, y_2, \ldots, y_k$ denote actually observed values corresponding to $x_1, \ldots, x_k$, assuming just one observed value for each x. If we wish to emphasize the random character of these observed values (as when talking about them before they are actually measured), we shall capitalize: $Y_1, \ldots, Y_k$.

The expected value, $E(Y_x)$, depends on x; this dependence is described by saying that $E(Y_x)$ is the *regression function*. We shall consider the special type of regression function which depends linearly on x:

$$E(Y_x) = \alpha + \beta x,$$

or, for the particular values of the controlled variable chosen:

$$E(Y_i) = \alpha + \beta x_i, \, i = 1, \ldots, k.$$

The random variables $Y_1, \ldots, Y_k$ will be assumed to be independent, an assumption which simplifies the discussion but which provides, even so, a very useful model. It will be assumed, further, that the variances var Y_i are all equal; again, this assumption does not leave the model without

† The situation is considerably more complicated when the supposedly controlled variable is subject to chance fluctuations approaching, in order of magnitude, those of the variable under observation. We shall not consider this possibility.

application and would probably be justified in the case of the pressure measurements described above.

In summary, then, the model we consider is defined in the following table:

Values of the Controlled Variable	Observed Values (Independent)	$E(Y_i)$	Var Y_i
x_1	Y_1	$\alpha + \beta x_1$	σ^2
x_2	Y_2	$\alpha + \beta x_2$	σ^2
.	.	.	.
.	.	.	.
.	.	.	.
x_k	Y_k	$\alpha + \beta x_k$	σ^2

12.2.1 The Principle of Least Squares

It is assumed that data are given in the form (x_1, y_1), . . . , (x_k, y_k). Each pair (x_i, y_i) can be represented in a system of plane coordinates, as indicated in Figure 12–2. Shown in the same figure is a possible regression

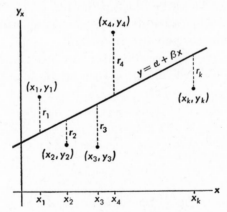

Figure 12–2.   Residuals about a Possible Regression Line

line, corresponding to a given slope β and intercept α. Also shown in the figure are the errors or "residuals" r_i. These are the amounts, at each x_i, by which the data point misses falling on the given regression line, and are given by:

$$r_i = y_i - \alpha - \beta x_i.$$

It is desired to choose α and β on the basis of the given data so as to estimate as well as possible the actual values of these parameters.   To see how to do this, let us apparently digress and consider a property of the sample mean. For a given set of observations $Y_1, \ldots Y_n$ with mean $\bar{Y}$, we know (the "parallel axis theorem," Chapter 7) that

$$\Sigma(Y_i - K)^2 = \Sigma(Y_i - \bar{Y})^2 + n(\bar{Y} - K)^2,$$

which has a minimum value when K is chosen equal to $\bar{Y}$. That is, the sum of squared deviations is a minimum about the sample mean.

In the regression problem, however, we do not have a single population mean, and $\bar{Y}$ does not, therefore, have its usual significance. Instead of choosing a constant K about which the sum of squared deviations is minimized, then, we choose a linear function $\hat{\alpha} + \hat{\beta}x$ about which the sum of squared deviations is minimized. The numbers $\hat{\alpha}$ and $\hat{\beta}$ are thus defined as those values of α and β which minimize

$$R(\alpha, \beta) = \sum_{i=1}^{k} r_i^2 = \sum_{i=1}^{k} (y_i - \alpha - \beta x_i)^2.$$

To minimize a function of two variables, we simply observe that if it is a minimum at $(\hat{\alpha}, \hat{\beta})$, it is a minimum as a function of α at $\alpha = \hat{\alpha}$ when β is held fixed and is a minimum as a function of β at $\beta = \hat{\beta}$ when α is held fixed. Necessary conditions are then that the partial derivatives with respect to α and β of $R(\alpha, \beta)$ must vanish at $\hat{\alpha}$ and $\hat{\beta}$:

$$\frac{\partial R}{\partial \alpha} = \sum_{i=1}^{k} 2(y_i - \hat{\alpha} - \hat{\beta}x_i)(-1) = 0$$

$$\frac{\partial R}{\partial \beta} = \sum_{i=1}^{k} 2(y_i - \hat{\alpha} - \hat{\beta}x_i)(-x_i) = 0.$$

In a form better exhibiting the dependence on α and β, these become:

$$\Sigma y_i = k\hat{\alpha} + \hat{\beta}\Sigma x_i$$
$$\Sigma y_i x_i = \Sigma x_i \hat{\alpha} + \hat{\beta}\Sigma x_i^2.$$

This is a pair of *linear* equations in $\hat{\alpha}$ and $\hat{\beta}$ which will have a unique solution if the determinant of the coefficients does not vanish. This determinant is:

$$\begin{vmatrix} k & k\bar{x} \\ k\bar{x} & \Sigma x_i^2 \end{vmatrix} = k \sum_{i=1}^{k} (x_i - \bar{x})^2.$$

It is not zero so long as the points $x_1, \ldots, x_k$ are not all the same point.

The equations obtained above for $\hat{\alpha}$ and $\hat{\beta}$ are sometimes called the *normal equations*. Their unique solution $(\hat{\alpha}, \hat{\beta})$ does actually minimize $R(\alpha, \beta)$, since this function must have a minimum value, being non-negative.

12.2.2 Solving the Normal Equations

The normal equations may be solved once and for all by leaving the general expressions general rather than putting in specific values of x_i and y_i. The solution is easily obtained—by elimination or by using determinants—and we call the pair of numbers which satisfy the equations $(\hat{\alpha}, \hat{\beta})$. They are given by the expressions:

$$\hat{\beta} = \frac{\frac{1}{k}\Sigma x_i y_i - \bar{x}\bar{y}}{\frac{1}{k}\Sigma x_i^2 - \bar{x}^2}, \quad \hat{\alpha} = \bar{y} - \hat{\beta}\bar{x}.$$

The denominator in the expression for $\hat{\beta}$ happens to be the variance s_x^2 of the set of numbers $x_1, \ldots, x_k$; however, these numbers are not observations on a random variable! This denominator is *not* a statistic; it is fixed when the values of the controlled variable to be used are fixed. Similarly, the numerator happens to be called the "covariance" of the numbers x_i and the numbers y_i, but has not the usual statistical significance of a covariance since the x's are not observations on a random variable.

If k is not too large, it is almost as easy to obtain the normal equations directly and solve as it is to work out the solution from the general solution given above. The first normal equation is just the result of summing the expressions $y_i = \alpha + \beta x_i$ which would be obtained if (x_i, y_i) lay on the line $y = \alpha + \beta x$. The second normal equation is obtained by multiplying these expressions through by the x_i to obtain $x_i y_i = \alpha x_i + \beta x_i^2$, and then summing from $i = 1$ to k.

Example 12–c

Suppose we have the following five points given: $(1, 3), (2, 3), (4, 7), (5, 6), (8, 12)$, the first coordinates being the values of a controlled variable, and the second, observations on the corresponding random variable.

Substituting these pairs of numbers successively in $y = \alpha + \beta x$, multiplying each by the corresponding x_i, and summing, we obtain the following:

$3 = a + b$	$3 = a + b$
$3 = 2a + b$	$6 = 4a + 2b$
$7 = 4a + b$	$28 = 16a + 4b$
$6 = 5a + b$	$30 = 25a + 5b$
$12 = 8a + b$	$96 = 64a + 8b$
$31 = 20a + 5b$	$163 = 110a + 20b$

The equations obtained by summing are the normal equations, and solving them simultaneously we obtain $\hat{\beta} = 1.3$ and $\hat{\alpha} = 1$.

The work can also be laid out in tabular form:

x_i	y_i	$x_i{}^2$	$x_i y_i$
1	3	1	3
2	3	4	6
4	7	16	28
5	6	25	30
8	12	64	96
20	31	110	163

$$\bar{x} = \frac{20}{5} = 4, \bar{y} = \frac{31}{5}$$

$$\hat{\beta} = \frac{\dfrac{163}{5} - \dfrac{124}{5}}{\dfrac{110}{5} - 16} = \frac{13}{10}$$

$$\hat{\alpha} = \frac{31}{5} - \frac{13}{10}4 = 1.$$

12.2.3 Estimation of the Parameters

The problem we set out to consider was the estimation of the coefficients α and β in the linear function giving the variation of $E(Y_x)$ with x. We might also wish to estimate var Y_x, which we assumed to be constant, σ^2. Thus we have three parameters, α, β, and σ^2, to be estimated. Again rather than derive "good" estimates of these quantities, we state the fact that $\hat{\alpha}$, $\hat{\beta}$, and

$$\hat{\sigma}^2 = \frac{1}{k} R(\hat{\alpha}, \hat{\beta}) = \frac{1}{k} \sum (y_i - \hat{\alpha} - \hat{\beta} x_i)^2$$

are in a sense as good estimates as can be found.

The quantities $\hat{\alpha}$, $\hat{\beta}$, and $\hat{\sigma}^2$ depend on the observed values y_i, so when we consider these observed values as random variables, the estimates $\hat{\alpha}$, $\hat{\beta}$, and $\hat{\sigma}^2$ are random variables—are *statistics*. They are good estimates of α, β, and σ^2, respectively, in the sense that the probability distribution of each tends to narrow and peak at the appropriate parameter value, just as with $\bar{x}$ in estimating μ (see Chapter 9).

Since $\hat{\beta}$ can be written as a sum of independent random quantities:

$$\hat{\beta} = \frac{1}{s_x{}^2} \frac{1}{k} \sum (x_i - \bar{x})(Y_i),$$

it is normally distributed if Y_x is normally distributed and asymptotically normally distributed in any case, according to a more general form of the Central Limit Theorem than that given in Chapter 7. The same is true of $\hat{\alpha}$, and it can also be shown that $\hat{\sigma}^2$ is asymptotically normal.

The expected value and variance of the distribution of $\hat{\beta}$ are readily calculated. For,

$$E(\hat{\beta}) = \frac{1}{s_x{}^2} \frac{1}{k} \sum (x_i - \bar{x}) E(Y_i)$$

$$= \frac{1}{s_x{}^2} \frac{1}{k} \sum (x_i - \bar{x})(\alpha + \beta x_i) = 0 + \beta,$$

the zero entering because the sum of the terms $(x_i - \bar{x})$ is zero, and the β being obtained using the fact that $s_x{}^2 = (1/k)\Sigma x_i(x_i - \bar{x})$. Thus, $\hat{\beta}$ is unbiased. The variance is computed as follows:

$$\text{var } (\hat{\beta}) = \frac{1}{s_x{}^4} \frac{1}{k^2} \sum (x_i - \bar{x})^2 \text{ var } Y_i = \frac{\sigma^2}{ks_x{}^2}.$$

Similarly, we can compute the expected value and variance of the distribution of $\hat{\alpha}$. First we write

$$\hat{\alpha} = \bar{Y} - \hat{\beta}\bar{x} = \frac{1}{k} \sum Y_i \left[1 - \frac{\bar{x}}{s_x{}^2} (x_i - \bar{x}) \right]$$

and, recalling that $E(Y_i) = \alpha + \beta x_i$, easily obtain $E(\hat{\alpha}) = \alpha$. Since the Y_i are assumed independent, we can again use the additivity property of the variance:

$$\text{var } (\hat{\alpha}) = \frac{1}{k^2} \sum \text{var } Y_i \left[1 - \frac{\bar{x}}{s_x{}^2} (x_i - \bar{x}) \right]^2 = \frac{\sigma^2}{k} \left(1 + \frac{\bar{x}^2}{s_x{}^2} \right).$$

A couple of interesting points should be observed. First, if we had happened to label the x axis in such a way that the origin is at the center of the fixed x_i's, i.e., $\bar{x} = 0$, the various formulas simplify considerably, and this choice is often made (although to be more honest, the motivation is that choosing $\bar{x}$ equal to 0 happens to make $\hat{\alpha}$ and $\hat{\beta}$ uncorrelated). Second, we, observe that if we take the x_i's as widely spaced as possible—make $s_x{}^2$ as large as possible—the variance of the regression coefficient estimate $\hat{\beta}$ is minimized. This is intuitively quite reasonable; the farther apart the observations along the x direction are, the better the estimate of the slope of the linear function $\alpha + \beta x$ is.

Example 12–d

Suppose that calculations for a given set of 100 points (x_i, y_i) yield $s_x{}^2 = 9.7$, $\hat{\alpha} = 1.1$, $\hat{\beta} = .02$, and $\hat{\sigma}^2 = .0036$. Construct a 90 per cent confidence interval for β. Because of the asymptotic normality of $\hat{\beta}$, we have

$$P \left(|\hat{\beta} - \beta| < 1.65 \frac{\sigma}{s_x \sqrt{k}} \right) \doteq .90.$$

In view of the relatively large sample size, we approximate σ^2 by $\hat{\sigma}^2$, and so obtain the approximate confidence limits

$$\hat{\beta} \pm 1.65 \frac{\hat{\sigma}}{s_x \sqrt{k}}$$

or, putting in the numerical values,

$$.02 \pm 1.65 \frac{.06}{10 \sqrt{9.7}}.$$

Thus, the 90 per cent confidence interval extends from .0168 to .0232.

Example 12–e

Using the data of Example 12–d, test the hypothesis $\beta = 0$ against the alternative $\beta \neq 0$, at the 5 per cent significance level.

The test statistic is of course $\hat{\beta}$, and intuitively the critical region should be $|\hat{\beta}| > K$. Using this rejection region, we have as the (large sample) operating characteristic function:

$$P_\beta(\text{accept } \beta = 0) = P_\beta(|\hat{\beta}| > K)$$
$$\doteq \Phi\left(\frac{K - \beta}{\hat{\sigma}/s_x \sqrt{k}}\right) - \Phi\left(\frac{-K - \beta}{\hat{\sigma}/s_x \sqrt{k}}\right).$$

The size of the type I error (which we had better not call α in this context) is then the value of the OC function at $\beta = 0$, or

$$.05 = 2\Phi\left(\frac{10K \sqrt{9.7}}{.06}\right),$$

and solving for K we find $K = .0038$. Since the observed $\hat{\beta}$ is farther from 0 than .0038, we reject $\beta = 0$, at the 5 per cent level.

12.2.4 Other Regression Problems

Having considered the *linear* regression problem, we mention briefly other types of regression functions to which the "least squares" principle is applicable.

Whenever the assumed regression function depends linearly on certain parameters, the corresponding "normal equations" are linear equations in those parameters. For instance, if it is assumed that

$$E(Y_x) = ax^3 + bx^2 + cx + d$$

(which is linear in a, b, c, and d), the minimization of the sum of the squared residuals leads to a system of four linear equations in a, b, c, and d. The solution of this system provides the least squares estimates of the four parameters.

Certain types of relationships among physical variables are not linearly dependent on parameters. However, if we make suitable a transformation of scales, such cases can sometimes be handled. For example, if pressure and temperature are connected by the relation

$$p = KT^\alpha$$

their logarithms are related as follows:

$$\log p = \log K + \alpha \log T.$$

The parameters $\log K$ and α are now involved linearly, and the least squares regression concepts are applicable to data in the form $(\log p_i, \log T_i)$. It must be realized, on the other hand, that the assumption of normality would now apply to the error in the *logarithms* of the measured pressures.

The principle of least squares can also be extended to cases in which the random variable depends on more than one controlled variable. For example, if Y depends on x and z, we might consider the linear regression function

$$E(Y) = ax + bz.$$

The problems would then be to test the validity of this linearity assumption and to estimate the parameters a and b. Such problems are referred to as multiple regression problems.

Problems

12-4. Determine the line which best fits the following points in the least squares sense: (0, 2), (1, 1), (4, 3), (5, 2).

12-5. The independent, normal random variables Y_x are assumed to have variance σ^2 independent of x and mean $E(Y_x) = \alpha + \beta x$. Fifty observations (x_i, y_i) are obtained, with these results:

$$\bar{x} = 8.2,\ s_x{}^2 = 10.24,\ \hat{\alpha} = 6.31,\ \hat{\beta} = .092,\ \hat{\sigma}^2 = 4.6.$$

Construct a 95 per cent confidence interval for β. Would you accept $\beta = 0$ at the 5 per cent level, against $\beta \neq 0$? (Observe that this is a test of equality of means of several populations.)

12-6. Suppose that the y axis, in Problem 12-5, is translated so that the *new* $\bar{x}$ is zero. Compute the new quantities $s_x{}^2$, $\hat{\alpha}$, $\hat{\beta}$, and $\hat{\sigma}^2$ with this change.

12-7. Construct confidence intervals for α and β using the data in Problem 12-5 modified (as described in Problem 12-6) so that $\bar{x} = 0$.

12.3 Analysis of Variance

In Chapter 11 we considered the problem of testing the null hypothesis of no difference in expected values or means of two populations, where the two populations correspond usually to two "treatments" (or two operators, or two machines, or two times of day, etc.). Basically, the "analysis of variance" extends the methods to cover the case of several treatments.

The technique employed is briefly as follows: One determines the total variability of all of the observations comprising samples from several populations (corresponding to several treatments) and breaks this down into two components of variability. One component is associated with the actual population variances, and the other component is associated with differences in population means. The latter is the key to testing for equality of population means.

More generally, methods can be developed which permit the designing of a statistical experiment to study simultaneously the effects of several factors (say, four operators, three machines, and five times of day). In this brief introduction we shall consider the "single classification" problem, in which we study the effect of a single factor on a given variable, and a two-factor problem.

The bulk of the work done in the field of analysis of variance assumes normal populations, and we restrict our discussion to this assumption. We should mention, however, that work has also been carried out along "nonparametric" lines, in which no assumption as to the nature of the population is made.

12.3.1 A Single Classification Problem

Let us again consider the data given in Example 10–1, which we repeat in the following tabulation:

	n_i	Observations x_{ij}	$\bar{x}_i$	$\sum_{j=1}^{n_i} (x_{ij} - \bar{x}_i)^2$
Sample 1	4	11, 9, 13, 11	11	8
Sample 2	6	25, 28, 31, 27, 30, 33	29	42
Sample 3	5	19, 23, 19, 21, 20	20.4	11.2
	$n = 15$			61.2

In Example 10–1 we computed a "pooled variance" by combining the sample variances as follows:

$$s^2 = \frac{1}{n - k} \sum_{i=1}^{k} \sum_{j=1}^{n_i} (x_{ij} - \bar{x}_i)^2 = \frac{1}{15 - 3} \times (61.2) = 5.1.$$

The assumption is that the variance of each population from which a sample was taken is σ^2, which is then estimated by this pooled variance.

Suppose that in place of s^2 we had computed the total variability of the set of fifteen numbers, just as though they had come from a single population. In fact, if the population means are the same, and the variances are the same, and they are normally distributed, we *could* consider the data as a sample of fifteen from a single population. This over-all variability is indicated by the total sum of squared deviations:

$$\sum_{i=1}^{k} \sum_{j=1}^{n_i} (x_{ij} - \bar{x})^2,$$

where $\bar{x}$ denotes the "grand mean" of all of the data:

$$\bar{x} = \frac{1}{n} \sum_{i=1}^{k} \sum_{j=1}^{n_i} x_{ij} = \frac{1}{n} \sum_{i=1}^{k} n_i \bar{x}_i.$$

For the data above, the grand mean is $21\frac{1}{3}$ and the "total sum of squares" is $845\frac{1}{3}$. Dividing this by 14 one gets a number on the order of 60, far in excess of the pooled variance, 5.1.

An examination of the data shows that such a result is not at all surprising. The ranges of the individual samples are less than ten, whereas the range of all of the data is twenty-four. The situation is so obvious for this data (and it was made up to be so) that one would probably not even bother with a statistical test to decide that the population levels are quite different. The wide range of the data, it is clear, is caused mainly by this variation in population levels and is little related to the variability within each population, σ^2.

These sources of variation can be isolated as follows:

$$\sum_{i=1}^{k} \sum_{j=1}^{n_i} (x_{ij} - \bar{x})^2 = \sum_{i=1}^{k} \sum_{j=1}^{n_i} [(x_{ij} - \bar{x}_i) + (\bar{x}_i - \bar{x})]^2$$

$$= \sum_{i=1}^{k} \sum_{j=1}^{n_i} (x_{ij} - \bar{x}_i)^2 + \sum_{i=1}^{k} \sum_{j=1}^{n_i} (\bar{x}_i - \bar{x})^2$$

$$+ 2 \sum_{i=1}^{k} \sum_{j=1}^{n_i} (x_{ij} - \bar{x}_i)(\bar{x}_i - \bar{x})$$

$$= \sum_{i=1}^{k} \sum_{j=1}^{n_i} (x_{ij} - \bar{x}_i)^2 + \sum_{i=1}^{k} n_i(\bar{x}_i - \bar{x})^2 + 0.$$

(The value 0 for the third term results from the fact that $\sum_{j=1}^{n_i} (x_{ij} - \bar{x}_i) = 0$, a property of the sample mean familiar to us from Chapter 7.) The above relation for the data at hand is as follows:

$$845 \frac{1}{3} = 61 \frac{1}{5} + 784 \frac{2}{15}.$$

The first term on the right is referred to as the "within sample" variation, and the second term as the "between samples" variation.

Of course, it should be realized that even if the population means are identical, there will still be some between-samples variation, since the *sample* means will not be identical; and the between-samples variation measures the variance of the sample means about the grand mean. It can be shown that under the null hypothesis of no differences in sample means, the expected values of total, within-sample, and between-samples variations are the terms in the following relation (in that order):

$$(n - 1)\sigma^2 = (n - k)\sigma^2 + (k - 1)\sigma^2.$$

Hence, the expected values of

$$\frac{1}{n-1} \sum_{i=1}^{k} \sum_{j=1}^{n_i} (x_{ij} - \bar{x})^2, \quad \frac{1}{n-k} \sum_{i=1}^{k} \sum_{j=1}^{n_i} (x_{ij} - \bar{x}_i)^2, \text{ and } \frac{1}{k-1} \sum_{i=1}^{k} n_i(\bar{x}_i - \bar{x})^2$$

are to each equal to σ^2 under the null hypothesis H_0 of equality of means. But the expected value of the second of these (i.e., of the pooled variance) is σ^2 even when the population means are *not* equal. Thus, it is reasonable to take the ratio

$$\frac{\dfrac{1}{k-1} \sum_{i=1}^{k} n_i(\bar{x}_i - \bar{x})^2}{\dfrac{1}{n-k} \sum_{i=1}^{k} \sum_{j=1}^{n_i} (x_{ij} - \bar{x}_i)^2}$$

as a statistic useful in detecting inequality among the population means. If this ratio is near 1, we accept the null hypothesis; but if it is too large, the between-samples variation is excessive, and the null hypothesis is rejected. How large is "too large" is determined by the significance level of the test and by the distribution of the statistic under H_0; this distribution can be shown to be the F distribution (Table IV, page 258) with $k - 1$ and $n - k$ "degrees of freedom" for numerator and denominator, respectively.

For the data above, the value of the test ratio is

$$\frac{784.133/2}{61.2/12} = 77,$$

whereas the ninety-fifth percentile of the F distribution $(2, 12)$ is 3.89. Since $77 > 3.89$, we reject H_0 at the 5 per cent significance level.

In a situation in which the population means can be considered equal, $\bar{x}$ can of course be used as an estimate of the common value and the total sum of squares as an estimate of $(n - 1)\sigma^2$. In other words, the data can be considered a random sample (of size n) from a single population. The t test would be used to test hypotheses concerning μ. However, the test variable for this t test would not be independent of the variable used above to test the hypothesis of equality of means. It would be best, then, to use different samples for the two purposes in order that the significance levels be really meaningful.

It is helpful to think of the model for the single classification problem in the following way. If we let $E(X_{ij}) = \mu_i$ (not necessarily the same for all i), and $\mu = (1/n)\Sigma n_i\mu_i$, the quantity $\theta_i = \mu_i - \mu$ can be thought of as a contribution associated with the factor being studied. We notice, indeed, that

$$E(\bar{x}_i - \bar{x}) = E\left\{\frac{1}{n_i}\sum_j X_{ij} - \frac{1}{n}\sum_i\sum_j X_{ij}\right\}$$

$$= \mu_i - \mu = \theta_i.$$

Thus, we may think of each observation X_{ij} as being made up of an over-all "expected value" μ, plus θ_i, a contribution to expected value associated with the factor, plus a random deviation ϵ_{ij} about $\mu + \theta_i$:

$$X_{ij} = \mu + \theta_i + \epsilon_{ij},$$

where $E(\epsilon_{ij}) = 0$. Testing equality of means is then equivalent to testing $\theta_1 = \theta_2 = \cdots = \theta_k = 0$.

Operating characteristic functions have been worked out for various analysis of variance tests and are given, for example, in *Techniques of Statistical Analysis*, Eisenhart, Hastay, and Wallis (eds.) (McGraw-Hill, 1947), and in *Analysis and Design of Experiments*, H.B. Mann (Dover, 1949).

12.3.2 A Two-Factor Problem

A simple extension of the model discussed in the preceding section is one in which one provides for two "factors," A and B. Observations would now be gathered for each combination of a level of factor A and a level of factor B. Corresponding to the ith level of A and the jth level of B, the data might be of the form

$$X_{ij1}, X_{ij2}, \ldots, X_{ijk}.$$

We shall only discuss the case of a "single observation per cell," that is, $k = 1$, and shall call the single observation in the ij cell by the name X_{ij}, where $i = 1, \ldots, p$ and $j = 1, \ldots, q$.

It is assumed that the X_{ij}'s are normally distributed and independent and that they have equal variances, σ^2. We write:

$$\mu_{ij} = E(X_{ij}), \qquad \mu_{i\cdot} = \frac{1}{q} \sum_{j=1}^{q} \mu_{ij}, \qquad \mu_{\cdot j} = \frac{1}{p} \sum_{i=1}^{p} \mu_{ij}$$

and

$$\mu = \frac{1}{q} \sum_{j=1}^{q} \mu_{\cdot j} = \frac{1}{p} \sum_{i=1}^{p} \mu_{i\cdot} = \frac{1}{pq} \sum_{j=1}^{q} \sum_{i=1}^{p} \mu_{ij}.$$

We then let

$$a_i = \mu_{i\cdot} - \mu, \qquad b_j = \mu_{\cdot j} - \mu,$$

and make the *assumption* that

$$X_{ij} = \mu + a_i + b_j + \epsilon_{ij},$$

where ϵ_{ij} is a random deviation with expectation zero. To test the hypothesis that factor A has no effect, we test $a_i = 0$.

The sample counterparts of the parameters μ, a_i, and b_j are $\bar{x}$, $\bar{x}_{i\cdot} - \bar{x}$, and $\bar{x}_{\cdot j} - \bar{x}$, respectively, where

$$\bar{x}_{i\cdot} = \frac{1}{q} \sum_{i=1}^{q} x_{ij}, \qquad \bar{x}_{\cdot j} = \frac{1}{p} \sum_{i=1}^{p} x_{ij}, \qquad \text{and } \bar{x} = \frac{1}{pq} \sum_{i=1}^{q} \sum_{i=1}^{p} x_{ij}.$$

(Notice that $\bar{x}$ can also be computed as the average of the $\bar{x}_{\cdot j}$ or the $\bar{x}_{i\cdot}$.) It is easily seen that the expected values of these statistics are the corresponding sample parameters.

Again to test the effect of a factor we consider the total sum of squared deviations about the grand mean $\bar{x}$, which sum is broken up as follows:

$$\Sigma\Sigma(x_{ij} - \bar{x})^2 = \Sigma\Sigma[x_{ij} - (\bar{x}_{i\cdot} - \bar{x}) - (\bar{x}_{\cdot j} - \bar{x}) - \bar{x}]^2$$
$$+ \Sigma\Sigma(\bar{x}_{i\cdot} - \bar{x})^2 + \Sigma\Sigma(\bar{x}_{\cdot j} - \bar{x})^2.$$

It can be shown that under the null hypothesis of no effect from either factor A or factor B, the expected values of these terms in the breakup are as follows, keeping the same order:

$$(pq - 1)\sigma^2 = (p - 1)(q - 1)\sigma^2 + (p - 1)\sigma^2 + (q - 1)\sigma^2.$$

Thus, for example, the quantity

$$\frac{1}{p-1} \sum_{i=1}^{p} \sum_{j=1}^{q} (\bar{x}_{i\cdot} - \bar{x})^2 = \frac{q}{p-1} \sum_{i=1}^{p} (\bar{x}_{i\cdot} - \bar{x})^2$$

is an estimate of σ^2, if $a_i = 0$ for $i = 1, \ldots, p$. On the other hand, if factor A has an effect, this quantity will tend to be larger than σ^2 owing to the more significant deviations of the various $\bar{x}_{i\cdot}$ from $\bar{x}$. The ratio

$$\frac{\dfrac{1}{p-1} \sum \sum (\bar{x}_{i\cdot} - \bar{x})^2}{\dfrac{1}{(p-1)(q-1)} \sum \sum (x_{ij} - \bar{x}_{i\cdot} - \bar{x}_{\cdot j} + \bar{x})^2}$$

which has the $F(p - 1, (p - 1)(q - 1))$ distribution under the null hypothesis, is used as a test statistic for the presence of factor A, inasmuch as the denominator is a form of "pooled variance" which is a valid estimate of σ^2 even if the a_i's are not all zero. The hypothesis that $a_i = 0$ for all i is rejected if the test ratio is "too large," as determined by the given significance level in conjunction with the F distribution.

Example 12–f

Consider two factors with three levels each, and assume that one observation per cell is obtained, with the results in the following array:

Factor B	Factor A			$\bar{x}_{i\cdot}$	$\bar{x}_{i\cdot} - \bar{x}$
	Level 1	Level 2	Level 3		
Level 1	3	5	4	4	-7
Level 2	11	10	12	11	0
Level 3	16	21	17	18	7
$\bar{x}_{\cdot j}$	10	12	11	$\bar{x} = 11$	
$\bar{x}_{\cdot j} - \bar{x}$	-1	1	0		

The breakup in the sum of squared deviations about $\bar{x}$ is easily computed to be as follows:

$$312 = 12 + 294 + 6.$$

The test ratio (for the effect of factor A) is then

$$\frac{294/(3 - 1)}{12/(3 - 1)(3 - 1)} = 49.$$

This is considerably greater than 6.94, the ninety-fifth percentile of the F distribution with 2 and 4 degrees of freedom in numerator and denominator respectively.

We observe that had we been interested in testing for the effect of factor B, the corresponding test ratio would have been 1, which does not call for rejection of $b_j = 0$.

The design in such an experiment permits testing for the influence of one factor in the presence of another factor. However, the two test statistics, for the effect of factor A and the effect of factor B, are not independent, and a *joint* conclusion concerning the presence of the two factors does not have the reliability indicated by a simple combination of significance levels of the individual tests. For instance, if one test is conducted at the 2 per cent level and the other at the 5 per cent level, the significance level of the joint test is not necessarily $1 - (.98)(.95) \doteq 7$ per cent, as would be the case if the test statistics were independent.

On the other hand, the conclusion drawn about one factor does not depend on the conclusion drawn about the other, since the numerators in the test ratios used are independent random variables. Thus, we can state, in the above example, that we reject the hypothesis of no effect of factor B at the 5 per cent level, whether or not the other factor is significant. We can also conclude that factor A has no effect, at the 5 per cent significance level, whether or not factor B has an effect. As long as we do not attempt to combine these levels for a joint type of statement, both conclusions are correct.

Problems

12-8. A tensile test measures the quality of a spot-weld of an aluminum clad material. Three spot-welding machines are used to determine whether there exists a "machines effect" when welding a specified gage material. The coded results of each test are as follows:

Machine	Sample Number				
	1	2	3	4	5
A	3.2	4.1	3.5	3.0	3.1
B	4.9	4.5	4.5	4.0	4.2
C	3.0	2.9	3.7	3.5	4.2

(a) Is there a significant difference between machines?
(b) Estimate the process variance, assuming that it is the same for each machine.

12-9. Four analysts determine the yield of a given process. For convenience eighty was subtracted from the original data to give the following table of values:

	Analyst		
1	2	3	4
8	7	4	1
5	12	−2	6
−1	5	1	10
6	3		8
5	10		
3			

(a) Do the analysts differ significantly in their determinations of yield?
(b) Estimate the variance in determinations of yield, assuming that it is the same for all analysts.
(c) Would the conclusions in (a) and (b) have been different if the eighty had not been subtracted in giving the data?

12-10. The data in the following table refer to the purity of a product determined by a given method. The four levels of factor A represent boiling times. The two levels of factor B represent the solvents used. Low values of the given results correspond to high purity.

Level of Factor B	Level of Factor A			
	1	2	3	4
1	3.1	2.7	3.3	3.0
2	4.7	3.5	3.9	3.6

(a) Is the purity significantly affected by differences in boiling time?
(b) Is it a matter of indifference whether solvent 1 or solvent 2 is used?

12-11. A wear testing machine consists of four weighted brushes under which samples of fabric are fixed, in order to measure their resistances to abrasion. The loss of weight of the material after a given number of cycles is used as a measure of the resistance to abrasion. The data denote the loss of weight of four fabrics tested.

Fabric	Brush Position			
	1	2	3	4
A	1.93	2.38	2.20	2.25
B	2.55	2.72	2.75	2.70
C	2.40	2.68	2.31	2.28
D	2.33	2.40	2.28	2.25

(a) Is there a significant amount of variation associated with brush position?
(b) Are there significant differences in the resistance to abrasion among the four fabrics?

12.4 Decision Theory

In studying the two-decision statistical decision problem, in Chapter 8, it was assumed that in practice someone would be willing to choose an α and a β, or to decide whether the operating characteristic of a given test does or does not give adequate protection. In making such choices one must make, consciously or unconsciously, a subjective evaluation of the penalties connected with the errors which can result in using a statistical test. To make this evaluation more objective, the subject of decision theory has evolved. More precisely, it is still evolving.

Although the multidecision problem is important, let us consider here only the case (as in Chapter 8) in which a decision is to be made between the *two* actions A and B. To aid in the decision an experiment of chance is performed—a sample is taken from that population which, if completely known, would tell exactly which action is correct. A rule which gives a choice between actions A and B corresponding to each possible outcome of the sampling experiment has been termed a test of a hypothesis. Here we use the terminology of "statistical decision function":

Definition: A *statistical decision function* is a function on the space of outcomes of the appropriate sampling experiment which assigns one of the possible actions to each outcome.

Example 12–g

A lot of articles is to be rejected (action A) or accepted (action B) on the basis of the quality of a sample of two articles. The possible samples (describing articles as defective (D) or good (G)) are as follows:

$$s = (D, D), (D, G), \text{ or } (G, G),$$

and there are therefore the following eight decision functions:

s	$d_1(s)$	$d_2(s)$	$d_3(s)$	$d_4(s)$	$d_5(s)$	$d_6(s)$	$d_7(s)$	$d_8(s)$
D, D	A	B	A	A	B	A	B	B
D, G	A	A	B	A	B	B	A	B
G, G	A	A	A	B	A	B	B	B

The number of possible decision functions is considerably increased if we were to admit the choice of sample size as part of the decision problem. To take this into account we should need to assess the cost of sampling. Clearly if sampling were "free," the best procedure is to take a large a sample as possible; this is not always the case.

In general, a decision function partitions the set of possible sampling outcomes into as many pieces as there are actions. Here we have the set of outcomes which (for a given decision function) result in choosing A, and the complementary set of those outcomes which result in choosing B. The former has been called the "critical region" of the statistical test which is defined by the decision function.

12.4.1 The Risk Function

To determine the quality of a given decision function, we define a *risk function*, in terms of the actual population distribution. Suppose that the population is indexed by a parameter θ. For a given decision function, and a given population distribution (called a "state of nature") as described by a given value of θ, a risk function assigns a numerical risk, or loss which would be incurred if that decision function is used in a case in which that value of θ is correct.

Let us assume that a choice is to be made between actions a_1, a_2, ... For each state of nature, and each action a_i we define a *loss function*, $L(\theta, a_i)$, as the numerical loss incurred if the state of nature is actually θ and action a_i is taken. The *risk function* is then defined, in terms of the loss function, corresponding to each state of nature and each decision function $d(s)$ as the expected loss:

$$\rho(\theta, d) = \Sigma L(\theta, d(s)) P_\theta(s),$$

where the sum extends over all outcomes of the sampling experiment, and $P_\theta(s)$ denotes the probability of a given outcome s, assuming that θ is the state of nature.

For the case at hand, $d(s)$ has only two "values," A or B, and thus we can write

$$\rho(\theta, d) = L(\theta, A) P_\theta [d(s) \text{ chooses } A] + L(\theta, B) P_\theta [d(s) \text{ chooses } B].$$

Example 12–h

Suppose that the articles of Example 12–g are flash bulbs and that action A is to reject the lot (junk the bulbs in the lot) and that action B is to pass the lot and sell the flash bulbs for 15 cents each, with a "double-your-money-back" guarantee. Suppose that the lot contains 200 bulbs, so that the lot fraction defective p is not changed appreciably when two are removed for testing. Testing consists in flashing the bulbs, a procedure which ruins them, so that only 198 bulbs can be sold. Let us assume a loss of one dollar, in having the lot hauled away, if the lot is rejected. The loss function is given as follows:

$$L(p, A) = 1.00,$$
$$L(p, B) = -.15 \times 198 + .30 \times (198p) = -.15 \times 198 \times (1 - 2p),$$

where $198p$ is the number of defectives in the untested portion of the lot. We can then evaluate the risk function, for each p and $d_i(s)$. Consider the decision function called $d_1(s)$ in Example 12–g, which calls for rejection of the lot no matter what the outcome of the sampling experiment. For each s, $L(p, d_1(s)) = 1.00$, and hence $\rho(p, d_1) = 1.00$. For decision function $d_6(s)$, which calls for rejection if both articles selected are defective, we have

$$\rho(p, d_6) = L(p, A)P_p(\text{reject lot}) + L(p, B)P_p(\text{accept lot})$$
$$= 1.00p^2 + [-.15 \times 198(1 - 2p)][(1 - p)^2 + 2p(1 - p)].$$

In similar fashion we can compute $\rho(p, d_i)$ for each of the eight decision functions possible, as a function of the state of nature, p.

12.4.2 Principles of Choice

Even though risks have been attached to each pair consisting of a decision function and a state of nature, it is not usually clear as to what is the *best* decision function. Several principles of selecting a "best" decision function have been proposed, among them these four: (1) minimax principle, (2) modified minimax principle, (3) minimax regret, and (4) the Bayes principle.

The minimax principle results in conservative behavior. It consists in choosing that decision function for which the maximum risk is a minimum, i.e., so as to achieve the "minimax risk":

$$\min_d [\max_\theta \rho(\theta, d)].$$

Then, no matter what the actual state of nature, the expected loss does not exceed this minimax amount. With this principle, one expects the worst and prepares for it.

The modified minimax principle selects a decision function d so as to minimize

$$\alpha \max_\theta \rho(\theta, d) + (1 - \alpha) \min_\theta \rho(\theta, \alpha)$$

where α measures one's optimism.

The minimax regret principle selects that decision function which minimizes the maximum "regret," which is defined as the loss we could have been spared had we known the state of nature:

$$r(\theta, d) = \rho(\theta, d) - \min_d \rho(\theta, d).$$

The principle of Bayes selects that decision function which minimizes the expected risk corresponding to a preassigned probability distribution on the states of nature, i.e., which maximizes

$$\sum_i P(\theta = \theta_i)\rho(\theta_i, d)$$

(written as though θ could assume only a discrete set of values).

Example 12–i

Referring to the preceding example, it is easily seen that for $p = 1$ the risks are at least 1.00 for every d, and hence the maxima are at least 1. The minimum maximum is therefore 1, which is attained by using action d_1; junk the lot no matter how the sample turns out.

If p can be considered as not possibly greater than 1/2, there are clearly some risks which are negative. An appropriate "a priori distribution" for p, to use Bayes' principle, might be that $200p$ is approximately a Poisson variable, with mean $200p_o$, where p_o is the probability (assumed constant) that the flash bulb manufacturing process turns out a defective bulb.

Example 12–j

To simplify the computations in illustrating the choices of decision function, let us consider that there are just three states of nature, θ_1, θ_2, and θ_3, and three decision functions, d_1, d_2, and d_3. Suppose further that the risk function is shown in the following array:

	θ_1	θ_2	θ_3
d_1	0	4	2
d_2	2	2	−2
d_3	5	−4	0

The minimum of the maxima in the rows is attained by using d_2, which is therefore the "minimax" solution of the problem.

The regret function is as shown in the following array:

	θ_1	θ_2	θ_3
d_1	0	8	4
d_2	2	6	0
d_3	5	0	2

The minimax regret is obtained by choosing d_3.

Finally, if we assume that θ_1, θ_2, θ_3 occur with probabilities 3/4, 1/4, 0, respectively, the expected risks are 1, 2, and 11/4, corresponding to d_1, d_2, and d_3, respectively. The minimum is achieved by selecting d_1, which is thus a Bayes solution.

We observe that each principle points to a different decision function as the "best."

Often the choosing of a decision function is considered as playing a game against "Nature," although the concept of "Nature" as a conscious force doing its best to get the better of the statistician may well be untenable. The theory of games is by no means complete and does not as yet offer absolutely optimal means of playing games (or of making statistical decisions). On the other hand, applying decision theory, even in its present form, serves to require a study of the numerical risks involved in wrong decisions. Such a study is certainly of value.

Problems

12-12. Refer to Example 12–g, and list the twelve possible decision functions if part of the decision is to decide whether to take a sample of size one or a sample of size two.

12-13. A coin is tossed once, and a statistician must choose between $p = 1/4$ and $p = 3/4$ as the probability of heads, on the basis of the outcome of that one toss.

(a) List the four possible decision functions.

(b) Let the loss function be $L(p, a) = (p - a)^2$, where p (the state of nature) has one of the values 1/4 or 3/4, and where a also has one of these values, representing the action of choosing the corresponding value as p. Determine (in tabular form) the risk function $\rho(p_i, d_j)$, that is, the expected loss if p_i is the state of nature and the decision function used is d_i.

(c) Determine the minimax decision function.

12-14. For the risk function given in the following array, determine the minimax decision function, the minimax-regret decision function, and the Bayes decision function corresponding to the assumed probabilities 1/4, 1/4, and 1/2 for the states of nature, in the order given.

Decision Functions	States of Nature		
	1	2	3
1	2	−3	−1
2	4	0	5
3	0	2	−2
4	1	1	−2

Appendix A
Notation

A major obstacle to becoming at ease in the study of a new technical subject is ∍ notation peculiar to it. This is especially true in statistics because of certain ᴛations which, while second nature to the working statistician, have a somewhat ᵉerent basis from that of usual mathematical notation.

In mathematical notation, the quantities $f(t)$ and $f(R)$ denote the values of a ᵖcific function $f(\ )$, obtained by "plugging" t and R, respectively, into that ᴀction. Thus, if $f(x) = x^2$, then $f(t) = t^2$ and $f(R) = R^2$. However, a common ᵗistical notation is that $f(t)$ and $f(R)$ refer to two distinct functions—the first, ∍ density function of the random variable t, and the second, the density function of ∍ random variable R (whatever those random variables might be). This is ᴀvenient, when understood. But it does lend further confusion to the concepts ᴀ random variable and of specific values of the random variable, and it becomes ᴵly mystifying when one attempts to translate the symbol $F(x)$ into probability ᵍuage: $F(x) = P(x \leq x)$.

In the earlier portions of the book we have consistently used capital letters ᵧ, etc.) to refer to random variables. Thus, X refers to a particular assignment ᵛalues to outcomes of a chance experiment, together with an appropriate proba- ᴛy distribution (defined either on the outcomes, or as a distribution function on ᵉset of corresponding values). We have used lower case letters to denote par- ᴵlar values of a random variable. A distribution function or a density function ᵉlated to the corresponding random variable by means of a subscript on the func- ᴀ, as in $F_X(x)$ and $f_X(x)$, although we have often dropped the subscript when ᵉe is no ambiguity in so doing. This notation emphasizes the distinction between ᵉrandom variable and the "dummy" variable used in writing a formula for the ᵣibution or density functions.

As to the multitudinous constants which occur in statistics, some classes of users ᵉ adopted (formally or informally) certain "standard" notations, but departures ᴵn these are so common that it hardly pays to present any one such system as the ᴵword. Most of the notations used in this book are used by many other writers, not by all.

The notation $E(X)$ for the expected value of a random variable resembles the

notation for a mathematical function, but it is not the same idea, of course, since
is not a specific number—rather a function. Mathematically, $E(X)$ is a linea
operator on X, symbolizing an averaging or integrating (with respect to the weigh
ing of values given by the distribution of probability among those values).

The symbols most frequently used in this book are listed in the following glossar
with brief explanations and references to the pages on which they are first introduce

Glossary of Symbols

Symbol	Explanation	Page referen
$n!$	$n(n-1) \cdots 3 \cdot 2 \cdot 1$	
$\binom{n}{k}$	The number of combinations of k things taken from n	
$E, F, \ldots$	Events, or sets of outcomes of a random experiment	
$P(E)$	The probability assigned to the event E	
p	Probability of "success" in a chance experiment with two outcomes, "success" and "failure"	23,
q	$1-p$	23,
n	(1) Number of trials in a binomial situation	23,
	(2) Sample size	
x_i	(1) One of the possible values of a discrete random variable	
	(2) One of the observations of a sample	
	(3) The center of the ith class interval in a frequency distribution	
$p(x_i)$	The probability assigned to the value x_i in a discrete distribution	
f_i	The frequency of the value x_i in a frequency distribution	
$\bar{x}$	Mean of a specific sample of observations on a random variable X	
$s_x{}^2$	The sample variance	
$X, Y, \ldots$	Random variables	

Symbol	Explanation	Page reference
$t, F, R, \chi^2, \ldots$	Certain statistics, or random variables computed from a sample	176, 220, 198, 83
X_i	The ith observation in a sample, considered as a random variable	109
$\overline{X}$	The sample mean, $\frac{1}{n} \sum X_i$, considered as a random variable	162
$F_X(x)$	$P(X \leq x)$, the (cumulative) distribution function of the random variable X	33
$F(x)$	The distribution function, when there is no ambiguity as to which random variable it describes	33
$f_X(x)$	The density function of the continuous random variable X, obtained as $\frac{d}{dx} F_X(x)$	72
$\mu_X, \mu,$ or $E(X)$	The expected value of X	46, 79
$\sigma_X^2, \sigma^2,$ or var X	The variance of X, $E[(X - \mu)^2]$	51, 80
Z	The standard normal random variable	87
$\Phi(z), \phi(z)$	The distribution and density functions of the standard normal variable. Note: $\Phi(z) = F_Z(z)$.	86
H_0, H_1	The hypothesis being tested and the alternative hypothesis	132
$P_\theta(E)$	The probability of the event E computed assuming that the parameter in question has the value θ	135
α, β	Sizes of the type I and type II errors	135
x_p	The $100p$th percentile of the distribution given by $F(x)$	42

Appendix B
Tables

REFERENCES FOR MORE EXTENSIVE TABLES

Fisher, R.A., and Yates, F., *Statistical Tables for Biological, Agricultural, and Medical Research*, Hafner Publishing Company, New York, 1949.

Hald, A., *Statistical Tables and Formulas*, John Wiley & Sons, New York, 1952.

Molina, E.C., *Poisson's Exponential Binomial Limit*, D. Van Nostrand Company, New York, 1949.

Pearson, E.S., (Ed), *Biometrika Tables for Statisticians*, Cambridge University Press, London, 1954.

Table I. Values of the Standard Normal Distribution Function

$$\Phi(z) = \int_{-\infty}^{z} \frac{1}{\sqrt{2\pi}} e^{-u^2/2} \, du = P(Z \le z)$$

z	0	1	2	3	4	5	6	7	8	9
−3.	.0013	.0010	.0007	.0005	.0003	.0002	.0002	.0001	.0001	.0000
−2.9	.0019	.0018	.0017	.0017	.0016	.0016	.0015	.0015	.0014	.0014
−2.8	.0026	.0025	.0024	.0023	.0023	.0022	.0021	.0021	.0020	.0019
−2.7	.0035	.0034	.0033	.0032	.0031	.0030	.0029	.0028	.0027	.0026
−2.6	.0047	.0045	.0044	.0043	.0041	.0040	.0039	.0038	.0037	.0036
−2.5	.0062	.0060	.0059	.0057	.0055	.0054	.0052	.0051	.0049	.0048
−2.4	.0082	.0080	.0078	.0075	.0073	.0071	.0069	.0068	.0066	.0064
−2.3	.0107	.0104	.0102	.0099	.0096	.0094	.0091	.0089	.0087	.0084
−2.2	.0139	.0136	.0132	.0129	.0126	.0122	.0119	.0116	.0113	.0110
−2.1	.0179	.0174	.0170	.0166	.0162	.0158	.0154	.0150	.0146	.0143
−2.0	.0228	.0222	.0217	.0212	.0207	.0202	.0197	.0192	.0188	.0183
−1.9	.0287	.0281	.0274	.0268	.0262	.0256	.0250	.0244	.0238	.0233
−1.8	.0359	.0352	.0344	.0336	.0329	.0322	.0314	.0307	.0300	.0294
−1.7	.0446	.0436	.0427	.0418	.0409	.0401	.0392	.0384	.0375	.0367
−1.6	.0548	.0537	.0526	.0516	.0505	.0495	.0485	.0475	.0465	.0455
−1.5	.0668	.0655	.0643	.0630	.0618	.0606	.0594	.0582	.0570	.0559
−1.4	.0808	.0793	.0778	.0764	.0749	.0735	.0722	.0708	.0694	.0681
−1.3	.0968	.0951	.0934	.0918	.0901	.0885	.0869	.0853	.0838	.0823
−1.2	.1151	.1131	.1112	.1093	.1075	.1056	.1038	.1020	.1003	.0985
−1.1	.1357	.1335	.1314	.1292	.1271	.1251	.1230	.1210	.1190	.1170
−1.0	.1587	.1562	.1539	.1515	.1492	.1469	.1446	.1423	.1401	.1379
−.9	.1841	.1814	.1788	.1762	.1736	.1711	.1685	.1660	.1635	.1611
−.8	.2119	.2090	.2061	.2033	.2005	.1977	.1949	.1922	.1894	.1867
−.7	.2420	.2389	.2358	.2327	.2297	.2266	.2236	.2206	.2177	.2148
−.6	.2743	.2709	.2676	.2643	.2611	.2578	.2546	.2514	.2483	.2451
−.5	.3085	.3050	.3015	.2981	.2946	.2912	.2877	.2843	.2810	.2776
−.4	.3446	.3409	.3372	.3336	.3300	.3264	.3228	.3192	.3156	.3121
−.3	.3821	.3783	.3745	.3707	.3669	.3632	.3594	.3557	.3520	.3483
−.2	.4207	.4168	.4129	.4090	.4052	.4013	.3974	.3936	.3897	.3859
−.1	.4602	.4562	.4522	.4483	.4443	.4404	.4364	.4325	.4286	.4247
−.0	.5000	.4960	.4920	.4880	.4840	.4801	.4761	.4721	.4681	.4641

Table I. Values of the Standard Normal
Distribution Function (Continued)

z	0	1	2	3	4	5	6	7	8	9
.0	.5000	.5040	.5080	.5120	.5160	.5199	.5239	.5279	.5319	.5359
.1	.5398	.5438	.5478	.5517	.5557	.5596	.5636	.5675	.5714	.5753
.2	.5793	.5832	.5871	.5910	.5948	.5987	.6026	.6064	.6103	.6141
.3	.6179	.6217	.6255	.6293	.6331	.6368	.6406	.6443	.6480	.6517
.4	.6554	.6591	.6628	.6664	.6700	.6736	.6772	.6808	.6844	.6879
.5	.6915	.6950	.6985	.7019	.7054	.7088	.7123	.7157	.7190	.7224
.6	.7257	.7291	.7324	.7357	.7389	.7422	.7454	.7486	.7517	.7549
.7	.7580	.7611	.7642	.7673	.7703	.7734	.7764	.7794	.7823	.7852
.8	.7881	.7910	.7939	.7967	.7995	.8023	.8051	.8078	.8106	.8133
.9	.8159	.8186	.8212	.8238	.8264	.8289	.8315	.8340	.8365	.8389
1.0	.8413	.8438	.8461	.8485	.8508	.8531	.8554	.8577	.8599	.8621
1.1	.8643	.8665	.8686	.8708	.8729	.8749	.8770	.8790	.8810	.8830
1.2	.8849	.8869	.8888	.8907	.8925	.8944	.8962	.8980	.8997	.9015
1.3	.9032	.9049	.9066	.9082	.9099	.9115	.9131	.9147	.9162	.9177
1.4	.9192	.9207	.9222	.9236	.9251	.9265	.9278	.9292	.9306	.9319
1.5	.9332	.9345	.9357	.9370	.9382	.9394	.9406	.9418	.9430	.9441
1.6	.9452	.9463	.9474	.9484	.9495	.9505	.9515	.9525	.9535	.9545
1.7	.9554	.9564	.9573	.9582	.9591	.9599	.9608	.9616	.9625	.9633
1.8	.9641	.9648	.9656	.9664	.9671	.9678	.9686	.9693	.9700	.9706
1.9	.9713	.9719	.9726	.9732	.9738	.9744	.9750	.9756	.9762	.9767
2.0	.9772	.9778	.9783	.9788	.9793	.9798	.9803	.9808	.9812	.9817
2.1	.9821	.9826	.9830	.9834	.9838	.9842	.9846	.9850	.9854	.9857
2.2	.9861	.9864	.9868	.9871	.9874	.9878	.9881	.9884	.9887	.9890
2.3	.9893	.9896	.9898	.9901	.9904	.9906	.9909	.9911	.9913	.9916
2.4	.9918	.9920	.9922	.9925	.9927	.9929	.9931	.9932	.9934	.9936
2.5	.9938	.9940	.9941	.9943	.9945	.9946	.9948	.9949	.9951	.9952
2.6	.9953	.9955	.9956	.9957	.9959	.9960	.9961	.9962	.9963	.9964
2.7	.9965	.9966	.9967	.9968	.9969	.9970	.9971	.9972	.9973	.9974
2.8	.9974	.9975	.9976	.9977	.9977	.9978	.9979	.9979	.9980	.9981
2.9	.9981	.9982	.9982	.9983	.9984	.9984	.9985	.9985	.9986	.9986
3.	.9987	.9990	.9993	.9995	.9997	.9998	.9998	.9999	.9999	1.0000

Note 1: If a random variable X is not "standard," its values must be "standardized": $Z = (X - \mu)/\sigma$. That is, $P(X \leq x) = \Phi\left(\dfrac{x - \mu}{\sigma}\right)$.

Note 2: For "two-tail" probabilities, see Tables Ic and IV.

Note 3: For $z \geq 4$, $\Phi(z) = 1$ to four decimal places; for $z \leq -4$, $\Phi(z) = 0$ to four decimal places.

Table Ib. Two-Tail Probabilities for the Standard Normal Distribution

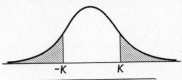

Table Ia. Percentiles of the Standard Normal Distribution

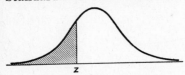

$P(Z \leq z)$	z
.001	-3.09
.005	-2.58
.01	-2.33
.02	-2.05
.03	-1.88
.04	-1.75
.05	-1.64
.10	-1.28
.15	-1.04
.20	$-.84$
.30	$-.52$
.40	$-.25$
.50	0
.60	.25
.70	.52
.80	.84
.85	1.04
.90	1.28
.95	1.64
.96	1.75
.97	1.88
.98	2.05
.99	2.33
.995	2.58
.999	3.09

K	$P(|Z| > K)$
1.04	.30
1.15	.25
1.28	.20
1.44	.15
1.64	.10
1.70	.09
1.75	.08
1.81	.07
1.88	.06
1.96	.05
2.05	.04
2.17	.03
2.33	.02
2.58	.01
2.81	.005
3.09	.002
3.29	.001

Table II. Percentiles of the Chi-Square Distribution

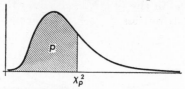

Degrees of Freedom	$\chi^2_{.005}$	$\chi^2_{.01}$	$\chi^2_{.025}$	$\chi^2_{.05}$	$\chi^2_{.10}$	$\chi^2_{.20}$	$\chi^2_{.30}$	$\chi^2_{.50}$	$\chi^2_{.70}$	$\chi^2_{.80}$	$\chi^2_{.90}$	$\chi^2_{.95}$	$\chi^2_{.975}$	$\chi^2_{.99}$	$\chi^2_{.995}$
1	.000	.000	.001	.004	.016	.064	.148	.455	1.07	1.64	2.71	3.84	5.02	6.63	7.88
2	.010	.020	.051	.103	.211	.446	.713	1.39	2.41	3.22	4.61	5.99	7.38	9.21	10.6
3	.072	.115	.216	.352	.584	1.00	1.42	2.37	3.66	4.64	6.25	7.81	9.35	11.3	12.8
4	.207	.297	.484	.711	1.06	1.65	2.20	3.36	4.88	5.99	7.78	9.49	11.1	13.3	14.9
5	.412	.554	.831	1.15	1.61	2.34	3.00	4.35	6.06	7.29	9.24	11.1	12.8	15.1	16.7
6	.676	.872	1.24	1.64	2.20	3.07	3.83	5.35	7.23	8.56	10.6	12.6	14.4	16.8	18.5
7	.989	1.24	1.69	2.17	2.83	3.82	4.67	6.35	8.38	9.80	12.0	14.1	16.0	18.5	20.3
8	1.34	1.65	2.18	2.73	3.49	4.59	5.53	7.34	9.52	11.0	13.4	15.5	17.5	20.1	22.0
9	1.73	2.09	2.70	3.33	4.17	5.38	6.39	8.34	10.7	12.2	14.7	16.9	19.0	21.7	23.6
10	2.16	2.56	3.25	3.94	4.87	6.18	7.27	9.34	11.8	13.4	16.0	18.3	20.5	23.2	25.2
11	2.60	3.05	3.82	4.57	5.58	6.99	8.15	10.3	12.9	14.6	17.3	19.7	21.9	24.7	26.8
12	3.07	3.57	4.40	5.23	6.30	7.81	9.03	11.3	14.0	15.8	18.5	21.0	23.3	26.2	28.3
13	3.57	4.11	5.01	5.89	7.04	8.63	9.93	12.3	15.1	17.0	19.8	22.4	24.7	27.7	29.8
14	4.07	4.66	5.63	6.57	7.79	9.47	10.8	13.3	16.2	18.2	21.1	23.7	26.1	29.1	31.3
15	4.60	5.23	6.26	7.26	8.55	10.3	11.7	14.3	17.3	19.3	22.3	25.0	27.5	30.6	32.8
16	5.14	5.81	6.91	7.96	9.31	11.2	12.6	15.3	18.4	20.5	23.5	26.3	28.8	32.0	34.3
17	5.70	6.41	7.56	8.67	10.1	12.0	13.5	16.3	19.5	21.6	24.8	27.6	30.2	33.4	35.7
18	6.26	7.01	8.23	9.39	10.9	12.9	14.4	17.3	20.6	22.8	26.0	28.9	31.5	34.8	37.2
19	6.83	7.63	8.91	10.1	11.7	13.7	15.4	18.3	21.7	23.9	27.2	30.1	32.9	36.2	38.6
20	7.43	8.26	9.59	10.9	12.4	14.6	16.3	19.3	22.8	25.0	28.4	31.4	34.2	37.6	40.0
21	8.03	8.90	10.3	11.6	13.2	15.4	17.2	20.3	23.9	26.2	29.6	32.7	35.5	38.9	41.4
22	8.64	9.54	11.0	12.3	14.0	16.3	18.1	21.3	24.9	27.3	30.8	33.9	36.8	40.3	42.8
23	9.26	10.2	11.7	13.1	14.8	17.2	19.0	22.3	26.0	28.4	32.0	35.2	38.1	41.6	44.2
24	9.89	10.9	12.4	13.8	15.7	18.1	19.9	23.3	27.1	29.6	33.2	36.4	39.4	43.0	45.6
25	10.5	11.5	13.1	14.6	16.5	18.9	20.9	24.3	28.2	30.7	34.4	37.7	40.6	44.3	46.9
26	11.2	12.2	13.8	15.4	17.3	19.8	21.8	25.3	29.2	31.8	35.6	38.9	41.9	45.6	48.3
27	11.8	12.9	14.6	16.2	18.1	20.7	22.7	26.3	30.3	32.9	36.7	40.1	43.2	47.0	49.6
28	12.5	13.6	15.3	16.9	18.9	21.6	23.6	27.3	31.4	34.0	37.9	41.3	44.5	48.3	51.0
29	13.1	14.3	16.0	17.7	19.8	22.5	24.6	28.3	32.5	35.1	39.1	42.6	45.7	49.6	52.3
30	13.8	15.0	16.8	18.5	20.6	23.4	25.5	29.3	33.5	36.2	40.3	43.8	47.0	50.9	53.7
40	20.7	22.1	24.4	26.5	29.0	32.3	34.9	39.3	44.2	47.3	51.8	55.8	59.3	63.7	66.8
50	28.0	29.7	32.3	34.8	37.7	41.4	44.3	49.3	54.7	58.2	63.2	67.5	71.4	76.2	79.5
60	35.5	37.5	40.5	43.2	46.5	50.6	53.8	59.3	65.2	69.0	74.4	79.1	83.3	88.4	92.0

Note: For degrees of freedom $k > 30$, use $\chi_p{}^2 = \frac{1}{2}(z_p + \sqrt{2k-1})^2$, where z_p is the corresponding percentile of the standard normal distribution.

This table is adapted from Table VIII of *Biometrika Tables for Statisticians*, Vol. 1, 1954, by E.S. Pearson and H.O. Hartley, originally prepared by Catherine M. Thompson, with the kind permission of the editor of *Biometrika*.

Table III. Percentiles of the *t* Distribution

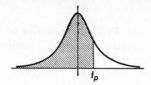

Degrees of Freedom	$t_{.55}$	$t_{.60}$	$t_{.65}$	$t_{.70}$	$t_{.75}$	$t_{.80}$	$t_{.85}$	$t_{.90}$	$t_{.95}$	$t_{.975}$	$t_{.99}$	$t_{.995}$	$t_{.9995}$
1	.158	.325	.510	.727	1.00	1.38	1.96	3.08	6.31	12.7	31.8	63.7	637
2	.142	.289	.445	.617	.816	1.06	1.39	1.89	2.92	4.30	6.96	9.92	31.6
3	.137	.277	.424	.584	.765	.978	1.25	1.64	2.35	3.18	4.54	5.84	12.9
4	.134	.271	.414	.569	.741	.941	1.19	1.53	2.13	2.78	3.75	4.60	8.61
5	.132	.267	.408	.559	.727	.920	1.16	1.48	2.01	2.57	3.36	4.03	6.86
6	.131	.265	.404	.553	.718	.906	1.13	1.44	1.94	2.45	3.14	3.71	5.96
7	.130	.263	.402	.549	.711	.896	1.12	1.42	1.90	2.36	3.00	3.50	5.40
8	.130	.262	.399	.546	.706	.889	1.11	1.40	1.86	2.31	2.90	3.36	5.04
9	.129	.261	.398	.543	.703	.883	1.10	1.38	1.83	2.26	2.82	3.25	4.78
10	.129	.260	.397	.542	.700	.879	1.09	1.37	1.81	2.23	2.76	3.17	4.59
11	.129	.260	.396	.540	.697	.876	1.09	1.36	1.80	2.20	2.72	3.11	4.44
12	.128	.259	.395	.539	.695	.873	1.08	1.36	1.78	2.18	2.68	3.06	4.32
13	.128	.259	.394	.538	.694	.870	1.08	1.35	1.77	2.16	2.65	3.01	4.22
14	.128	.258	.393	.537	.692	.868	1.08	1.34	1.76	2.14	2.62	2.98	4.14
15	.128	.258	.393	.536	.691	.866	1.07	1.34	1.75	2.13	2.60	2.95	4.07
16	.128	.258	.392	.535	.690	.865	1.07	1.34	1.75	2.12	2.58	2.92	4.02
17	.128	.257	.392	.534	.689	.863	1.07	1.33	1.74	2.11	2.57	2.90	3.96
18	.127	.257	.392	.534	.688	.862	1.07	1.33	1.73	2.10	2.55	2.88	3.92
19	.127	.257	.391	.533	.688	.861	1.07	1.33	1.73	2.09	2.54	2.86	3.88
20	.127	.257	.391	.533	.687	.860	1.06	1.32	1.72	2.09	2.53	2.84	3.85
21	.127	.257	.391	.532	.686	.859	1.06	1.32	1.72	2.08	2.52	2.83	3.82
22	.127	.256	.390	.532	.686	.858	1.06	1.32	1.72	2.07	2.51	2.82	3.79
23	.127	.256	.390	.532	.685	.858	1.06	1.32	1.71	2.07	2.50	2.81	3.77
24	.127	.256	.390	.531	.685	.857	1.06	1.32	1.71	2.06	2.49	2.80	3.74
25	.127	.256	.390	.531	.684	.856	1.06	1.32	1.71	2.06	2.48	2.79	3.72
26	.127	.256	.390	.531	.684	.856	1.06	1.32	1.71	2.06	2.48	2.78	3.71
27	.127	.256	.389	.531	.684	.855	1.06	1.31	1.70	2.05	2.47	2.77	3.69
28	.127	.256	.389	.530	.683	.855	1.06	1.31	1.70	2.05	2.47	2.76	3.67
29	.127	.256	.389	.530	.683	.854	1.05	1.31	1.70	2.04	2.46	2.76	3.66
30	.127	.256	.389	.530	.683	.854	1.05	1.31	1.70	2.04	2.46	2.75	3.65
∞	.126	.253	.385	.524	.674	.842	1.04	1.28	1.64	1.96	2.33	2.58	3.29

Note 1: For the lower percentiles, use the relation $t_\alpha = -t_{1-\alpha}$. In particular, $t_{.50} = -t_{.50} = 0$. For example, for 6 degrees of freedom, $t_{.35} = -t_{.65} = -.404$.

Note 2: For two-tail probabilities, see Table IV.

This table is abridged from Table II of Fisher and Yates, *Statistical Tables for Biological, Agricultural, and Medical Research* (5th ed.)/Fisher, *Statistical Methods for Research Workers*, published by Oliver and Boyd, Ltd., Edinburgh, by permission of the authors and publishers.

Table IVa. $F_{.95}$, Ninety-Fifth Percentiles of the F Distribution

Numerator Degrees of Freedom

	1	2	3	4	5	6	8	10	12	15	20	24	30
1	161	200	216	225	230	234	239	242	244	246	248	249	250
2	18.5	19.0	19.2	19.2	19.3	19.3	19.4	19.4	19.4	19.4	19.4	19.5	19.5
3	10.1	9.55	9.28	9.12	9.01	8.94	8.85	8.79	8.74	8.70	8.66	8.64	8.62
4	7.71	6.94	6.59	6.39	6.26	6.16	6.04	5.96	5.91	5.86	5.80	5.77	5.75
5	6.61	5.79	5.41	5.19	5.05	4.95	4.82	4.74	4.68	4.62	4.56	4.53	4.50
6	5.99	5.14	4.76	4.53	4.39	4.28	4.15	4.06	4.00	3.94	3.87	3.84	3.81
7	5.59	4.74	4.35	4.12	3.97	3.87	3.73	3.64	3.57	3.51	3.44	3.41	3.38
8	5.32	4.46	4.07	3.84	3.69	3.58	3.44	3.35	3.28	3.22	3.15	3.12	3.08
9	5.12	4.26	3.86	3.63	3.48	3.37	3.23	3.14	3.07	3.01	2.94	2.90	2.86
10	4.96	4.10	3.71	3.48	3.33	3.22	3.07	2.98	2.91	2.85	2.77	2.74	2.70
11	4.84	3.98	3.59	3.36	3.20	3.09	2.95	2.85	2.79	2.72	2.65	2.61	2.57
12	4.75	3.89	3.49	3.26	3.11	3.00	2.85	2.75	2.69	2.62	2.54	2.51	2.47
13	4.67	3.81	3.41	3.18	3.03	2.92	2.77	2.67	2.60	2.53	2.46	2.42	2.38
14	4.60	3.74	3.34	3.11	2.96	2.85	2.70	2.60	2.53	2.46	2.39	2.35	2.3
15	4.54	3.68	3.29	3.06	2.90	2.79	2.64	2.54	2.48	2.40	2.33	2.29	2.25
16	4.49	3.63	3.24	3.01	2.85	2.74	2.59	2.49	2.42	2.35	2.28	2.24	2.1
17	4.45	3.59	3.20	2.96	2.81	2.70	2.55	2.45	2.38	2.31	2.23	2.19	2.1
18	4.41	3.55	3.16	2.93	2.77	2.66	2.51	2.41	2.34	2.27	2.19	2.15	2.1
19	4.38	3.52	3.13	2.90	2.74	2.63	2.48	2.38	2.31	2.23	2.16	2.11	2.0
20	4.35	3.49	3.10	2.87	2.71	2.60	2.45	2.35	2.28	2.20	2.12	2.08	2.0
21	4.32	3.47	3.07	2.84	2.68	2.57	2.42	2.32	2.25	2.18	2.10	2.05	2.0
22	4.30	3.44	3.05	2.82	2.66	2.55	2.40	2.30	2.23	2.15	2.07	2.03	1.9
23	4.28	3.42	3.03	2.80	2.64	2.53	2.37	2.27	2.20	2.13	2.05	2.01	1.9
24	4.26	3.40	3.01	2.78	2.62	2.51	2.36	2.25	2.18	2.11	2.03	1.98	1.9
25	4.24	3.39	2.99	2.76	2.60	2.49	2.34	2.24	2.16	2.09	2.01	1.96	1.9
30	4.17	3.32	2.92	2.69	2.53	2.42	2.27	2.16	2.09	2.01	1.93	1.89	1.8
40	4.08	3.23	2.84	2.61	2.45	2.34	2.18	2.08	2.00	1.92	1.84	1.79	1.7
60	4.00	3.15	2.76	2.53	2.37	2.25	2.10	1.99	1.92	1.84	1.75	1.70	1.6

Denominator Degrees of Freedom

This table is adapted from Table XVIII in *Biometrika Tables for Statisticians* Vol. I, 1954, by E.S. Pearson and H.O. Hartley, originally prepared by M. Merrington and C.M. Thompson, with the kind permission of the editor of *Biometrika*.

Table IVb. $F_{.99}$, **Ninety-Ninth Percentiles of the F Distribution**

Numerator Degrees of Freedom

	1	2	3	4	5	6	8	10	12	15	20	24	30
1	4050	5000	5400	5620	5760	5860	5980	6060	6110	6160	6210	6235	6260
2	98.5	99.0	99.2	99.2	99.3	99.3	99.4	99.4	99.4	99.4	99.4	99.5	99.5
3	34.1	30.8	29.5	28.7	28.2	27.9	27.5	27.3	27.1	26.9	26.7	26.6	26.5
4	21.2	18.0	16.7	16.0	15.5	15.2	14.8	14.5	14.4	14.2	14.0	13.9	13.8
5	16.3	13.3	12.1	11.4	11.0	10.7	10.3	10.1	9.89	9.72	9.55	9.47	9.38
6	13.7	10.9	9.78	9.15	8.75	8.47	8.10	7.87	7.72	7.56	7.40	7.31	7.23
7	12.2	9.55	8.45	7.85	7.46	7.19	6.84	6.62	6.47	6.31	6.16	6.07	5.99
8	11.3	8.65	7.59	7.01	6.63	6.37	6.03	5.81	5.67	5.52	5.36	5.28	5.20
9	10.6	8.02	6.99	6.42	6.06	5.80	5.47	5.26	5.11	4.96	4.81	4.73	4.65
10	10.0	7.56	6.55	5.99	5.64	5.39	5.06	4.85	4.71	4.56	4.41	4.33	4.25
11	9.65	7.21	6.22	5.67	5.32	5.07	4.74	4.54	4.40	4.25	4.10	4.02	3.94
12	9.33	6.93	5.95	5.41	5.06	4.82	4.50	4.30	4.16	4.01	3.86	3.78	3.70
13	9.07	6.70	5.74	5.21	4.86	4.62	4.30	4.10	3.96	3.82	3.66	3.59	3.51
14	8.86	6.51	5.56	5.04	4.69	4.46	4.14	3.94	3.80	3.66	3.51	3.43	3.35
15	8.68	6.36	5.42	4.89	4.56	4.32	4.00	3.80	3.67	3.52	3.37	3.29	3.21
16	8.53	6.23	5.29	4.77	4.44	4.20	3.89	3.69	3.55	3.41	3.26	3.18	3.10
17	8.40	6.11	5.18	4.67	4.34	4.10	3.79	3.59	3.46	3.31	3.16	3.08	3.00
18	8.29	6.01	5.09	4.58	4.25	4.01	3.71	3.51	3.37	3.23	3.08	3.00	2.92
19	8.18	5.93	5.01	4.50	4.17	3.94	3.63	3.43	3.30	3.15	3.00	2.92	2.84
20	8.10	5.85	4.94	4.43	4.10	3.87	3.56	3.37	3.23	3.09	2.94	2.86	2.78
21	8.02	5.78	4.87	4.37	4.04	3.81	3.51	3.31	3.17	3.03	2.88	2.80	2.72
22	7.95	5.72	4.82	4.31	3.99	3.76	3.45	3.26	3.12	2.98	2.83	2.75	2.67
23	7.88	5.66	4.76	4.26	3.94	3.71	3.41	3.21	3.07	2.93	2.78	2.70	2.62
24	7.82	5.61	4.72	4.22	3.90	3.67	3.36	3.17	3.03	2.89	2.74	2.66	2.58
25	7.77	5.57	4.68	4.18	3.86	3.63	3.32	3.13	2.99	2.85	2.70	2.62	2.54
30	7.56	5.39	4.51	4.02	3.70	3.47	3.17	2.98	2.84	2.70	2.55	2.47	2.39
40	7.31	5.18	4.31	3.83	3.51	3.29	2.99	2.80	2.66	2.52	2.37	2.29	2.20
60	7.08	4.98	4.13	3.65	3.34	3.12	2.82	2.63	2.50	2.35	2.20	2.12	2.03

Denominator Degrees of Freedom

This table is adapted from Table XVIII in *Biometrika Tables for Statisticians*, Vol. I, 1954, by E.S. Pearson and H.O. Hartley, originally prepared by M. Merrington and C.M. Thompson, with the kind permission of the editor of *Biometrika*.

Table V. Distribution of the Standardized Range $W = R/\sigma$
(Assuming a Normal Population)

	2	3	4	5	6	7	8	9	10	12	15
$E(W)$	1.128	1.693	2.059	2.326	2.534	2.704	2.847	2.970	3.078	3.258	3.472
σ_W	.853	.888	.880	.864	.848	.833	.820	.808	.797	.778	.755
$W_{.005}$	.01	.13	.34	.55	.75	.92	1.08	1.21	1.33	1.55	1.80
$W_{.01}$	.02	.19	.43	.66	.87	1.05	1.20	1.34	1.47	1.68	1.93
$W_{.025}$	.04	.30	.59	.85	1.06	1.25	1.41	1.55	1.67	1.88	2.14
$W_{.05}$	.09	.43	.76	1.03	1.25	1.44	1.60	1.74	1.86	2.07	2.32
$W_{.1}$	.18	.62	.98	1.26	1.49	1.68	1.83	1.97	2.09	2.30	2.54
$W_{.2}$	.36	.90	1.29	1.57	1.80	1.99	2.14	2.28	2.39	2.59	2.83
$W_{.3}$	.55	1.14	1.53	1.82	2.04	2.22	2.38	2.51	2.62	2.82	3.04
$W_{.4}$	.74	1.36	1.76	2.04	2.26	2.44	2.59	2.71	2.83	3.01	3.23
$W_{.5}$	.95	1.59	1.98	2.26	2.47	2.65	2.79	2.92	3.02	3.21	3.42
$W_{.6}$	1.20	1.83	2.21	2.48	2.69	2.86	3.00	3.12	3.23	3.41	3.62
$W_{.7}$	1.47	2.09	2.47	2.73	2.94	3.10	3.24	3.35	3.46	3.63	3.83
$W_{.8}$	1.81	2.42	2.78	3.04	3.23	3.39	3.52	3.63	3.73	3.90	4.09
$W_{.9}$	2.33	2.90	3.24	3.48	3.66	3.81	3.93	4.04	4.13	4.29	4.47
$W_{.95}$	2.77	3.31	3.63	3.86	4.03	4.17	4.29	4.39	4.47	4.62	4.80
$W_{.975}$	3.17	3.68	3.98	4.20	4.36	4.49	4.61	4.70	4.79	4.92	5.09
$W_{.99}$	3.64	4.12	4.40	4.60	4.76	4.88	4.99	5.08	5.16	5.29	5.45
$W_{.995}$	3.97	4.42	4.69	4.89	5.03	5.15	5.26	5.34	5.42	5.54	5.70

This table is adapted from Tables XX and XXII in *Biometrika Tables for Statisticians*, Vol. I, 1954, by E.S. Pearson and H.O. Hartley, with the kind permission of the editor of *Biometrika*.

Table VI. Control Chart Constants
Sample Size

	2	3	4	5	6	8	10
A_2	1.880	1.023	.729	.577	.483	.373	.308
D_1	0	0	0	0	0	.387	.687
D_2	3.686	4.358	4.698	4.918	5.078	5.307	5.469
D_3	0	0	0	0	0	.136	.223
D_4	3.268	2.574	2.282	2.114	2.004	1.864	1.777
d_2	1.128	1.693	2.059	2.326	2.534	2.847	3.078

More extensive tables of control chart constants are found in the *ASTM Manual on Quality Control of Materials*, published by the American Society for Testing Materials. The above table is adapted from Table III of that *Manual*.

Table VIIa.   Acceptance Limits for the Kolmogorov-Smirnov Test of Goodness of Fit

Sample Size (n)	Significance Level				
	.20	.15	.10	.05	.01
1	.900	.925	.950	.975	.995
2	.684	.726	.776	.842	.929
3	.565	.597	.642	.708	.829
4	.494	.525	.564	.624	.734
5	.446	.474	.510	.563	.669
6	.410	.436	.470	.521	.618
7	.381	.405	.438	.486	.577
8	.358	.381	.411	.457	.543
9	.339	.360	.388	.432	.514
10	.322	.342	.368	.409	.486
11	.307	.326	.352	.391	.468
12	.295	.313	.338	.375	.450
13	.284	.302	.325	.361	.433
14	.274	.292	.314	.349	.418
15	.266	.283	.304	.338	.404
16	.258	.274	.295	.328	.391
17	.250	.266	.286	.318	.380
18	.244	.259	.278	.309	.370
19	.237	.252	.272	.301	.361
20	.231	.246	.264	.294	.352
25	.21	.22	.24	.264	.32
30	.19	.20	.22	.242	.29
35	.18	.19	.21	.23	.27
40				.21	.25
50				.19	.23
60				.17	.21
70				.16	.19
80				.15	.18
90				.14	
100				.14	
Asymptotic Formula:	$\dfrac{1.07}{\sqrt{n}}$	$\dfrac{1.14}{\sqrt{n}}$	$\dfrac{1.22}{\sqrt{n}}$	$\dfrac{1.36}{\sqrt{n}}$	$\dfrac{1.63}{\sqrt{n}}$

Reject the hypothetical distribution $F(x)$ if $D_n = \max |F_n(x) - F(x)|$ exceeds the tabulated value.

(For $\alpha = .01$ and $.05$, asymptotic formulas give values which are too high—by 1.5 per cent for $n = 80$.)

This table is taken from F.J. Massey, Jr., "The Kolmogorov-Smirnov Test for Goodness of Fit," *J. Amer. Stat. Assn.* (1951), 46: 68–78, except that certain corrections and additional entries are from Z.W. Birnbaum, "Numerical Tabulation of the Distribution of Kolmogorov's Statistic for Finite Sample Size," *J. Amer. Stat. Assn.* (1952), 47: 425–441, with the kind permission of the authors and the *J. Amer. Stat. Assn.*

Table VIIb. Acceptance Limits for the Kolmogorov-Smirnov Test of $H_0: F_1(x) = F_2(x)$

					Sample Size n_1							
Sample Size n_2	**1**	**2**	**3**	**4**	**5**	**6**	**7**	**8**	**9**	**10**	**12**	**15**
1	* *	* *	* *	* *	* *	* *	* *	* *	* *	* *		
2		* *	* *	* *	* *	* *	* *	7/8 *	16/18 *	9/10 *		
3			* *	* *	12/15 *	5/6 *	18/21 *	18/24 *	7/9 8/9		9/12 11/12	
4				3/4 *	16/20 *	9/12 10/12	21/28 24/28	6/8 7/8	27/36 32/36	14/20 16/20	8/12 10/12	
5					4/5 4/5	20/30 25/30	25/35 30/35	27/40 32/40	31/45 36/45	7/10 8/10		10/15 11/15
6						4/6 5/6	29/42 35/42	16/24 18/24	12/18 14/18	19/30 22/30	7/12 9/12	
7							5/7 5/7	35/56 42/56	40/63 47/63	43/70 53/70		
8								5/8 6/8	45/72 54/72	23/40 28/40	14/24 16/24	
9									5/9 6/9	52/90 62/90	20/36 24/36	
10										6/10 7/10		15/30 19/30
12											6/12 7/12	30/60 35/60
15												7/15 8/15

Reject H_0 if

$$D = \max |F_{n_1}(x) - F_{n_2}(x)|$$

exceeds the tabulated value. The upper value gives a level at most .05 and the lower value gives a level at most .01.

Note 1: Where * appears, do not reject H_0 at the given level.

Note 2: For large values of n_1 and n_2, the following approximate formulas may be used:

$$\alpha = .05: \quad 1.36 \sqrt{\frac{n_1 + n_2}{n_1 n_2}}$$

$$\alpha = .01: \quad 1.63 \sqrt{\frac{n_1 + n_2}{n_1 n_2}}$$

This table is derived from F.J. Massey, Jr., "Distribution Table for the Deviation Between Two Sample Cumulatives," *Ann. Math. Stat.* (1952), **23**: 435–441. Adapted with the kind permission of the author and the *Ann. Math. Stat.* Formulas for large sample sizes were given by N. Smirnov, "Tables for Estimating the Goodness of Fit of Empirical Distributions," *Ann. Math. Stat.* (1948), **19**: 280–281.

Table VIII. Rejection Limits for the Wilcoxon-Mann-Whitney Test

n \ m	3	4	5	6	7	8	9	10
2			0 (4.7)	0 (3.6)	0 (2.8)	0 (2.2) 1 (4.4)	0 (1.8) 1 (3.6)	0 (1.5) 1 (3.0)
3	0 (5.0)	0 (2.8)	0 (1.8) 1 (3.6)	1 (2.4) 2 (4.8)	0 (.83) 1 (1.7) 2 (3.3)	0 (.61) 2 (2.4) 3 (4.2)	0 (.45) 1 (.91) 3 (3.2) 4 (5.0)	0 (.35) 1(.70) 3(2.5) 4 (3.9)
4		0 (1.4) 1 (2.9)	0 (.79) 1 (1.6) 2 (3.2)	0 (.48) 1 (1.0) 2 (1.9) 3 (3.3)	0 (.30) 1 (.61) 3 (2.1) 4 (3.6)	1 (.40) 2 (.81) 4 (2.4) 5 (3.6)	1 (.28) 3 (.98) 5 (2.5) 6 (3.8)	2 (.40) 3 (.70) 5 (1.8) 7 (3.8)
5			0 (.40) 1 (.79) 2 (1.6) 4 (4.8)	1 (.43) 2 (.82) 3 (1.5) 5 (4.1)	1 (.25) 3 (.88) 5 (2.4) 6 (3.7)	2 (.31) 4 (.93) 6 (2.3) 8 (4.7)	3 (.35) 5 (.95) 7 (2.1) 9 (4.2)	4 (.40) 6 (.97) 8 (2.0) 11 (5.0)
6				2 (.43) 3 (.67) 5 (2.1) 7 (4.7)	3 (.41) 4 (.70) 6 (1.8) 8 (3.7)	4 (.40) 5 (.63) 8 (2.1) 10 (4.1)	5 (.38) 7 . (88) 10 (2.5) 12 (4.4)	6 (.37) 8 (2.0) 11 (2.1) 14 (4.7)
7					4 (.35) 6 (.87) 8 (1.9) 11 (4.9)	5 (.47) 7 (1.0) 10 (2.0) 13 (4.7)	7 (.39) 9 (.82) 12 (2.1) 15 (4.5)	9 (.48) 11 (.93) 14 (2.2) 17 (4.4)
8						7 (.35) 9 (.74) 13 (2.5) 15 (4.2)	9 (.39) 11 (.76) 15 (2.3) 18 (4.6)	11 (.43) 13 (.78) 17 (2.2) 20 (4.2)
9							11 (.39) 14 (.94) 18 (2.5) 21 (4.7)	13 (.38) 16 (.86) 20 (2.2) 24 (4.7)
10								16 (.45) 19 (.93) 23 (2.2) 27 (4.5)

Note: See explanations on page 264.

The four entries for each pair of sample sizes are rejection limits when it is desired to have:

a one-sided test at .5 per cent or a two-sided test at 1 per cent;
a one-sided test at 1 per cent or a two-sided test at 2 per cent;
a one-sided test at 2.5 per cent or a two-sided test at 5 per cent;
a one-sided test at 5 per cent or a two-sided test at 10 per cent.

The entries in the table are lower limits; corresponding upper limits are $mn - u$. The number in parentheses after a value u is the probability (in per cent) that $U \leq u$.

Example: If a two-sided test at 5 per cent is desired for $m = 5$ and $n = 8$, use $6 < U < 34$ as the acceptance region. For this test,

$$\alpha = P_{H_0}(U \leq 6 \text{ or } U \geq 34) = 2 \times (.023) = .046,$$

which is less than .05 as desired.

This table is adapted from those given in H.B. Mann and D.R. Whitney, "On a Test of Whether One of the Two Random Variables Is Stochastically Larger than the Other," *The Annals of Mathematical Statistics* (1947), **18:** 50–60, with the kind permission of *The Annals of Mathematical Statistics.*

Appendix C
Some References for Further Study

Burr, I.W., *Engineering Statistics and Quality Control*, McGraw-Hill Book Company, New York, 1953.

Dixon, W.J., and W.J. Massey, *Introduction to Statistical Analysis*, McGraw-Hill Book Company, New York, 1951.

Duncan, A.J., *Quality Control & Industrial Statistics*, Richard D. Irwin, Chicago, 1952.

Feller, W., *An Introduction to Probability Theory and Its Applications*, Vol. 1, 2nd ed., John Wiley & Sons, New York, 1957.

Fisher, R.A., *The Design of Experiments*, 6th ed., Hafner Publishing Company, 1951.

Fisher, R.A., *Statistical Methods for Research Workers*, 11th ed., Hafner Publishing Company, New York, 1951.

Fraser, D.A.S., *Statistics: An Introduction*, John Wiley & Sons, New York, 1958.

Fry, T.C., *Probability and Its Engineering Uses*, D. Van Nostrand Company, New York, 1928.

Hald, A., *Statistical Theory with Engineering Applications*, John Wiley & Sons, New York, 1952.

Kempthorne, O., *The Design & Analysis of Experiments*, John Wiley & Sons, New York, 1952.

Mood, A.M., *Introduction to the Theory of Statistics*, McGraw-Hill Book Company, New York, 1950.

van der Waerden, B.L., *Mathemetische Statistik*, Springer-Verlag, Berlin, 1957.

Wald, A., *Sequential Analysis*, John Wiley & Sons, New York, 1947.

Walker, H.M., and Lev, J., *Statistical Inference*, Henry Holt and Company, New York, 1953.

Williams, J.D., *The Compleat Strategyst*, McGraw-Hill Book Company, New York, 1954.

Answers to Problems

1-31. 5/1944, 1/6, 7/162

1-32. .411

1-33. 1/4, 5/16, 5/16

1-34. $\displaystyle\sum_{11}^{20}\binom{20}{k}(.45)^k(.55)^{20-k}$

1-35. $\displaystyle\sum_{11}^{20}\binom{45}{k}\binom{55}{20-k}\Big/\binom{100}{20}$

1-36. $(7/3)(5/6)^5$, $13/3^6$

1-37. $55

1-38. $3.50

1-39. 2

1-40. About 31 cents

Chapter 2

2-1. .63

2-2. .999

2-3. $(.5)(.95)^9$

2-4. .48, .65

✗ 2-7. $F(x) = \begin{cases} 0, \text{ if } x < 0 \\ x, \text{ if } 0 \le x \le 1 \\ 1, \text{ if } x > 1 \end{cases}$

2-8. .5, .6, .9, 1, 0, .4

2-9. $1 - 1/e$, $1 - 1/e$, $1/e^2$, $\log_e 2$

2-10. $3/4e^2$, 1/4, 1/4, 0, $1 - 3/4e^3$

2-11. .3174, .0007, .9544, .0498

2-13. (a) 0, if $x < -4$; $(x + 4)/2$, if $-4 \le x \le -2$; 1, if $x > -2$

 (b) 0, if $x < -2$; $(x + 2)/4$, if $-2 \le x \le 2$; 1, if $x > 2$

 (c) 0, if $x < 0$; x, if $0 \le x \le 1$; 1, if $x > 1$

2-14. $F_V(x) = \begin{cases} 0 \text{ if } x < 0 \\ 1 \text{ if } x \ge 0 \end{cases}$

2-16. 1/2, $\log 2$, $\log (3/2)$

2-18. -1.645, 1.645

2-19. 2.75, .32

Chapter 3

3-1. $p(k) = (6 - |k - 7|)/36$, $(k = 2, \ldots, 12)$

3-2. $p(k) = 1/5$, $(k = 1, 2, 3, 4, 5)$

3-3. $p(k) = \binom{10}{4-k}\binom{3}{k}\Big/\binom{13}{4}$, $(k = 0, 1, 2, 3)$

3-4. $p(k) = \binom{4}{k}p^k(1 - p)^{4-k}$, $(k = 0, 1, 2, 3, 4)$

3-5. $p(k) = 1/2$, $(k = 0, 1)$

3-6. $p(k) = (1/6)(5/6)^{k-1}$, $(k = 1, 2, 3, \ldots)$

3-7. 7

3-8. 3

3-9. 12/13

3-10. 4p

3-11. 1/2

3-12. 6

3-13. $(1 + e^t)/2$

3-14. 287/6

3-16. 35/6

3-17. 2

3-18. 90/169

3-19. $4p(1 - p)$

3-20. 1/4

3-21. 35/12

3-22. 1/2

3-23. 1

3-24. 3.3

3-25. 97

3-26. 2.83

3-27. .0337, .96, e^{-5T}

3-28. .184

3-29. .082, .544, .713

3-30. .0183, .0916

3-31. .919, 20

3-32. $-2/3$, 5/9

3-33. .55, .2475

3-34. .9606, .996, 1/2

3-35. 200, 10

3-36. 270, 15

3-37. 4, 1/3, 4/3, 8/9; 65/81

3-39. $1/5$; $\dbinom{2}{k}\dbinom{8}{4-k}\bigg/\dbinom{10}{4}$, $k = 0, 1, 2$; 4/5, 32/75

3-40. $\dbinom{13}{2}\dbinom{13}{3}\bigg/\dbinom{52}{5}$; 13/4, 507/272

3-41. $\dbinom{4}{3}\dbinom{4}{2}\bigg/\dbinom{52}{5}$; $13 \cdot 12 \dbinom{4}{3}\dbinom{4}{2}\bigg/\dbinom{52}{5}$; 1, 12/17

3-42. $13/8\sqrt{e}$

3-43. e^{-5}, $e^{-5} 5^x/x!$, $1 - 6e^{-5}$

3-44. $\displaystyle\sum_0^2 \dbinom{100}{k}\dbinom{400}{75-k}\bigg/\dbinom{500}{75} \doteq 3.2 \times 10^{-6}$

3-45. .140

3-46. Poisson: .0498, .149, .224, .224, .168
Binomial: .0476 .147 .225, .227, .171.

Chapter 4

4–1. (a) $F(x) = \begin{cases} 0, \text{ if } x < 0 \\ (1 - \cos x)/2, \text{ if } 0 \le x \le \pi \\ 1, \text{ if } x > \pi \end{cases}$

(b) 1/4

(c) $\pi/2$

4–2. 1, uniform on $0 < x < 1$, 0, 1/2

4–3. 1/4

4–4. $f(x) = \begin{cases} \lambda e^{-\lambda x}, \; x \ge 0 \\ 0, \; x < 0 \end{cases}$

4–5. $F(\theta) = \begin{cases} 0, \; \theta \le 0 \\ \sin \theta, \; 0 \le \theta \le \pi/2 \\ 1, \; \theta > \pi/2 \end{cases}$

4–6. 1/2, 1/12

4–7. 13/6, 11/36

4–8. $1/\lambda$, $1/\lambda^2$

4–9. $\pi/2 - 1$, $\pi^2/4 - 2$

4–10. $k/2$

4–11. 1/4

4–12. 2/3

4–13. No

4–14. .5, .1574, .9974, 0, .0456

4–16. .0082, .8904, 0, .8426

4–17. (8, 4) or (2, 64)

4–18. about 6'4''

4–19. 4.8%, non-negative, 3.78k

4–20. 1.7%, 127.3, 123.4 to 136.6, 85.3%

Chapter 5

5–1. 100 oz., .1 oz.

5–3. 0, 9.2 (in the fourth decimal place)

5–4. 2×10^6 ft.^{2}

5–5. .30

5–6. 25/8 hours

5–7. .0655

5–8. .0513

5–9. .0058

5–10. .1303

5–11. .0179, .7262, .0485

5–12. .1829

5–13. .0185

5–14. Normal .6401, Poisson .6767, Binomial .6772

5–15. Yes, tolerance in the series combination is $\pm$.707%, which is less than required.

5–16. .49929

5–17. 1.5 inches, $\pm$.00458 inches

5–18. 1.12 miles

Chapter 7

7-6. 14.5, 14.7
7-13. 16, 24.21, 4.3
7-14. 30.4, 32.1
7-16. 1.75
7-17. 1.90

Chapter 8

8-1. (a) Both sides are heads or both are tails; composite.
      (b) Accept H_0 regardless of the outcome of the tosses; 0.
      (c) 1/8
8-2. Simple; composite; in general composite, although if the distribution of X is determined by $E(X)$, the hypothesis is simple; simple; composite; composite.
8-3. .103
8-4. .0054, .063
8-5. $K = 27, \beta = 1.000$
8-6. $n = 95$
8-8. .2743, .6554
8-9. $(10 - M)(9 - M)/90$
8-10. $3p(1 - p)$
8-11. .29, .29, .181
8-12. $\displaystyle\sum_{0}^{1} \binom{M}{k}\binom{10 - M}{4 - k} \bigg/ \binom{10}{4}$
8-15. $\chi^2 = 9 > 6.63$, reject $p = 1/2$
8-16. (a) $\chi^2 = 3.16 < 13.4$, accept
      (b) $\chi^2 = .89 < 10.6$, accept
8-18. $D_n = .145 > .122$, reject at 10% level
8-19. $D_n = .075 < .0815$
8-20. **Right to left:**   42 to 46 runs above and below median, reject.
                            120 to 124 runs up and down, reject.
      Top to bottom: 79 to 85 runs above and below median, reject.
                            134 to 136 runs up and down, accept.
      (Note: Number of runs depends on how ties are broken.)
8-21. 51 to 59 runs above and below median.
      30 to 36 runs up and down.   Reject at 5% level.

Chapter 9

9-1. .3174, .0456
9-2. 663, 1089
9-3. 5'9.2'' to 5'10.8''
9-4. $2.3 \pm .0514, 2.3 \pm .0392$
9-5. 661
9-7. (.61, .77), (.64, .75)
9-8. (.57, .80)

9–9. (.055, .174)

9–10. (.52, .76), (.515, .747)

9–11. (1.67, 2.39)

9–12. (a) $z = 3.67 > 1.65$, reject $\mu = 16$
  (b) .0618

9–13. $\bar{X} > 1.414$, $n = 32$

9–14. More than 40

9–15. 134, 18

9–16. .1611

9–17. $t = 1.46$, accept

9–18. (3.60, 3.78)

9–19. $t = 4.36$, reject

9–20. CL 15, UCL 18.72, LCL 11.28; .014; .0278 (assuming normality)

9–22. $n = 49$, reject if sample median exceeds .107

9–23. $b \log 2$, $b/\sqrt{n}$, (med.)/(log $2 \pm 1.96/\sqrt{n}$), $31.6 < b < 42.1$

9–24. Reject at 5% level

9–25. .01, .896

9–26. .9533

Chapter 10

10–1. Normal: $(35.7, 63.5) \times 10^{-8}$, Chi-square: $(35.2, 62.2) \times 10^{-8}$

10–2. Reject if $s_x^2 > 28.6$

10–4. Reject, since $4s_x^2 > 11.98$; accept, since $4s_x^2 < 18.98$; (1.65, 12.1);
  (53.6, 58.0)

10–5. 7.7×10^{-6}, $(4.9, 14.2) \times 10^{-6}$

10–6. 1.58

10–7. 2.54×10^{-3}, $(2.0, 3.49) \times 10^{-3}$

10–8. (2.51, 6.32), (2.81, 6.69)

10–9. .068, .000

10–10. CL 10, UCL 18.6, LCL 1.36

10–11. 3.70; LCL 3.47, UCL 3.93; LCL 0, UCL .719

Chapter 11

11–1. Reject at 5% level, accept at 1% level ($D = .2$)

11–3. There is a difference, (.81, 1.59)

11–4. (a) $z = -3.9 < -1.65$, reject at 5% level
  (c) $t = -3.5$, reject at 5% level
  (d) $(-.0033, -.0009)$

11–5. Reject equality of levels in each case (at 5% level).

11–6. Accept equality of levels in each case (at 5% level).

11–7. "   "   "   "   "   "   "   "   "   "

11–8. Variance ratio is $5.79 > 3.01$, reject at 5% level.

11–9. Accept equality of variances, since $\dfrac{1}{2.17} < 1.6 < 2.17$.

11–10. Reject equality.

Chapter 12

12–2. $1/4 < \left(\frac{1}{5}\right)^{s_n} \left(\frac{9}{5}\right)^{f_n} < 4$

12–3. $|\Sigma x_i| < .275$

12–4. $6x - 34y + 53 = 0$

12–5. $(-.094, .278)$, yes

12–6. Only change is in $\hat{\alpha}$, which is now 7.06.

12–7. $(6.47, 7.65)$, $(-.094, .278)$

12–8. Yes, at 5% level, since test ratio is $8.42 > 3.89$; .199

12–9. Not at 5% level, since test ratio is $2.44 < 3.34$; no; 11.7

12–10. No, test ratio $= 2.16 < 9.28$; no, test ratio $= 1.57 < 10.1$

12–11. No, $3.51 < 3.86$; yes, $14.8 > 3.86$ (5% level)

12–13. (c) Choose $p = 3/4$ if outcome is heads, $p = 1/4$ if outcome is tails.

12–14. Minimax 4, minimax regret 1, Bayes 1

Index